MAN

and

HIS BODY

THE WONDERS OF THE HUMAN MECHANISM

by

BENJAMIN F. MILLER, M.D.

and

RUTH GOODE

With illustrations by Cal Sachs

SIMON AND SCHUSTER
NEW YORK / 1960

LIBRARY OF CONGRESS CATALOG CARD NUMBER: 60-10993
MANUFACTURED IN THE UNITED STATES OF AMERICA

CONTENTS

To Zelma Miller and Gerald Goode

ACKNOWLEDGMENTS

Since this book deals with many areas of specialized knowledge of the human body, the authors were concerned to have the most authoritative reading of the manuscript in these several fields. They are therefore deeply indebted to Drs. Bernard C. Wexler, Richard Goldsmith, J. Park Biehl, George Kittinger, Paul Nathan, Clair Paine, Philip Edlin, and Edmond Ricanati, who gave generously of their time and provided valuable suggestions.

Excellent service in checking reference materials was contributed by Mr. Robert Lefkowitz, Librarian of the May Institute. Mrs. Elsie Lincoln Rosner, biologist and experienced editorial researcher, very kindly read the book in galleys. The authors also acknowledge their warm gratitude to Dr. Zelma Miller, who prepared the basic material for several chapters.

The authors found it a genuinely rewarding experience to work with the book's editor, Mr. Henry Simon, whose interest was always stimulating and constructive.

Finally, thanks are due to the secretaries, Ruth Keyes, Priscilla O'Donnell, and Mary Ellen Sweet, who helped in typing the manuscript.

B. F. M.
R. G.

PART I

THE

MAGNIFICENT

WHOLE

1 | BEGINNINGS

THERE WAS A TIME when our planet knew no life. Torn from the sun, it flamed molten in the black void, a pin point of light whirling around its blazing parent. Slowly it cooled; its hardening crust wrinkled and formed mountains, valleys, and ocean deeps.

The young planet swinging through its orbit was barren of life, but it was far from quiet. Its turbulent marrow boiled and belched through its crust in fearful volcanic outbursts, and the sun blazed through its thin, steaming atmosphere of carbon dioxide, nitrogen, ammonia and marsh gas. Swirling vapors shuddered with electrical storms and condensed to drench the jagged crust with torrential rains, and the torrents raced down the valleys, carrying all manner of materials to the seas.

The land burned by day and froze by night; but the waters warmed and cooled more slowly and maintained a gentler temperature. In the warm shallows, atoms of carbon, hydrogen, nitrogen and oxygen became fused—perhaps by shafts of lightning, perhaps by cosmic irradiation—into the long molecular chains we call protein molecules. With favoring temperatures and a plentiful supply of electrical energy, these peculiar molecules developed the power to synthesize replicas of themselves out of the chemically rich waters in which they drifted.

Then such a molecule developed a membrane around it, like the film of scum on a bubble, and within this tenuous shelter it began to conduct ever more intricate chemical transactions with its environment. Thus was born the living cell.

The seas nourished many such forms, single-celled and many-celled. Animal forms came into being that could extract oxygen from the water and feed on each other. Plant forms appeared that could take carbon dioxide from the atmosphere and combine it with water molecules, in sunlight, to make carbohydrates for their nourishment. In the course of this process, which we call photosynthesis, they released oxygen into the earth's atmosphere.

Thus gradually, thanks to the plants, the atmosphere became converted to the sheltering, tempering, oxygen-rich envelope of air that we know. The environment was ready for a land-dwelling, air-breathing animal. Then the time came when such an animal crept out of the sea and breathed its oxygen directly from the air.

MAN EMERGES

In the violent environmental changes that beset life on the young planet, many species perished. But many survived, and by the compelling processes of evolution these gave rise, step by step, to forms ever more highly organized, self-contained, and adaptable. The warm-blooded creatures won independence from the environment's changing temperatures. The mammals bore their young alive and fed them through infancy from their own bodies. Finally came the most highly organized, most adaptable animal of all the milliards of living forms on the planet, one that could develop the power to control its own environment: the genus man.

How long had it taken for humankind to be born? Scientists today believe that the matter composing our universe, from the farthest galaxies to the fleeting particles within the atom, came into being ten billion years ago, and that living organisms are a billion, perhaps two billion, years old. A hundred thousand years ago there were men who used fire, covered their hairless bodies with animal hides, and hunted with weapons. Taking shelter in caves, men survived the Ice Age; fifty thousand years ago they were painting on their cave walls beautiful images of the animals they hunted, perhaps for aesthetic pleasure and perhaps to gain magic power for their hunting. Some ten thousand years ago or less there were men who planted grains and herded gentle grass-eating animals for milk and meat. Thus arose villages and cities, law, religion, trade, and written language. Thus began history and, in time, the scientific study of man.

BODY AND MIND

Gazing down the long, twisting corridors of evolution, we tend to think of man as differing from his animal relatives mainly because of his remarkable brain, and that is so. The cleverest of the apes never built a fire, devised a tool, or planted a crop. No animal but man ever prayed to unseen spirits or attempted by ritual and magic to influence his own destiny.

Yet what could such a brain, however remarkable, do without a body to act at its bidding? The anthropologists find their clues to man's emergence in the fossil bones not only of his skull but also of his trunk and limbs. Thanks to a curious change in his pelvis, he was able to walk erect, not haltingly as did the apes but steadily; he could hold his head up and look about him whether he stood, walked, or ran. And he could use his hands. By another happy circumstance he retained the marvelously flexible five-fingered hand of his tree-dwelling ancestors, with a thumb that he could oppose separately to each of his fingers, so that he could hold and guide a tool. Even his circulatory system developed a refinement for propelling the blood upward against gravity and keeping his busy, inquiring brain ever nourished.

The scientists are still seeking evidence of how and in what order these changes came about; they surmise that the erect posture, the free and remarkably articulated hands, the wide field of vision of a head held high on its slender flexible neck—all these must have influenced the fabulous growth of the human brain. Other species have had one or more of these characteristics. Some of the dinosaurs walked upright; the giraffe has a far wider field of vision than any man and so have the birds. But none has had, all at once, the posture, the hands, and a skull which can house a brain of human size. Nor has any other species a brain so little encumbered with inborn instinctual patterns, so free to grow and develop new patterns of association within each individual's own lifetime and out of his own experience.

Probably all these separate advances had to occur together, and in a favoring environment, before the upright Java and Peking men, not far above the apes, yielded place to the low-browed, heavy-jawed Neanderthal man who had fire and hunting weapons, and he in turn yielded to the cave painter and skilled artisan. This Stone Age man of Europe, whom we call Cro-Magnon, was in every way a modern man except that he had no recorded history. He was a man who could learn to plan for his future and record his past, who would one day make poetry, music, and machines. Above all, he was a man who could study the world around him, and himself.

The more man has learned, the more he has wondered about himself. "What is man, that Thou art mindful of him?" mused the poet in Biblical Judea. In the 3,000 years since his day the record of man's deeds and misdeeds has filled vast libraries. Yet the psalmist lived only yesterday, and it was only the day before yesterday that man had begun to wonder about himself and write down his wonderment.

By the same reckoning it is only today, and virtually within the last hour, that man has begun to appreciate the unmatched wonder of his body.

THIRTY TRILLION CELLS

From a single-celled creature, man emerged at the end of evolution's corridor, an organism of thirty trillion highly specialized, interacting and interdependent cells. A human life today still begins with one cell and reaches maturity with thirty trillion. Each of these cells is, on the average, less than a thousandth of an inch long. It would take 1,250 of them laid side by side to make an inch; a box measuring one inch on each side could hold nearly two billion. Each of these microscopic body cells carries on specific and highly organized activities, and their sum total is a human being.

It is tempting and convenient to call the body a machine and to describe its functioning in the mechanical terms of a machine civilization. No mechanism yet devised by our technological era can compare with the efficiency of the body's organs and systems, the combined mechanisms of its thirty trillion living cells functioning together.

No engineering genius has invented a pump like the human heart, which pulsates seventy times a minute, forty million times a year; through it pass seven thousand quarts of fluid a day, nearly 200,000 tons in an average lifetime; and this powerful mechanism weighs just a pound. No manufacturer of industrial devices can offer a high-pressure filter apparatus like the human kidneys, with two million filter units, complete with filter sheet, strainer, and reabsorbing mechanism, capable of filtering nearly two hundred quarts of fluid daily, in two structures each small enough to fit into the palm of a man's hand.

Like the motor of an automobile, the six hundred muscles of the body burn a high-grade fuel; in the body, we call this conversion of fuel to energy the process of metabolism. The muscles are supplied by a feed line, the arterial system; they are sparked by an electrical—or electrochemical—impulse produced by a battery, the brain. We can play this game of mechanical analogies, in fact, with the body as a whole: in machine terms the body represents an engine of six hundred cylinders each complete with piston, ignition apparatus and conduction wires, moving more than a hundred articulated parts. Furthermore, it is a self-regulating, self-servicing engine that manufactures its own fuel out of raw materials gathered by itself, does its own cleaning and its ordinary —and sometimes extraordinary—repairs, replaces its own worn-out cellular units by the million every day, and reproduces itself —with the collaboration of another engine of the same basic design plus certain complementary parts.

Most tempting to the machine-minded is the brain with its fifteen billion cells and its intricate nerve pathways carrying electrochemical messages to and from every part of the body, receiving and interpreting the messages of the senses, controlling movement, speech, and thought, memories and emotions, the capacity to learn and to create. There are electronics experts who brilliantly describe every one of these functions of the brain in terms of open and closed circuits and feedback mechanisms. And there are among them a few dreamers who are confident they can build a machine that will perform all these functions and also gather and process its own food and reproduce itself, even adaptating to changes in its environment, a machine version of evolution. In the biochemical laboratory, meanwhile, other imaginative scientists are reproducing in a test tube the cataclysmic conditions of the young planet on which life first began, and they have succeeded in putting together sixteen of the twenty-three amino acids of that singular chemical unit, the self-replicating giant molecule that constitutes the heart of a living cell.

These activities of men in the workshops of physical and chemical science make the miracle of our bodies and brains not less but actually greater. For these are men who are working such marvels, and each of these men, with their billions of brilliantly co-ordinating brain cells, once grew from a single cell.

None of them has yet predicted that he could reproduce the greatest of life's powers, its ability—indeed its intense driving compulsion—to survive and to grow. This is the still inexplicable mystery, the beginning of a new human life.

THE FIRST CELL

Babies are born every day, and yet each one of them is something of a miracle. Each has begun with a single cell whose germ of growth lay in the meeting of two cells, from the bodies of two separate human beings. In that meeting, and the burst of orderly growth that follows it, there is still the baffling strangeness of the first protein molecules which inexplicably found the power to reproduce themselves and so became living cells and the parents of all life on the young earth.

That it takes two human beings, a male and a female, to create each new human being is a most commonplace, though inexhaustibly interesting, fact of life. It is a fact that irradiates our private and our social worlds and motivates our behavior in a thousand subtle and unsubtle ways. It lies behind great deeds and evil ones, deeds both creative and destructive; it lifts us to sublimity and casts us down into despair.

As an evolutionary development, sexual reproduction began quite early. There are single-celled organisms that reproduce by simply dividing themselves but must also periodically mate with a member of the species not of their own progeny, or they dwindle and die. The survival value of sexual reproduction is clearly enormous: uniting within itself the separate heritages of two individuals, each new individual of a species multiplies its possible variations and adaptations, and with succeeding generations these added chances to produce new structures of value in a changing environment increase virtually by geometric progression. We cannot even estimate how much the fact of sexual reproduction contributed to the growth of higher species. And among many species, such as the birds, some mammals and especially man, the institution of the family provided the newborn also with two parents and often a whole clan of experienced providers, protectors, and teachers. This social development, too, had its roots in the biological fact of sex.

Commonplace though it is, the fact of sexual reproduction is awesome to contemplate. And when we consider the biological mechanisms by which it operates, we find the tale almost too fantastic to believe. We will leave for a later chapter the complexities of the male and female reproductive structures, the interweaving endocrine and nervous networks that activate and support them, the still mysterious biological time clock that sets in motion impulses, desires, attractions and emotions along with the physiological processes of sex. Yet, even though we narrow our focus to the end result, the meeting of two incomplete cells to make a single complete one, capable of growing into a human being, is a challenge to the imagination.

It takes place on a microscopic scale, within a small tube in the woman's body; so miniature is the drama that she is not at all aware of it. The intense meeting of the lovers' bodies is hours past and their passion and pleasure in each other has accomplished its biological function, which was to place the male's reproductive cell within the female's body. Actually, with the prodigality characteristic of nature especially in the reproductive processes, not one but between 200 and 500 million sperm cells are conveyed in one ejaculation, and, if the act of intercourse takes place around the time when a ripe ovum is present in the Fallopian tube of the female partner's body, millions of sperm cells will make their way to it. Yet only one of them is needed to create life with the ovum.

The girl child is born with thousands of immature ova, or egg cells, lying dormant in her ovaries, and from puberty through all her childbearing years one of these ova matures and leaves the ovary during each menstrual month, to make its leisurely way down the Fallopian tube toward the uterus. The boy begins at puberty to form and store up sperm cells in his testes, and in a single act of sexual intercourse during his mature years he makes his gift of millions of potential life-giving mates to the waiting ovum. If ovum and sperm cell do not meet, neither can survive.

Of the hundreds of mature ova that the woman's body produces in her fertile years, all but a few end in disintegration, and of the millions of sperm cells that the man delivers with each act of intercourse, even if conception takes place, except in the rare instance of multiple birth, only one can achieve its goal and live. The union of ovum and sperm cell is literally a matter of life or death to both.

At the moment of union these two tiny grains of living matter hold all the physical inheritance handed down from generations of forebears to the future human being. They hold the color and texture of skin and hair, the shape of face and body, the gifts and talents, the sex and the tendency to live or not to live to a ripe old age. Chance will place the new life in a kind or unkind setting, and chance will present the new individual with many turns of fortune, good or ill, that will not be of his own making. How he will respond to these challenges is to some extent already determined in the ovum and the sperm cell whose meeting constitutes the beginning of his life. His inborn potential is carried in an egg cell weighing about one millionth of an ounce and a sperm cell 100,000 times smaller than that, a minuscule tadpolelike cell with a length of only one five-hundredth of an inch.

Chance also determines which of the mother's thousands of immature ova will be ready for fertilization and which of the father's millions of sperm cells will succeed in uniting with it. Each of these reproductive cells, both the female and the male, has only about forty-eight hours of independent life and only one chance to accomplish the union that means a continuing existence. Characteristically, the female cell can only wait, but the male cells have their own motive power and can actively seek her. They have a journey of some ten inches to make from the vagina through the uterus and into the Fallopian tubes. The distance is long for such tiny swimmers, and even with the help of muscular contractions in the uterus and hairlike fibers that direct them on their way, it takes them four or five hours to reach their goal.

Many do not complete the journey. Yet within a few hours the ovum is surrounded by millions of intensely active sperm. Motion pictures have been made which show the desperate, though microscopic, struggle that ensues; again and again the sperm cells hurl themselves against the walls of the ovum, so intense is the biological will to live, even in an infinitesimally small cell.

Conception occurs when one at last succeeds in breaching the wall. Its head and neck slide abruptly inside the ovum, the tail drops away and, in that magic moment of completion, the finality of the act is accented by an instantaneous thickening of the ovum's surface which shuts out the millions of competing sperm cells. Fertilization has been achieved; the now fulfilled ovum continues in microscopic majesty toward its prepared dwelling in the uterus, and a new human life begins.

THE HERITAGE

Within the first cell, a minute dot barely visible to the unaided eye, is contained the heritage not only of the new human being's individual father and mother but also of the species. Compressed into hours and days of uterine life will be the successive stages through which the species developed in the course of millions of years, from single cell to cell cluster, through a fishlike stage and an amphibianlike stage and a stage when it resembles its mammal cousins, including the tail. Not until its seventh week of uterine life does the embryo show the unmistakably human characteristics of the child it is destined to be.

All this, plus the individual inheritance that will make it unique even among human beings, is already contained in the first cell. Half of it, the mother's half of the heritage, was in the original ovum, and the other half was in the father's cell, the tiny head of the sperm. How so much is transmitted in so little space, by what biochemical code this pair of cells determines in advance the trillions of highly specialized cells that will eventually form the new human body—on this we can so far only speculate. But we do know the mechanism by which the heritage is carried.

Contained within the ovum and forming almost all of the sperm cell's head is a biochemical substance called chromatin. This is the material of the chromosomes, and set in its strands, like beads on a string, are the genes. The chromosomes are biological entities, independent bits of protoplasm which have the power to reproduce themselves. The genes that they carry are highly specialized. They are also remarkably durable, for they not only determine the particular characteristics each parent passes on to the child, but they also influence those that the child will give to his children, and so on through countless generations.

When a cell is preparing to reproduce itself—that is, to divide into two cells—the chromatin in which the genes are imbedded separates into strands; these are the chromosomes. The body cells of the various species, both plant and animal, have each a characteristic number of chromosomes. The fruit fly, for example, has eight; a lily, a trout, and a mouse happen to have the same number, twenty-four. The cells in the human body each have forty-six, and each chromosome probably carries thousands of genes. The chromosomes are arranged in pairs, and in the ordinary cell's process of reproducing itself each chromosome divides in half. Thus each of the two daughter cells emerges with the same number of chromosomes as its parent cell.

In the case of the ovum and sperm cells, the cells destined to produce a new individual, a different division takes place in the sex glands of the parents: the chromosomes themselves do not divide in half, but instead the pairs divide. Thus each ovum and each sperm cell comes from the parents' reproductive glands with twenty-three chromosomes instead of twenty-three pairs. Not until the ovum and sperm cell unite are the chromosomes once more paired. Then the fertilized ovum goes on its way with a complete set of forty-six chromosomes, the characteristic number for the human species.

By this fascinating piece of natural mathematics, mother and father contribute equally to the heredity of a child. Only one item of its inheritance is not equally shared between the parents, and that is the rather significant one of its sex. The decisive chromosome for this is in the father's sperm cells.

Under the microscope the drama of sex differentiation can be observed. Both the father's and the mother's cells, before dividing for reproduction, have their twenty-three pairs of chromosomes. In the mother's, all the pairs are fairly well matched. This is also true of the sex-determining pair. Both these chromosomes in the mother's reproductive cells are X chromosomes, which can produce only a female child. In the father's reproductive cells, however, the two sex-determining chromosomes are strikingly different. One is an X chromosome like those in the mother's cells. The other, considerably larger and hooked at the end, is a Y chromosome.

When the father's cells divide in preparation for their role as sperm cells, half of them receive the X chromosomes and half the Y chromosomes. If the sperm cell that eventually fertilizes the ovum carries the X chromosome, the child will be a girl; if the Y chromosome, a boy. The chances are nearly even. For every one hundred girls born there are 104 boys. Even if it were desirable to do so, science knows of no way to alter this ratio in human births.

Sometimes two separate ova are released at the same time; if both are fertilized and grow to maturity together in the uterus, the result is twins. Twins of this fraternal kind, born of separate pairs of ova and sperm cells, are no more alike than any two children in the same family and they may be of the same or opposite sex. Sometimes a fertilized egg, its cells dividing and redividing as it grows, separates into two independent cell masses at an early stage of its development, and each mass grows into a separate individual. These are identical twins, born of the same egg and sperm cell union, sharing the same set of chromosomes, and they are inevitably of the same sex.

Triplets may come of three separate and separately fertilized ova, or they may be a pair of identical twins and a fraternal twin. Quadruplets may be fraternal, or a pair of identical and two fraternal twins, or even two pairs of identical twins, and the sexual and other characteristics will be determined either by their origin from a single egg or by chance, as in the cases of other brothers and sisters. Science cannot tell us the reason for multiple births; we do know that it is an inherited tendency, and that it seems to be transmitted in the mother's genes more often than in the father's.

When a characteristic is inherited predominantly by one sex rather than the other, it is said to be sex-linked; that is, it is carried on the chromosomes that determine sex. Color blindness is one such sex-linked characteristic, and so is hemophilia, the defect in blood coagulation that plagued the Hapsburg dynasty. Both these characteristics are inherited in a curious way: they are transmitted by daughters but appear almost exclusively in sons. In other words, a boy inherits color blindness by way of his mother from her father or her maternal grandfather who was color blind; only 5 per cent of inherited color blindness occurs in girls.

Many beliefs about what a child inherits are based more on folklore than science: for example—if the firstborn is a daughter, she will tend to resemble her father; if a son, he will favor his mother. In finding out about the significant aspects of a child's inheritance, those that influence health, adaptability, and resistance to disease, geneticists today are making impressive strides. But their task seems endless, for they must deal with all the possible combinations of between 10,000 and 40,000 genes. That is the number of these microscopic transmitters of our inheritance with which each new human being is born.

THE BLUEPRINT OF GROWTH

Whatever the new cell contains of individual characteristics, it must still follow the species' blueprint of growth. Within a day or a little more after sperm and ovum combine, the embryonic unit begins to multiply by dividing, first into two cells, then four, eight, sixteen, thirty-two, always by a multiple of two. Even while it is still traveling along the Fallopian tube toward the safe nest prepared for it in the uterus, it becomes a mulberrylike mass of cells. Fluid begins to form in the center, forcing the cells into a spherical shape.

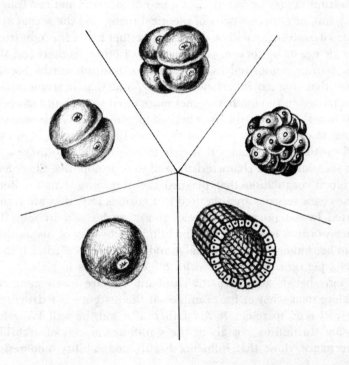

And now the cells begin to differentiate, following the orderly stages foreordained in the genes. First they separate into an outer and an inner layer, and then a few cells separate from the outer layer's underside and a third, middle layer forms. Each of these layers is destined to form a specific portion of the body's structure.

The innermost layer, or entoderm, will become the digestive and respiratory systems with their accessory organs. It rolls up first to form a tube which expands in the center, making a primitive stomach, while another portion develops the winding loops of the intestines. The inner surface of the canal becomes modified into its characteristic structure, and from its outer wall bloom small balloons which will become liver, pancreas, and most of the highly specialized organs and glands of digestion.

From the outer layer of cells, the ectoderm, will develop the skin and the nervous system. Its outer surface sends out cells that will eventually form hairs, and below them the layers of the skin and its sweat- and oil-producing glands. At the same time an indentation appears in the ectoderm; this in turn closes to form a tube, and this—the neural tube—will in time become the brain, the spinal cord, and the vast network of nerves running to and from every part of the body.

The middle layer, or mesoderm, is meanwhile preparing the beginnings of the body's bony skeleton, its muscles, and the circulatory system of heart and blood vessels. It divides first into five tubelike segments, like five pipes lying side by side. The center tube becomes the vertebral column, the backbone from which the whole skeleton will radiate. Ribs grow out of this column, encircling and protecting the embryonic intestinal organs, and eventually arms and legs, fingers and toes, and all their elaborate jointed articulation will bud outward from the little body. The two tubes flanking this central, skeletal tube will become the musculature clothing bones and joints, giving the body its motive power. The two outermost tubes will form the heart, blood vessels and blood, the kidneys and the bladder.

The role of each layer in developing its specific structures in the body is not quite so exclusive as might appear from this schematic account. There is some collaboration among the separate cell groups to make these exquisitely detailed and complex mechanisms. For example, while the innermost layer is mainly responsible for the digestive system, the outermost layer contributes the salivary glands, and the middle layer forms the smooth muscle of the digestive, respiratory and circulatory systems as well as the striped skeletal muscle. The mesoderm produces the kidneys and the bladder, but the entoderm gives rise to their inner linings, while the ectoderm lines the nose and mouth and puts the dental enamel on the teeth.

All this goes on at a marvelous rate of speed. In two weeks the three germinal layers have formed, and two weeks later the embryo is no larger than a match head but it has a brain, a mouth, and the outline of its jaw. In another week the budding arms and then the legs begin to thrust forth, and the heart, though only a tiny bulge in the circulatory tube, is already beating. When its uterine age is two months, the embryo is still only one inch long; but it has grown to 175 times its original size and it is a distinctly human individual, although it has a vast amount of growing and developing still to do before it will be ready for the world. During its nine months of life in the uterus it will increase its weight nearly six billion times. By contrast, it will become only twenty times heavier in the twenty years from birth to adulthood.

LIFE IN THE UTERUS

Fish lay their eggs in river and ocean beds and leave them there to hatch as best they can; snakes and turtles hide or bury their broods but also leave them to mature unprotected; while the birds, warm-blooded like ourselves, cover their unhatched young with their own bodies and strive anxiously to protect them from the hazards of life in tree and bush and meadow grass.

A few mammal species such as the kangaroo and the opossum, the marsupials, bear their young alive but far from ready for the world and carry them in a pouch outside the body. Somewhere along the evolutionary way, the mammals gained an organ that answered all the survival needs of a warm-blooded embryo: a constant temperature, ideal metabolic conditions, and protection from shock and injury. It is a home, moreover, that expands as the occupant grows, from a size no larger than a woman's fist, perhaps three inches long and weighing only a few ounces, to a length of as much as sixteen inches and a weight of more than two pounds. Except for the first three or four days of its life, the embryo lives in this extraordinary, endlessly accommodating uterine dwelling.

The muscle fibers of the uterus grow and thicken, providing an increasingly sturdy surrounding wall, and its blood vessels increase tremendously in size and number to nourish its expanding muscle tissue. Meanwhile the embryo contributes to its own shelter a surrounding sac, thin but tough-walled and filled with fluid, called the amnion. Within this it floats in a world of its own, protected even from its mother; no nerves connect mother and child, and no blood from the mother's body actually enters the child's circulation.

Yet the child grows and builds bone, muscle, blood and body tissues, and it excretes the wastes of its busy voracious metabolism. This is made possible by another remarkable structure, the placenta. Both the embryo and the mother contribute to the growth of this uterine feeding station; during the early weeks of pregnancy the proliferating lining of the uterus and the tiny but rapidly growing embryo both send cells to form this organ, and while it is developing the infant organism is nourished by the yolk sac of its original ovum. About the twelfth week the placenta takes over the embryo's nutrition.

The blood vessels of mother and child meet in the placenta. They have no connection; each is sealed off from the other and their circulations flow independently. But in the placenta the blood vessels of each are separated by only the thinnest of membranes. Across the placental membrane the mother's blood sends the necessary sugars, the proteins, vitamins, and minerals to nourish the baby, and the baby's blood yields up its carbon dioxide and other metabolic waste products to be eliminated by the mother through her lungs and kidneys. Through the umbilical cord, connecting the baby with the placenta, run two arteries and a vein, and through these vessels the baby's circulation carries on its vital traffic to and from the placenta. Together the umbilical cord and the placenta are a tree of life for the child, a tree that sends its roots deep into the mother's body for nourishment and yet has no direct connections with the mother. The placental membrane is highly selective, allowing passage to very few kinds of material that are not directly essential to the child's growth.

The child's growth is continuous before and after birth. The birth itself, dramatic though it is, is an incident, not an interruption. To some extent the kidneys and digestive system and the nervous system are immature at birth and need further time to reach full functioning. Parents notice that their newborn's eyes do not focus. They also know that the sphincter muscles of anus and bladder are not yet under the baby's conscious control, and it is no use to attempt toilet training until they are.

One change is dramatic, sudden, indeed almost instantaneous at birth. In the moment when the child becomes an air-breathing creature, there is a miraculous revision in the functioning of the heart.

THE GREAT CHANGE-OVER

In its uterine Nirvana the child does nothing for itself but build new tissues and grow. Its breathing, like its eating and waste disposal, is done for it. Its lungs develop early, but they lie collapsed and dormant, ready for the moment of birth when their work will begin. The only blood that circulates through them is for the nourishment of their own tissues.

When the lungs are doing their own work, they have their own circulatory system. All the body's blood must flow through these blood vessels, giving up its carbon dioxide to the air in the lungs' air sacs and taking oxygen from them. The lungs then expel carbon dioxide and take in a new supply of oxygen with each breath. This is the mechanism that makes us land-dwelling, air-breathing animals.

This air-breathing mechanism gives the heart two separate circulations to manage. One side, the right, receives the bluish blood from the great veins and sends it out to the lungs to be aerated. The other side, the left, receives it red with oxygen from the lungs and sends it out again, through the great arteries, on its circuit of the body. Within the heart the two sides are completely shut off from each other, as though they were two separate pumps propelling the blood in two different directions at the same time.

While the embryo is in the uterus there is no need for its blood to go to the lungs for aeration. The exchange of carbon dioxide and oxygen is made with the mother's blood across the thin membrane of the placenta, and comes back through the umbilical cord ready to nourish the body tissues of the child.

For this way of breathing during its uterine life, the heart has two special arrangements. There is an oval opening between its two sides, allowing much of the blood that would travel through the lungs to go instead directly into the body's circulatory system. And there is a small bypass artery on the route to the lungs, which detours additional blood into the main circulation and leaves only enough flowing to the lungs to keep them well nourished and healthy. With the moment of birth the baby is on its own and breathing for itself. Its first cry tells us that its lungs are unsealed, expanded and filled with air. In that same moment the two special devices, the oval opening and the bypass artery, cease to function. A flap valve closes over the oval opening and before very long it is sealed like a vulcanized patch on a tire tube. The bypass artery clamps down, begins to shrivel, and in a few days it is no more than a fibrous string.

How does this miracle occur? There have been many theories. An interesting recent one is an almost entirely mechanical explanation, a matter of sudden changes in blood pressure. With the expansion of the lungs, their blood vessels, hitherto tightly coiled, uncoil and the blood rushes into them. The sudden rush of blood into newly opened channels momentarily lowers the volume of blood in the body's system and hence its pressure. In particular the pressure is suddenly reversed at the oval opening and in the bypass artery. In the one, the flap valve closes. In the other, the muscular walls of the little artery themselves clamp together when there is no longer enough volume or pressure of blood in them to keep them open.

Thus with its own first protesting cry, the new human being sets the mechanics of its own heart in order and is ready to take up life in the world and the family of man.

2

THE BODY IN MOTION

I N NATURE all living things move, and there is infinite diversity in their motion. Some creatures move with marvelous swiftness and control. The dragonfly darts and hovers; the hawk swoops or it soars with outspread wings; the small garden snake glides like a shadow out of the path into grassy invisibility. And some forms of life move as imperceptibly as the hour hand on the clock: thus the plant turns to the sun and its blossoms open and close. But slowly or swiftly, they all move. Even the amoeba moves in a leisurely saraband to embrace its dinner.

Human beings are almost never still. Eyes move, eyelids blink, hands and feet and torso shift even as you sit quietly reading this book. The sleeper changes his position many times during the night; contrary to the popular notion about sleeping like a log, the most restful sleep is not totally inert. And in our deepest sleep or, conversely, in our most attentive waking moments, when we seem entirely motionless, even then we are kept in constant though scarcely noticeable motion by the heart's steady beating and the muscles of respiration contracting and relaxing as they work the bellows of the lungs.

Of the thousand thousand movements that our bodies enact each day, most are performed without our awareness and a great many are outside of our voluntary control. Breathing, the propulsion of blood through body and limbs, and of food through the digestive tract—these movements are powered by muscles that function rhythmically and continuously without our bidding. There are many reflex actions of which we are quite unconscious, even as we execute them. There are movements of great complexity, involving the precise timing and co-ordination of many muscles big and small, that we habitually go through with no notion of how we perform them: walking, for instance, or the uttering of meaningful organized sounds that we call speech. These, once learned, have become automatic, and there is no need for the thinking brain to supervise their performance; it can concentrate on the purpose or meaning of the act rather than on the act itself.

A young growing organism, a puppy or a child, is in constant, restless, often explosive motion through its waking hours and only comparatively quiet in sleep. As we grow older, we convert much of this energy into the organized physical activity of our daily tasks and recreations, and many of us replace physical activity largely with activity of the mind, which needs no muscles to leap the barriers of time and space. Many fortunate adults manage to preserve a bit of childhood's kinetic pleasure through the years, in the co-ordinated muscular activity of sports.

Whether or not we stretch our own muscles on the golf course or the ski slope, we can all share the exhilaration of the pole vaulter soaring through his precipitous arc, the football player swiveling down the field, the catch, pivot and throw of a double play in the ritualistic ballet of the baseball diamond. Only man enjoys the special delight of physical movement by proxy.

Most of the movement of which our bodies are capable we share with other species, including even the complicated learned co-ordinations. The fish swims, the bird flies as automatically and skillfully as a man walks. Some actions only a human being can perform. Only man can combine muscle with intelligence and imagination, plan and purpose, to plow and plant a field, to create a museum masterpiece or the "Gettysburg Address." And only man trains to perform the most highly co-ordinated forms of bodily motion for their own sake, in the expressive and athletic arts. We applaud this skill in our species every time we clap our hands for a ballerina or a circus aerialist.

And there is still another kind of motion peculiar to man. Consider the pitcher, the artist of the mound. He bends forward, takes the catcher's signal, makes the mysterious gestures which he believes are essential to his art, and stands motionless for a second. Then he takes a deep breath, draws back, and goes through the series of motions, each one flowing into the next, that constitute the windup and the pitch. As the ball leaves his hand, he has completed a perfect demonstration of the beauty of human motion. If the pitch happens to be a third strike and a third out, he may also smile as he walks off the mound, and this is the human grace note. Many animals can produce a grimace or a snarl. But only man is equipped with such an exquisitely differentiated set of muscles—the mimetic musculature of the face—with no other function than to express and communicate feelings.

THE GENERATORS OF MOTION

We say of an athlete, "He's in condition," and in this simple statement we embrace a world of physiological meaning. When an athlete is in condition, all the systems and organs of his body are functioning in superb integration. Heart and lungs accelerate smoothly, blood courses at an increased rate and pressure to carry fuel to the muscles and waste products away from them; kidneys efficiently filter out the wastes and return the purified fluids to the body. Eyes are sharp, reflexes quick; brain and nerves sort perceptions and co-ordinate actions with that economy that we recognize in the simplest motions of a fine performer. No part of the body is inert; the whole splendid organism is committed when a skilled athlete is at the top of his form. And all this integrated functioning is focused on the group of special tissues that generate movement: the muscles.

A muscle, any muscle, is a collection of long slender cells with a characteristic peculiar only to them: they have the power to contract their length. Because of their shape and toughness we generally call them fibers. Each muscle is a bundle of these fibers laid side by side; in the human body the muscle fibers range in length from a few hundred-thousandths of an inch to an inch or an inch and a half. Each fiber is sheathed in its own thin protective covering and equipped with its own nerve endings. Each has its small stored supply of high-grade fuel, the particular sugar, glycogen, to which the body's chemistry converts a large part of the food we eat. At the signal of an impulse traveling down the nerve, the muscle fiber converts the chemical energy of this fuel into mechanical energy, and the result is motion.

The principle is the same as in any conversion of energy from a chemical to a physical state. We are familiar with it in our automobile engine: the spark ignites the vaporized gasoline, the piston moves, and it keeps moving in response to a series of these small explosions as long as the ignition is turned on and there is fuel to burn. A muscle cell performs the functions of both the spark and the piston; the cell itself splits a molecule of fuel and also exerts the resulting physical power.

We do not know exactly how the muscle fiber turns its chemical energy into the motion peculiar to it—that is, the contraction or shortening of its length. It produces heat in the process, but it is not a heat engine like the gasoline motor, which gets its power from the sudden expansion of heated gases. According to one very recent theory, the contraction is the effect of a folding up of one of the muscle's proteins, called myosin, each of whose molecules is a long chain of amino acids. The myosin molecules, says this theory, fold up in response to the chemical change induced by the splitting of the fuel molecule. When the chemical energy cycle is completed the myosin molecule opens out again; that is, the muscle fiber relaxes, or returns to its uncontracted length.

All this happens in fractions of seconds, unless the nerve impulse that stimulates the cycle is repeated, and the muscle is thus required to continue working. The entire process is on an infinitesimal scale, molecule by molecule. The motive power is delivered not in explosive quantities and at high temperatures, as in a man-made engine, but in tiny packets and at little more than body temperature. Each fiber, shortening, pulls only a fraction of its own tiny length.

The shortest fibers are those of the smooth muscles, and it is not too difficult to imagine that they may do their work in these minute fractions of power. For these are the muscles of our internal organs. They form the walls of the blood vessels and, in combination with elastic tissue and sometimes cartilage, also of the respiratory passages. They power the digestive tract from esophagus to anus; it is these muscle fibers that churn our food in the stomach and propel it along its alimentary pathway, by the wavelike contractions called peristalsis. Smooth muscle fibers form the flat rings about the pupil of the eye, widening and narrowing the opening and allowing more or less light to fall on the retina within. There is a tiny bundle of smooth muscle at the base of every hair in the skin. When these muscles contract, we experience that bumpy phenomenon, goose flesh.

Smooth muscle fibers are controlled by our involuntary, or autonomic, nervous system; we have no conscious control over them. They are part of the steadily functioning mechanism that keeps the body going night and day, making constant adjustments to the external environment, to the body's own internal activities, and to the demands we make on the body hour by hour. These muscle tissues have a remarkable power to remain in a state of contraction for long periods without fatigue, and they also are endowed with a rhythmic function that is apparently inherent in the tissue itself. They may be inactive for long periods, even for years, and yet they are always ready when called upon. The uterus, for example, may rest inert through half a woman's lifetime, but when a child is ready to be born the smooth muscle fibers of the uterus are able to perform one of the body's most challenging tasks.

Quite a different order of muscle tissue is that of the skeletal muscles, the ones of whose working we are not only conscious but also in control. They even look different under the microscope, showing marked regular stripes running laterally across the fibers. For this reason they are also called striped or striated muscles. They have other differences from smooth muscle: they weaken with disuse and they become tired and demand rest. They have fibers many times longer than the smooth muscle, and we know from experience that they can exert astonishing power.

Yet how can these tiny structures muster enough power to lift a leg, let alone a whole body? To add to the wonder, there is still a third kind of muscle, the muscle of that unique organ, the heart, which is a combination of both the other kinds, possessing the tirelessness and the inherent rhythm of smooth muscle plus the dynamic power of skeletal muscles like the biceps.

It is hard to believe that even the longest muscle fiber can do the work that we know our muscles can do. Still, there are thousands of such fibers in each muscle bundle; with some 600 striped muscles in the body, we have a total of about six billion muscle fibers. Each of these fibers is composed of approximately a thousand smaller units, the fibrils. The sum of these many tiny contractions is powerful enough to lift and lower and move ourselves and the objects around us countless times a day. The heart muscle alone accomplishes more than one thousand foot-pounds of work in an ordinary day; once a minute it propels more than ten pounds of fluid through the body at a pressure that could lift the load seven feet into the air.

The total number of foot-pounds of work performed by the muscles of one moderately active human being in the course of the day is easily in the millions. An average man does about 300 foot-pounds of work in the simple act of stepping up into a bus.

When we measure our muscular achievements in these mechanical terms, it seems as though we ought to be exhausted merely by getting out of bed in the morning. But when the man getting on the bus lifts his 150 pounds to the height of two feet, no pair of muscles alone has to expend 300 foot-pounds of energy to do the job. Many muscles collaborate on the task. And they have the help of a remarkable apparatus, the human skeleton.

THE ARTICULATED LEVER SYSTEM

When our muscles move us about, they do it by working a series of articulated levers that make a most efficient use of every ounce of muscular motive power. The levers are the bones of the body's framework, fitted together with the neatness of jigsaw pieces and hinged by joints that must win the admiration of any mechanic.

The bony structure is in itself something of an engineering marvel, strong enough to support weight and carry burdens, yet flexible to cushion shocks and allow for an extraordinary variety of motion. It is an apparatus built of 206 bones and sometimes a few more; about one person in twenty has a thirteenth pair of ribs, which in the rest of us disappeared before birth.

The bones are fitted to each other with a variety of joints bound by tough fibers of connective tissue, the ligaments; the ends of the bones, where they meet, are covered by cartilage, a tissue related to bone but smoother and softer. A lubricant, the synovial fluid, released by the joints themselves greases them and prevents friction. Further cushioning is provided by the bursae, little sacs filled with fluid; they take their name from *bursa*, the Latin word meaning "purse," which they resemble. The muscles are connected to the bones by another set of connective tissues, the tendons; the tapering muscle fibers in their sheaths gather into tendons at one or both ends, and the tendons merge with the sheath of protective tissue that covers each bone. Thus the muscle is bound securely to the bone by a continuous tissue structure.

Some joints permit no motion at all: the skull bones are jointed together, but the joints serve their function only once, at the beginning of life, when they permit enough motion so that the infant head can be pushed through the narrow birth canal. After that they become fixed, providing a solid vaulted case for a precious and sensitive organ.

The other joints permit different degrees of motion; there are four primary kinds and their names are descriptive. Saddle joints connect the vertebrae, giving the twice-curved column of the backbone forward motion along most of its length but less motion backward and from side to side. Ball-and-socket joints allow a good deal of motion in the hips, where the fingers meet the hand, and especially in the shoulders. The fingers themselves have hinge joints; they can double themselves up forward to grasp objects and make a fist, but they cannot bend sideways, or backward to any extent except in very flexible-fingered individuals. The rotary joint of the elbow can double up forward like a hinge and also revolve; together with the very mobile shoulder joint, it gives the hand a wonderfully wide range of fine movements.

THE MECHANICS OF MOTION

Most of the skeletal muscles are attached to two bones across the joint that connects them. When the muscle contracts, it pulls the second bone toward the first one.

You can see the mechanics of this by bending your elbow to lift this book toward your eyes. Look at your biceps muscle, and you will see it shorten and thicken. You can also feel and possibly see the tendon become taut across the inside of the elbow; this is the tendon that connects the biceps, from its site on the bone of the upper arm, diagonally across the elbow to the inner bone of the forearm, called the radius.

Let us say that the two bones are like two pieces of wood, with the elbow joint as the fulcrum between them, and the muscle with its tendon is like a rope running from a pulley in the upper piece and fastened to the lower piece. When you flex your biceps you pull the rope and the lower piece comes up at an angle from the fulcrum. Just so, the elbow bends, your forearm rises and with it the book in your hand.

Now suppose you want to put the book down again. If your

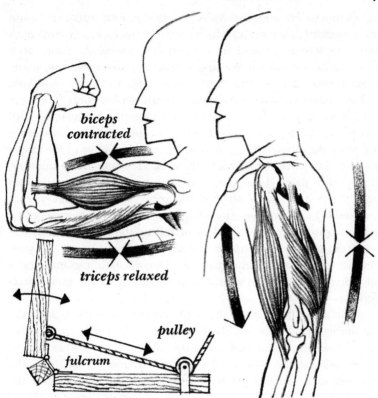

biceps contracted

triceps relaxed

pulley

fulcrum

biceps simply let go—abruptly released its tension—then forearm, hand, and book would fall of their own weight, and if you were reading at a desk or table you would undoubtedly suffer a sharp rap on the knuckles. That is what would happen if your arm were merely like two pieces of wood with a rope and pulley arrangement. But the apparatus is a good deal more interesting than our simple analogy.

The act of straightening your arm again is also a muscle-controlled motion. Another muscle, the triceps, connects the upper and lower bones; specifically, it runs from the back of the upper arm across the outside of the elbow to the ulna, the other bone of the forearm. To lower the book, the triceps contracts against the gradual release of the biceps; the elbow straightens, the forearm is extended, and the book is gently lowered to the desk.

This is a commonplace motion, one that we perform many thousands of times a day. It makes use of one of the simplest of the body's muscle-bone-joint devices. Yet it is, on examination, quite extraordinary. Two muscles have been called into play, and both have functioned in the same way and in the same direction; both have contracted toward the upper arm. Yet you have moved the book in two opposite directions, toward you and away from you, and you have made both movements with perfect control.

This is thanks to the fact that your upper arm is equipped with two paired muscles, so placed that they pull against each other and work the elbow joint in opposite directions. Most of the major muscles that move the body's framework are arranged in this way, in opposing pairs. There are some two hundred such pairs controlling the movements of head and torso, arms and legs, fingers and toes. There are even tiny antagonists, six of them arranged in pairs, surrounding the eyeballs, controlling the movements of our eyes from side to side and up and down. What is more, the muscles of each eye are synchronized to the corresponding muscles of the other so that our eyes turn simultaneously in the same direction.

In our experiment with the book, another anomaly may strike the mechanically minded: both the biceps and the triceps have pulled the forearm toward the upper arm; yet the upper arm to which each muscle is attached is also highly mobile, and so is the shoulder to which it is jointed. Why do not the muscles pull the upper arm and shoulder down toward the forearm, instead of vice versa, or else pull both book and shoulder toward each other?

In order for the upper arm muscles to move the forearm with precision, they must have a fixed base from which to operate; the upper arm has to be held firm. And we find this is exactly what happens. When we want to move the forearm, the group of powerful muscles of the shoulder tense to hold the upper arm firm, and other muscles that are even more remote also become taut to stabilize the shoulder. If you were lifting something really heavy instead of only a book, you would possibly be aware of the tensing of these co-ordinating muscles. They are called synergists, meaning that they work together. Without their teamwork, we would never be sure how any movement that we initiated might end up. With them, we are able to move exactly the member that we want to move, to exactly where we want to move it.

Paired antagonists and related synergists work together in this way throughout the body's framework. They keep us erect, maintain our balance and, by their beautiful co-ordination, they permit us to make our movements precise. We can put out a hand as far as necessary, and no farther, to turn the page. We can also exert exactly enough power to lift a page, a book, or a brief case full of books, all with the same hand and the same set of muscles.

Judgment and experience enter into these movements; the brain interprets the messages of our eyes, as well as messages from the muscles and parts of the body. On the basis of these perceptions and the experience behind them, the brain guides the direction and power of each movement. Each striated muscle is equipped with sensory nerves as well as motor nerves; the sensory nerves are part of the proprioceptive—self-perceiving—senses of the body that keep us informed of the position of our limbs, head, and torso in relation to each other and in relation to our environment. The sensory nerves in the muscles indicate to the brain the state of contraction of each one, and thus the motor messages from the brain are based on information as to how matters stand at each moment.

In addition, the muscles have a characteristic reflex of their own, the stretch reflex, and this is particularly important in keeping us balanced whether we are sitting, standing, or moving about. Each time a muscle is stretched it reflexively contracts; it does this automatically, without an instructing message from the conscious brain. Thus we respond to the pull of gravity and the shifting of our weight as we move. Even as we stand or sit still, there is an imperceptible sway caused by breathing and the coursing of the blood, and without the stretch reflex we probably should often be on the verge of toppling over. Involuntary and virtually instantaneous, this reflex is an essential part of the combined system of eyes, semicircular canals, and self-perceiving senses that guide us in maintaining our posture and equilibrium.

Our voluntary movements are not automatic reflexes, like the stretch reflex, but we begin to learn the refinements of judgment and muscular control at a very early age, and they soon become automatic. We see the curb of the sidewalk, and we raise a foot just high enough to step up on it, without being aware either of the visual perception of the distance or of the muscular co-ordinations that are necessary to negotiate it. Each experience of the kind adds to the exactness of our judgment of distance, and each act of muscular co-ordination confirms the nerve pathways of that particular movement.

To the spectator watching the ball game, it seems like sheer magic when the outfielder runs the instant after the ball has been hit and then stands waiting for it as it comes down out of the sky, holding out his glove to make the catch. How does he know just how fast and how far to run, and where to stop and wait? But what he does is only the furthest extension, by talent and training, of a power that we all share to some degree and make use of with virtually every movement that we perform. It is the power of co-ordinated muscular control that is responsive and obedient to learned judgment and the sum of our perceptions.

THE WORKING MUSCLE

The more a muscle works the stronger it grows, for example, the formidable musculature of a tennis champion's playing arm. A wrestler's knotty biceps and the softly curved upper arms of a young girl contain approximately the same number of fibers. Not the number of muscle fibers, but their size and strength have been increased by the wrestler's line of work.

A muscle also works better after it has been working for a while than when it first begins. Athletes, acrobats, dancers, and even home gardeners, if they are wise, take care to begin their exertions with mild preparatory exercise. The warm-up is literally what the familiar term suggests. Muscles work faster and better at higher temperatures than at lower ones. Cold-blooded animals like turtles and frogs move slowly and sleepily as the weather turns cold, and when it becomes really cold they dig in and go to sleep until spring. The warm-blooded species, except for those that hibernate, maintain a steady body temperature regardless of the weather. But the muscles at work do raise the temperature. At the end of a three-mile race an athlete's temperature may be as high as 105° Fahrenheit. The heat generated by the muscles themselves increases the speed and power of their performance, because the power source is a chemical reaction, and chemical reactions speed up by a measurable rate as the temperature rises.

The major factor in the muscle's improved performance after a warm-up comes from its increased supply of blood, and hence of oxygen. This the muscle itself also helps to bring about, for among the chemical products of its activity are some that stimulate the increased blood flow. At the peak of physical activity as much as twelve quarts a minute may be pumped through the muscles, more than twice the heart's entire output while we are resting. There comes a time when the muscle tires. How soon this fatigue point is reached depends on how well developed the muscle is. An experienced typist may type all day without a sign of fatigue in her fingers, but her leg muscles may ache after a quarter of a mile of brisk walking. If you tapped a single finger steadily and rapidly you would find after a while that the finger itself would stop; you could not continue tapping it no matter how hard you willed to do so.

It was believed for many years that the muscle's own fatigue product, lactic acid, was the cause of fatigue; when enough lactic acid accumulated in the muscle, it would be unable to continue working. More likely it is not the muscle, however, that goes on strike, but the nervous connection. Nerves themselves are remarkably resistant to fatigue, but along the nerve pathways there are spaces across which the impulse jumps from one nerve to the next. It is at such gaps, called synapses, that fatigue sets in. When the motor impulse fails to reach the muscle, then of course the muscle stops working.

In the complete chemical cycle of a working muscle, lactic acid is reclaimed as rapidly as it is produced, provided the blood is able to supply oxygen fast enough for the reclamation. In strenuous work or exercise the muscles use tremendous quantities of oxygen, and even when the heart and lungs of a well-trained athlete are working at top efficiency they cannot supply enough oxygen to meet the demand. And here we see a remarkable phenomenon. The muscles keep going at the pace that we demand of them, and they do it in spite of the lack of sufficient oxygen. They simply incur an oxygen debt. This is why the runner, in top condition though he is for the race, collapses panting after he has crossed the finish line; he continues to pant and gasp for air until he has paid off his muscles' oxygen debt and their chemistry is once more in order.

In our civilized world the power of our muscles to go into oxygen debt and still keep working merely makes for good fast competition in sports. To primitive man, pitting his hunter's cunning against the strength and swiftness of powerful beasts, it must often have meant survival.

MUSCLES OF EMOTION

We have talked about the smooth muscles that provide motion in the inner systems and organs and the striped muscles that move the body's framework. A few muscles do not move bones but give support and motion, for example, to the eyes. Some human beings retain the ability to wiggle the ears. In the lower animals these muscles have the useful function of turning the pinna, the external flap, of the ear so as to catch the least sound, but in man the auricular muscles serve only to amuse.

And there are the muscles of the face, the mimetic muscles. They are uniquely human, and they are also unique among the muscles in the human body. They are slender, delicately differentiated, and as responsive to our feelings as a leaf to every breeze. Most of them do not move bones, and some have no bony attachment at all. Dimples, and eventually the lines and grooves of habitual facial expression, mark the places where these muscles are attached to the skin.

Small though they are, the facial muscles are among the strongest in the body. Somehow these interesting muscles were ignored through the centuries by the physiologists. Not even the artist-anatomists of the Renaissance, not Leonardo da Vinci or the pupils of Titian who produced the superb anatomical drawings for Vesalius, took note of this singularly human and appealing group of muscles. It was not until the last century that the British artist-scientist Sir Charles Bell eloquently called attention to "phenomena the most surprising in the whole extent of nature, and the most affecting to human sympathies." Charles Darwin concurred and attempted to trace the evolution of emotional expression in man back to animal expressions of primitive rage and fear. Bell, and other investigators after him, linked the facial expression of strong emotion to the respiratory functions, which also respond characteristically in times of emotional stress. How and why the many separate muscles developed that reveal all the fine nuances of human feeling—this remains a mystery.

There are some sixteen muscles in the group, most of them in pairs for the two sides of the face. The largest and most powerful one, a singleton, is called the platysma. It is the last remnant in man of the thick over-all blanket of skin muscles by which animals shiver and shrug off insects. It extends from the chest to the lower jaw, lip, and cheeks, and by its downward pull it exaggerates all the dark emotions. When the platysma contracts, fear becomes terror, sorrow becomes anguish, surprise turns to horror; it is the muscle of melodrama.

A branch of the platysma is the "grin muscle," the risorius, which pulls the corners of the mouth back into a dry grin or even a sneer. With the co-operation of what nineteenth-century physiologists named the muscles of laughter, the zygomatic muscles extending from the cheekbones, the sneer becomes a smile. And with a little more encouragement from these muscles the nose wrinkles up and we are laughing.

Five separate muscles converging on the corners of the mouth contribute to its mobility and astonishing variety of expression; in the textbooks they all have their Latin names, but medical writers of the past gave them evocative labels. The "muscle of sorrow," as they called it, draws the corners of the mouth down; a different muscle lifts the lip and nostril in grief—this is the one we sternly inhibit for a stiff upper lip. A versatile muscle in the chin, which physiologists of another era called superbus, the "haughty muscle," indicates degrees of firmness, disdain, or petulance, or it sets the chin and lower lip trembling, a warning that tears are not far off. The mouth is equipped with four muscles for sorrow and only two for joy; what significance that has, if it has any, is a question for philosophers to ponder.

In the upper part of the face, "muscles of attention" wrinkle the forehead transversely, raise the eyebrows, and open the eyes wide, and "muscles of reflection" pull the brows together and draw vertical lines between them. The paired "muscles of pain" raise the brows in an oblique angle, an unhappy expression that may range from mild concern to acute distress.

Looking into each other's faces to read the emotional meaning there, we generally look first to the eyes and mouth. These features are the focal points of expression, for three reasons: the three powerful orbicular muscles. There is one of these for the mouth and a pair of double ones for the eyes; they are circular muscles that work like purse strings, pulling the circle tight when they contract. The orbicular of the mouth relaxes when we laugh and the orbiculars of the eyes pull the lids together and wrinkle the corners; they are responsible for the genial laugh wrinkles, or crow's-feet. The pair circling the eyes work in opposition to the one that purses the mouth, and most of the other facial muscles are antagonists of one or the other of these. That is, they work in opposition to each other: you wrinkle your eyes and open your mouth to laugh, but when you are astonished it is your mouth muscle that pulls up tight, while your eye muscles relax and your eyes open wide. There are almost no limits to the shades and intensities of expression that these muscles, working with and against each other in every sort of combination, can produce.

Every human face is different from every other, and the eloquent facial muscles contribute vastly to the differences. Their position, the points at which they are attached to the skin, even the number of their distinct fiber bundles differ from one individual to another. Families pass on some resemblances from generation to generation, and there are some basic resemblances among members of each of the broad racial divisions of man. But in the mixed inheritance of each one of us the individual differences are more striking than the similarities.

As we mature, each of us tends to use certain muscles and combinations of muscles rather than others. Each of our faces acquires a characteristic set of expressions that those who know us learn to read. Thus, through the years, we write our personalities, our strengths and weaknesses, our very identities in the unmistakable tracings of our mimetic musculature.

All the muscles by which we move contribute to this identity. The way we walk, stand, or sit, the way we hold our heads and move our hands, all these express both the whole person and the state of mind and body of the moment. In the face, our window on the world, the plastic muscles of expression speak our most personal language.

3

THE SELF-PROTECTING,

SELF-REPAIRING BODY

COMPARED WITH its environment, the body seems alarmingly fragile. Almost every object it encounters is harder, sharper, more solid and more resistant than tender skin and yielding flesh. We have only to watch a young child's first independent explorations to become aware of the potential menace of the physical world in which we live. Indoors, the furniture bristles with inimical points, sharp edges, legs to trip the unwary walker. Outdoors, rocks lurk to stub the toes, ascents and descents and a variety of obstacles impede the way. Everywhere, small foreign objects lie in wait to invade the eyes, nose, and mouth, while large ones threaten to pierce the skin and bruise the flesh and bones.

Or so it seems. Yet most of us pursue our busy active lives without ever experiencing serious injury to this apparently vulnerable body. Indeed, the species survived and prospered through hundreds of thousands of years, in environments probably far more hostile than any we can imagine from the vantage point of our sheltering civilization.

Today we encounter only in the pages of books, or in our dreams, the tusked mammoth and saber-toothed tiger, but our ancestors roamed the wild forests and Ice Age tundras in search of these animals and conquered them for food. Prehistoric men lived dangerous lives, and many of them died of the accidents to which they were hourly exposed. Their life span has been estimated as less than thirty years. Despite the hazards of their world, enough of them lived to rear children or we would not be here to study the fossil records of their lives.

The body is far tougher than it looks. Through the ages of its evolution, by mutations and adaptations, it gained ever new and better equipment for survival. From cushioned toe to thatched poll, from its bony architecture to the chemical composition of its blood, the human body is prepared to protect itself against injury and repair itself when injury occurs. And all of its safety devices and repair services are built in, automatic, and ready on demand for emergencies around the clock.

Part of the body's protection is in its architecture and the materials of which it is made. When, in a heated discussion, you pound your fist into your palm, the skin remains unbroken, the flesh compresses without bruising, the bones do not shatter; no damage is done to sensitive nerves or thin-walled arteries and veins. If in the course of the day you should suffer a bump or bruise, prick or nick, the injury may hurt a bit, but you know in advance that the swelling and soreness will vanish, the blood will stanch itself, the break in the skin will seal itself up again. A gash in the flesh, a torn ligament or broken bone will take longer, but the body will repair those too. And with reasonably favoring conditions the injured part will mend as good as new, often with no help beyond the body's own resources.

THE BODY'S ARCHITECTURE

The human skeleton is a remarkable piece of functional architecture. Human builders for centuries have been rediscovering the same principles that living species long ago evolved. Uncounted ages before the architects of Rome swung the first dome atop the Pantheon and built arches to support their aqueducts, the dome of the skull already roofed the human head in its present perfection, the arches of the foot provided a strong, springy support for the body's weight in motion, and the arched ribs formed a light, flexible cage sheltering the organs within the thorax. The columns of the Greeks and the Egyptians were antedated by the columns of animal and human legs, and the first curved portal in man's experience was the gateway of the pelvis through which he entered the world.

Bones are not the longest-lasting building materials, but they weather the years remarkably well, and for combined strength and

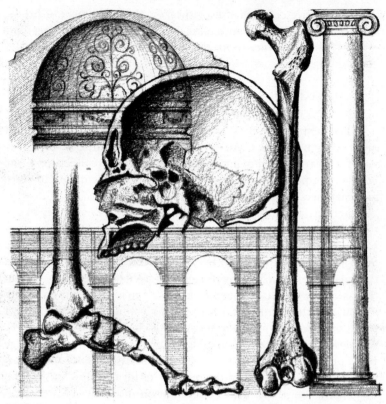

flexibility they outdo many materials devised by man and are far lighter besides. A shin made of bricks would not support a man of average weight, but the shinbone can bear thirty times the weight of the man who rests on it; it would hold up an automobile with four or five passengers. Iron itself would be no stronger, and iron would be too rigid to take the stresses of the body in motion and far too heavy for practical purposes.

Over its bony framework the body lays tissues that neither splinter, chip, nor weather away as do wood, brick, cement, stucco, and paint. Ligaments like wire cords tie the frame together. Flesh, muscles, and fat fill in the chinks. The outer covering, or skin, is tough and comes in attractive colors suitable to various climates. Finger tips and toes come equipped with a hard, horny layer of skin that grows to a projecting overhang of protection, the fingernails and toenails. Teeth grow an enamel resistant to chemicals that are strong enough to digest food. The eyes, the windows of this house, have curtains of eyelashes, overhanging eaves of brows, and shutters that close automatically. The structure's outer covering is able to produce protecting hairs where needed.

ROOMS IN THE HOUSE

The body's structure must serve two functions: like a building, it must safely house its occupants, and like a machine it must provide for a variety of moving parts. The interior architecture of the body is compartmental, guarding its precious occupants in separate chambers and by a variety of sheltering devices.

The heart and lungs have a room virtually to themselves in the thorax, a springy, expanding cage of bones and muscle. Two armor plates, the scapulae or shoulder blades, reinforce the upper and outermost quadrants of the back. The ribs, the bony supports of this cage, are arched, providing great strength in proportion to their weight; they are hinged fore and aft to allow for the vital inflation and deflation of the lungs in breathing. The diaphragm forms the powerful muscular floor of this chamber.

Below the diaphragm is the abdominal cavity, the second large room of the house. Here the walls are mainly muscle; the framework is the inwardly curved ridge of the lower spine and a solid bone floor, the pelvis, which rises high on the sides. This gives an armor-plate protection to the organs enjoying its shelter, in this case the reproductive organs nestled deep within this girdling bone.

Some other organs have special protection; the liver, for example, is tucked securely up on the right under the diaphragm and the lower ribs. The kidneys are sheltered by the spinal column and the powerful back muscles, and by the intestines, coiled muscular tubes filled with liquid and gases, which make ideal bumpers.

Over the whole torso is the heavily layered muscular wall, thickest on the exposed back. By comparison the breast and belly seem vulnerable, but they have the arms and legs to ward off blows and the flexible backbone allows the torso itself to fold forward like a jackknife. Furthermore the eyes see to the front and can warn of danger to the tender underside.

The house of the body also has its sheltered passageways. The trachea and esophagus, passages for air and food, and the major blood vessels running to the head are encased in the muscular column of the throat, with its bony vertebral support. The vital arteries to the body's extremities are imbedded deep in the arms and legs, and, where they come close to the surface at the joints, they are on the inner side. The sensitive spinal cord runs within its own bony corridor, the shaft that descends through the center of the spinal column like the concrete elevator shaft in a skyscraper.

The brain is most carefully safeguarded, for the body would be too often helpless and adrift if its master control center could be shaken by every passing blow. Its domed bony roof provides great strength by its shape as well as its material, and most blows glance harmlessly off its rounded surface. The thick skin of the scalp, well supplied with cushiony tissue, adds further insulation, and it is topped with a thatch of resilient hair. Just inside the roof of the skull, a thin, very tough wrapping—the dura mater—surrounds and protects the brain.

One more device guards the tender occupants of the body's house. A fluid barrier as a shock absorber is familiar to engineers, and the bottle that drifts unbroken across thousands of miles of stormy ocean, carrying a castaway's message, is a classic detail of adventure stories. The body's fluids surround all the organs and systems of the body; indeed every cell and tissue is bathed in this inland sea. Surrounding the brain and spinal cord there are special fluid compartments, and the brain has its own fluid-filled chambers, the ventricles, distributed among its lobes and regions.

The body's master plan provides even for future contingencies during a lifetime. In the blueprint for the female body is the plan for another such fluid compartment, to be developed when the need arises. This is the amniotic sac, or bag of waters, in which the unborn infant floats in safety throughout its nine prenatal months. The sac grows and fills with fluid within the uterus around the growing embryo, and at birth when its usefulness is ended it empties and is discarded.

The body is not merely built to stand, like a house, or to move, like a machine or a vehicle. It is also built to grow and to respond to and act upon its environment. It is alive, a restless, dynamic organism. It is in almost constant action and, being human, its action is more often than not a wrestling match with objects in its environment. Man moves not only himself but virtually everything else as well. He has been making over his environment to suit himself since he first carried animal hides into a cave to make its stone floor softer to lie on and set up flaming sticks to light its darkness and drive out its chilly damp. He has to be built to survive the shocks and jolts of his own activity.

To be sure, many of our animal relatives need this kind of body structure. Many of its features we have in common with them. But some are exclusive with man, who walks and runs on two feet, voluntarily lifts and carries burdens sometimes nearly his own weight, and performs more kinds of movements than any other animal. A cat climbs, an antelope leaps, a chamois scales mountains. Man, without their special physical equipment, accomplishes all these feats and many more besides that only he has thought of.

He can perform all these extravagant movements that meet his needs or please his fancy, because he has such a marvelously plastic body structure. He has strong straight leg bones to support his weight, but also springlike forms, such as his S-curved spine and his arched feet, to take the bumps. Even his bones are flexible, up to a point; they are spongy rather than solid and they contain many wirelike fibers. They have ends of soft cartilage that will yield and spring back instead of chipping as a harder material would do. Cartilage discs act as buffers between the vertebrae of his remarkably flexible spine. His joints are lubricated and cushioned, as we have seen, and the tendons that bind the muscles to his bones have the strength of steel chains and the resilience of the finest hard rubber. The flesh, too, is resilient, springing back into shape; the skin is elastic, and there are pads of extra fat in strategic places.

This dynamic structure is also adapted to his needs at every stage of his growth. In the child not yet born, the bones are actually not quite bone but closer to cartilage. They have little or no strength to bear the body's weight, but he does not need this strength. On the other hand, they are extremely flexible, and flexibility is what he does need in order to pass without injury through the narrow birth canal. The bones of his skull, the largest part of him at this stage, are not only soft but are still separated from each other and can be safely compressed during birth.

In the young child walking, running, climbing—and often falling—the bones are harder but still soft enough to absorb the ordinary jolts of trial and error without breaking. As he grows, gaining weight, but also strength and physical skills, his bones harden. Most of the rubbery cartilage is gradually replaced by calcium phosphate, the rigid material of bone tissue. During the first year of life the proportion of soft to hard material in the bones is eight to one. At the age of eighty the ratio is exactly reversed, one to eight. Presumably at eighty we are less inclined to physical adventure and we are also possessed of the wisdom and experience to avoid accident.

SAFETY DEVICES

The structure, built for action and growth, is also equipped with a battery of safety devices. Some of these are structural, like the fringe of eyelashes and the overhanging ridge of the brows that protect the eyes. The nose also has its screen of little hairs, and the inner nasal passages are lined with fine hairlike fibrils that filter the air we breathe, trapping a vast proportion of dust and other particles before they can be carried into the lungs via the bronchial tubes.

Other devices go into action automatically when needed. The eyes and nose are kept constantly moist by the mucous membrane, and if an invader does get past their other defenses the nose is promptly flooded by an increased flow of mucus and the eyes by a gush of tears from the lachrymal glands. The respiratory system also has explosive ejection methods: we sneeze if the invader is in the nose and cough if it is in the windpipe or beyond.

Sneezing and coughing are reflexes. So is the blink of the eyelid when a moving object, or even the shadow of one, approaches too close to the eye. The sensitive middle ear has a similar protective device, a set of tiny muscles and bones which keep the eardrum from vibrating to a sound that may be loud and sudden enough to cause damage.

We are hardly aware of the vast number of reflexes which protect us from harm without our even knowing that harm threatens. The stretch reflex of the muscles, which keeps us from falling, has already been mentioned. The reflexes work automatically without involving the thinking brain; their nerve connections are by way of centers in the spinal cord. Here the message comes in from the receptor or sensory nerve, and the impulse is instantly converted into action by way of the motor nerves. We move first, and the conscious brain learns about it afterward. In some instances a whole group of motor nerves and their muscles may be co-ordinated in a reflex action. When the hand jerks back from a hot surface in the familiar hot-stove reflex, all the muscles of the arm and shoulder are called into play, and so are muscles of the torso and legs to keep us from losing our balance in making the sudden move.

The hot-stove reflex is only one of a large group of automatic protective responses; we pull back in the same way from a pinprick, or from the unexpected sharp pebble when we are walking barefoot on soft grass or a sandy beach. All our senses are protective to some extent, warning us of danger, but the sensory nerves that bring us sensations of a disagreeable nature, the nerves of pain, are specific safeguards. They are spread through the skin, a network of protection all over the body, and they are thickly clustered in exposed spots like the finger tips, the eyes, and the face.

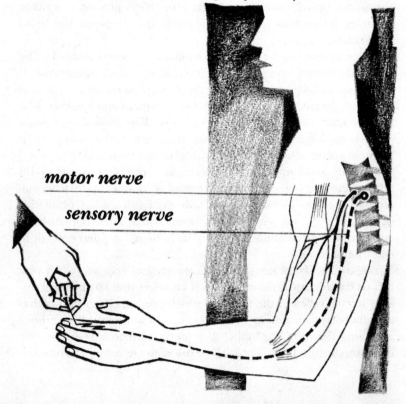

motor nerve

sensory nerve

Pain, unpleasant though it is, has an indispensable function; it is the body's most efficient biological protective device. In combination with the safety reflexes it jerks us back from danger before we are too severely hurt. And when we do suffer injury, pain obliges us to keep the injured part quiet, so that rest and the body's repair services can do their work.

THE BODY'S OWN FIRST AID

When an injury occurs to the body the first-aid mechanisms are automatically turned on. The blood vessels in the neighborhood of the injury dilate and an increased blood supply comes in. At the same time the pores in the thin walls of the tiny blood vessels, the capillaries, also open, letting more plasma than usual flow through to the injured tissues. The immediate result is twofold: the increased flow of blood and plasma brings the body's repair materials to the spot in large quantities, and incidentally the increase in fluid at the spot distends tissues, presses on nerves, raises the local temperature. The word we have for all this is inflammation. Inflammation causes pain, which puts the injured part out of action. As we have observed, this in itself is one of the body's protective devices, and not the least important of them by any means.

If the skin is broken and there is bleeding, another mechanism is brought into action, and this is one at which scientists do not cease to marvel. It is also the very one that most of us accept with utter casualness. When we sustain a small cut, we simply wait for it to stop bleeding or to dry up, and perhaps we are annoyed because it does not stop or dry up quickly enough to suit our convenience.

It all seems quite simple. Yet it is anything but simple. It is one of the body's most astonishing performances. The blood does not merely stop flowing, nor does it dry up by evaporation. It forms a cork that stops up the opening.

This is nothing less than a change from liquid to solid, a miraculous change that occurs automatically in response to any break in a blood vessel, even a pinprick in a tiny capillary in the skin. The blood-clotting mechanism goes into operation at the site of the injury—and not elsewhere. Elsewhere in the system the blood continues in the fluid state, coursing through the veins and arteries on its normal rounds.

The mystery of how the blood can remain fluid and continue circulating through the body, and also turn solid at the site of an injury so that it does not drain away, has tantalized research men in medicine, biology, chemistry, physics, genetics. Today we know how to encourage and discourage coagulation of the blood, and we can describe in fair detail how the mechanism works, although we still have not found the answers to all our questions about this remarkable property of the blood.

Four different substances are chiefly involved in clotting, and all four are essential. Only three are ordinarily present in the blood; the fourth is locked in the tissues. Not until tissue is damaged, and the fourth substance is liberated, is the coagulating mechanism put to work.

What happens then is that the substance liberated by the wound, called thromboplastin, acts upon one of the constituents of the blood, called prothrombin, and in the presence of calcium, also a normal constituent of the blood, the prothrombin changes to a similar but active material, thrombin. (The word element *thrombo,* which occurs in all these names, means to curdle or congeal.) Now the newly formed thrombin reacts with another chemical in the blood, fibrinogen, to form fibrin. This substance, the end product of the series of chemical reactions, is insoluble, spongelike, and has the property of being able to contract, or shrink. It forms a network of threads that enmesh the red blood cells; it pulls them together, as it contracts, into a tough little mass. And that is a clot.

Nor is this all, for other agents are active in the process. In the blood, along with the red and white blood cells, there are tiny fragments of protoplasm, the blood platelets. Where they come from we do not precisely know—perhaps from the red bone marrow that makes the red blood cells, or perhaps from the disintegration of red blood cells that goes on continuously in the body, as does also the formation of new ones.

Every quart of blood contains about one thousand billion of these minute bits of living material; each one of them is about one-fourth the size of a red blood cell, and even smaller in comparison with the white cells, which are of various sizes but all larger than the red cells. But size is not a measure of importance, especially in the body.

Even though no more than a few drops of blood may flow from a cut, platelets by the tens of thousands come in contact with the rough edge of injured tissue, and they disintegrate. Thus they liberate thromboplastin at the spot where it is needed. Their scientific name, one that indicates their important role in the blood-clotting mechanism, is thrombocyte, or blood-clotting cell.

The platelets help to stop the flow of blood in two additional ways. They release a chemical that stimulates the muscle walls of nearby blood vessels to contract, narrowing the channels along which blood is flowing to the cut and also narrowing the cut end that needs to be plugged. And the platelets themselves, being sticky, act as a natural adhesive, helping to seal up the cut. They are both chemical and mechanical agents.

Now we see why the blood does not clot by itself. Its prothrombin and fibrinogen, and the calcium which acts as catalyst in the reaction, are always present, but they are inactive unless thromboplastin is released and sets off the chain of events. And in case some active thrombin should be present in the blood, the plasma normally contains an antagonist—called, suitably enough, antithrombin—which neutralizes the unnecessary and normally unwanted thrombin. With an injury, however, the liberation of thromboplastin sets in motion the creation of an emergency supply of thrombin and the clotting proceeds. Incidentally the level of prothrombin in the blood, in readiness for emergency, is kept up by the vitamin K that we take in our food, mainly in green vegetables.

The clotting process has taken a good number of words to describe, even in a short summary that leaves out many technical details. In action it is quite rapid. Normal blood in a test tube takes between four and eight minutes to change from a fluid to a gelatinous mass that will not pour out of the tube. In a half hour it has separated into a clear amber fluid, the blood serum, and a semisolid red clot which is quite tough.

THE READY REPAIR SERVICES

The same materials that arrest bleeding prepare the site for mending. The fibrin threads contract and pull together the edges of the wound under the natural adhesive patch of the clot, and the repair cells go to work. These repair cells are a variety of connective tissue, long and spindle-shaped, with fibrous branches; they bind the edges of the wound together with the neatness of an expert seamstress. This done, their work is ended; their remnants and the remnants of cells damaged in the injury are cleared away by scavenger cells, cellular sanitation squads that keep all kinds of microscopic debris from cluttering the body tissues.

When a cut is relatively clean and small, the edges of tissue are brought together in a neat seam and there is no visible evidence of the repair; often it cannot be seen even under a microscope. The repair cells have acted as basting stitches, and they are disposed of when the tissues themselves effect a permanent juncture with their own cells. But when the wound is extensive, with uneven edges, the repair cells are unable to pull the edges together. Instead, they must build a bridge across the gap, and this they proceed to do. Unfortunately, these cells of connective tissue, the fibroblasts, can no more change into skin than the cement used to plug a damaged tree trunk can turn into bark. So, in much the same manner as cement, the fibroblasts harden, changing into tough, contracting, white scar tissue.

The scars of this kind of healing, the best the body can do and remarkable enough under the circumstances, may nevertheless be unsightly and they may also interfere with nerves, blood vessels and muscles. When such a wound occurs, the physician lends a hand by stitching the edges of the damaged tissues together, giving the body the conditions under which it can do its own beautiful repair work.

When a bone is broken, the repair mechanism works on similar principles; but the task requires different material, as strong as the original bone and capable of hardening rapidly. The first repair cells bind the broken ends of bone together, and along these bonds the osteoblasts, bone-forming cells, begin at once to grow. Callus, a tough binding material, holds the break firm until the new bone is properly hardened, and eventually it also turns into true bone. When the task is done, bone-scavenger cells clear away excess repair cells and trim the mended area to nearly its original size. When the break is jagged and the ends out of alignment, the body's repair mechanisms fill in with their mending materials, but often not adequately. Again man's medical skill steps in to help the natural process, in this case by setting the fracture and giving the body the necessary start for a good bone-repair job.

Some injuries cause damage the body cannot repair; some tissues, once destroyed, will not grow again. The body nevertheless may continue to function adequately, even perfectly. We are equipped for contingencies.

Our bodies are built on a generous scale. We have pairs of eyes, ears, lungs, kidneys. Furthermore most organs have a good deal more tissue than they actually need to perform their functions for the body. Each of the two kidneys contains one million filter units to remove waste products from the blood, but the body can manage with only one-fourth that number and could survive with even fewer. Only half the body's lung tissue is needed for any but strenuous exertion; with only one-fifth, a man could live quietly to a respectable old age.

If a vein or artery is put out of action, the blood switches course; like a brook making its way through a valley the blood finds new channels through another vessel or several vessels. In many areas of the body, nerves can substitute for one another; neighboring muscles pick up the load of a disabled muscle. The senses compensate for one that is weakened or lost.

Man shares most of these physical repair systems and compensating mechanisms with the higher animals. They, too, have spare parts and can use them to some extent. But there is one immeasurable difference between man and even his most intelligent animal relative, a difference that means not only survival but compensation on a grand scale, and that is the human mind.

The mind gives man the added powers of intellect, imagination, ingenuity to overcome disabilities that are beyond the body's powers to repair. It gives him the conscious will to live and to perform to his fullest capacity. It gives him, further, the support of other men's minds, of their science, skill, and encouragement. When the body's healing mechanisms have reached their limit, then its master organ, the brain, takes up the challenge. The marvels of the body's healing do not end with its chemical and physical powers of repair. There is still the mind, the determined and often brilliant rehabilitator of muscle movement and nerve co-ordination, the creator of artificial limbs and of techniques for replacing tissues and even organs by grafting and transplantation.

4

CO-EXISTENCE IN THE
MICROCOSM

MODERN MAN in his steel and concrete cities scarcely sees himself as part of the struggle for survival. He has pushed the visible boundaries of nature so far out of sight that he tends to look upon nature's basic law with the detachment of a visitor to the zoo. The pacing tiger and the baleful-eyed buzzard, there behind the bars, cause him only a pleasurable shiver of excitement. The raw rivalry of all life for food and living space seems as remote. As far as he is concerned, it too has been caged.

This is an illusion. The biological will to live is a powerful force. It exists in all of nature's marvelous multiplicity of living forms, and it cannot be caged. The primitive struggle for survival goes with man right into his cities. Rats prowl in his sewers and subway tunnels, and birds of prey hunt in his skyscraper canyons. Above the heads of a Manhattan lunch-hour throng a peregrine falcon catches in midflight a starling for his own lunch. A red-shouldered hawk pursues a rat through the open door of an East Side garage and catches it under the eyes of a startled mechanic. A dozen or so varieties of winged hunters, including the bald eagle, are regular visitors during migrating seasons and some are habitués of the metropolis. If mice, rats, and a vast avian population take up quarters with man in his cities, the species that feed on them will follow them there.

In the air-conditioned, electrically powered world of our own making it is easy to forget that we are biological organisms, subject to the same natural laws as the hawk and the rat. Our bodies, fortunately, do not share our illusion. Our bodies continue to fight the biological battle of all living creatures, though in our modern world it is fought mainly in a dimension invisible to the unaided eye. For this unseen struggle we have inherited a set of defenses that have kept the human species alive through eons of microscopic warfare.

THE CROWDED MICROCOSM

Like the city, the body is a highly organized community; also like the city, its population includes not only its permanent residents, the cells, but a number of transients which find it a good place to visit. These are the microbes; their name comes from two Greek words meaning "small" and "life."

These minute organisms exist everywhere in the world of living creatures. Incredible numbers of them float in every droplet of water and every thimbleful of air, and the soil teems with them. They live with, upon, and within every plant and every animal, including the human animal. They have their own multiplicity of forms and species. And, like all life, they too must compete for a living.

The microscopic world has its struggle for survival, but its struggle is on a far larger than microscopic scale. The world of the microorganisms invades every chink and cranny of our world. Its rivalries seethe in a different dimension, but they involve us at a thousand points.

With some of the microorganisms we merely co-exist. Others are essential to the continuance of life on earth, and some of these are specifically useful to human life. A few of the microbes are our enemies, against which the body automatically mobilizes its microscopic defenses.

Among the microorganisms that are classed as animal are the one-celled amoebas, the Protozoa, and the many-celled Metazoa. In the vegetable microkingdom are the fungus varieties, both the kind that afflict us with ringworm and athlete's foot, and the kind that give us penicillin and an ever lengthening list of antibiotics derived from molds.

Finally there are the viruses, and it is hard to classify them as either animal or vegetable, or even as living forms. They reproduce as do living organisms, but they cannot function independently as living organisms. They must take up residence in a living cell.

Like all forms of life, the microorganisms must feed and they must reproduce. They multiply so rapidly that one of them can produce an army in less time than it takes to count its offspring. Bacteria reproduce approximately every twenty minutes; one microorganism could result in a colony of 500 billion billion in twenty-four hours, provided nothing interfered with its growth.

Ordinarily something does interfere with this fantastic power of reproduction, and often that something is another microorganism. The struggle for survival is as keen in the microscopic world as everywhere else in nature. One species feeds on another or competes for the same food supply with another, and the result is what we call the balance of nature. Now and then, for reasons that are still mysterious to science, one or another variety bursts out of bounds and overruns its part of the unseen world. But then its natural enemy also prospers on this sudden increase in food supply and presently the balance is restored.

The discovery of antibiotics showed us how to turn these natural enmities to our own use. The word *antibiotic* means literally "anti-life"; it describes in scientific shorthand a method of pitting one microscopic living form against another. When we introduce the product of an antibiotic fungus culture into the body to combat an infection, we are using a potential natural enemy of the infecting bacteria to attack it and thus either kill the bacteria outright or check their growth to the point where the body's own forces can conquer them.

These natural enmities are for the most part quite specific. Just as certain microorganisms live only in man and the higher apes, perhaps only in certain tissues of their chosen hosts, in the same way their natural enemies live only on certain of the bacteria. Thus it was discovered very early in the development of antibiotics that penicillin was effective against a number of bacteria but not against viruses. Other antibiotics are specific only against certain bacteria. And we have found also, to our dismay, that some species of bacteria are all too quick to develop immunity to some antibiotics, so that our research scientists are kept feverishly busy seeking out new varieties of molds to combat each newly immune strain of bacteria.

Turning the natural struggle for survival to our own ends is not, we learn, a simple task. Each time we dip our fingers into this complex world we suffer some disagreeable surprise. The natural balance is so delicately maintained, it seems, that a human touch on the scales upsets it in many unforeseen ways. When we spray DDT against mosquitoes, we find we are killing bees and other beneficent insects and either poisoning or starving out a good part of our valued bird population. The same unwished-for consequences attend many of our efforts to take control in the microscopic world. Often the conscientious scientist, striving to ameliorate our human struggle for survival among the microorganisms, feels himself a very awkward bull in nature's crowded china shop.

But the scientific road, though long, is always full of new and hopeful turnings. We need only look back a century or so to see how far we have come in how short a time. Most of what is set down in this chapter has been learned in less than a hundred years, and a great part of it in less than thirty.

MICROSCOPIC FRIENDS AND FOES

A microorganism's taste in food determines the habitat in which it will thrive and multiply, and the tastes of the many varieties range over the whole organic world. We find them, consequently, performing all sorts of functions without which life would be less pleasurable, and in many instances not even possible.

The molds are the leaveners of our bread and the fermenting agents that produce our wine, beer, and cheese. Scavenger bacteria that break down organic matter keep the world from becoming an unbearable clutter of garbage; they turn the wastes instead into the rich nutrient soil that gives us our food, our flowers, and our trees. There are bacteria that convert nitrogen compounds into the nitrates that nourish plants, and there are bacteria that add to this supply of essential plant food by transforming the inert nitrogen from the air into chemicals useful for life.

There are the beneficent bacteria that dwell in our own bodies, specifically the intestinal flora. These feed on other microorganisms that might be harmful to us, and they are capable of synthesizing most of the factors of the vitamin B-complex, vitamin C, and vitamin K, which is essential to the coagulating properties of the blood. All these augment our vitamin intake from food.

So much for the microorganisms whose functioning happens to be good for us. It would be astonishing and contrary to all our experience of nature if all the species in the invisible domain were working on our side. So we come to the enemy microbes.

They are enemies because they find a favorable habitat in the human body, and in their struggle for survival they are destructive to their host. In this they are not too different from ourselves. For many centuries man has been destroying the natural resources on which his life depends, and he is learning only now, in the nuclear age, that he is in danger of destroying the earth itself.

The enemy microbes are no strangers to us; they are the agents of the infectious diseases. As animal species evolved, the microorganisms evolved with them, and man was not exempt from their invasions. Even as he emerged in the distant evolutionary dawn, disease germs that had found a home in the tissues of other warmblooded animals adapted themselves to the new, yet not too different, human environment, and in due time some of them became specialists in human tissue. Wherever man prospered and multiplied, the microscopic enemies also prospered; their record is written with his in prehistoric fossil bones. Stone Age men suffered abscessed teeth and infected bones. Clustered in their neolithic villages, our human ancestors were plagued by the ancestors of our diphtheria and tuberculosis germs and the forebears of the viruses that cause smallpox and poliomyelitis.

When men came to write their history, they recorded not only their wars with each other but also their microbe wars. The microbe invaders were often far deadlier than the human ones, and in more than one historic conflict the issue was decided not by kings and captains but by the microorganisms of disease. Glorious Athens was conquered by plague as well as by Sparta; mighty Rome lost many a campaign not to the barbarians but to the epidemics that decimated her legions.

History is full of these gruesome battles. In the mid-fourteenth century a fourth of the population of Europe, and two-thirds in some countries, perished in the onslaught of the Black Death, mainly bubonic plague, also cholera and other diseases. Three hundred years later the bubonic plague wiped out a sixth of London's population, 68,000 people, in the space of a year and one month.

Other diseases took a similar toll through the centuries. Revolutionary New York reeled under the impact of yellow fever, and a half century later cholera and typhus played havoc with the forty-niners in the golden California hills. Waves of epidemic death swept across the country repeatedly during the nineteenth century.

The pestilences have been progressively shorn of their terror for mankind as the sciences of medicine and public health have improved their armaments and spread protection over increasing numbers of the world's population. But in all the centuries when the human community had little organization for public health and no scientific weapons to wield against the foe, indeed no knowledge of the invisible assailant's nature, what saved mankind then? What prevented the genus Homo from being wiped from the earth even before men learned to give themselves a name?

Through all those centuries the body's only protection lay in its own biological defenses. Medical men were fighting in the dark against enemies they did not see and could scarcely imagine. Greek physicians speculated a good deal about invisible particles carried in the air that might transmit disease, but it was not until the seventeenth century, when the Dutch scientist Anton van Leeuwenhoek first saw them under his microscope, that men could be sure such tiny organisms really existed.

Late in the nineteenth century it was still hard to believe that these organisms were the cause of disease, even after Pasteur and Koch, Semmelweis, and the American Dr. Oliver Wendell Holmes had demonstrated how infection was carried from one person to another, and Lister had shown how it could be prevented in surgery by antiseptic techniques. Poisonous vapors—miasmas—were still held to be the cause of most diseases; malaria came from bad—*mal*—air, and influenza was due to an influence of the heavens, *ex influentia coelesti*. Normally half the patients died in the surgical hospitals and sometimes as much as 90 per cent.

The wonder is that any survived. Yet millions did, and the fact that they did is a tribute to the body's defenses.

THE OUTER FORTIFICATIONS

The enemy microorganisms do their damage in several ways. They may destroy body cells directly, or they may do it indirectly by depriving them of their essential nutrition. They also release into the body the products of their own metabolism which interfere with the body's chemistry. The toxin produced by the diphtheria bacillus, for example, has a chemical resemblance to snake venom and can cause just about as much havoc in the body if it is not met with an antidote.

The viruses, those organisms on the borderline between living and nonliving matter, operate in their own peculiar way. They enter into the body cell itself and convert its metabolism to their own. They are like an invader who does not merely take the inhabitants' land and produce but forces them also to work for him without allowing them even a bare subsistence.

The enemy can do none of these things, however, unless it can first make its way into the body, and that is far less easy than it appears at a glance. The body has a most efficient set of outer fortifications against even a microscopic foe.

We have already discussed the effectiveness of the skin as protection against injury. It is also an effective barrier against microscopic invaders. It is an elastic and flexible suit of armor; so long as it is uninjured, no microbes can penetrate it nor can they harm its surface. Like armor, however, it does have its chinks. There are openings both large and small. The smallest openings are those of the hair follicles and the sweat and sebaceous glands. The large ones are the orifices by which the body takes in its food, fluids, and oxygen and discharges its wastes.

At all of these openings there are safeguards. The skin washes its tiny portals with its own exudations of sweat and oil. The way into the nose is guarded by little hairs, and farther on by sticky secretions of the mucous membrane. Mucous membrane similarly protects the excretory and genital orifices. The eyes are continuously bathed by fluids which wash away microorganisms.

Tears and saliva also contain a bacteria killer, called lysozyme. Oddly enough, the peoples of antiquity did not know of the existence either of bacteria or of the bactericidal agent; but they knew that saliva was curative, simply from observing that animals lick their wounds and the wounds heal. In the temples of Aesculapius, the sanatoria of the ancient world, the priests kept dogs whose task was to lick away the infection from wounds and sores.

Microbes that make their way into the digestive system with food and drink are destroyed by the digestive juices. And if they survive the juices they are pushed through the canal by the peristaltic waves of muscular contractions, along passages whose mucous lining gives them no place to catch hold.

If the outer fortifications should be breached, and hostile microorganisms take up residence in some part of the body, then a new series of defenses goes into action.

THE CELLULAR ARMY

We have already noted that, when the body suffers an injury, the vessels of the circulatory system in the vicinity open wide, and blood and plasma rush to the area like rescue squads to the scene of an accident. What we see—and suffer—are the swelling, redness, and heat of inflammation. We also suffer pain as a result of the distention and pressure on nerves, and the pain obliges us to rest the injured part.

The same rush of rescue forces to the area occurs when the injury is not mechanical, the result of physical accident, but is chemical, the effect of toxins released by the invading microbes. The swelling, redness, and fever of an infection are the work not only of the invader but also of the body's defenses.

The flooding of body fluids to the spot brings an army of white cells whose principal function is to do combat with the enemy. Like the red cells, these white ones, the leukocytes, develop in the bone marrow and are a regular constituent of the blood. When all is well in the body, there is a fairly constant proportion of these cells in the blood and indeed throughout the body. They are highly mobile, and they circulate without hindrance through the organs and tissues, cellular knights errant on the biological roads and pathways.

When a foreign substance breaks through the body's outer defenses, these free-lance cells swarm to the defense. Once there, they perform an extraordinary double duty. Certain of their number surround the infected area and quarantine it by making a wall with their own bodies. Within the barricade, the rest of the leukocytes fall upon the enemy and—literally—eat them up.

This is no figure of speech. Another name for the leukocytes is phagocytes, "eating cells." The body's first line of interior defenders are these cannibal soldier cells. What they do is not unheard of in the microscopic world, to be sure. The one-celled amoeba enfolds its food in much the same way. But the phagocytes will do this with any intruder whether it is a thorn or splinter, a surgical suture, a shell fragment, even a bullet or piece of shrapnel. If they cannot destroy it by devouring it, they erode and loosen it until eventually it is ejected from the body.

When the invaders are enemy microbes, the phagocytes descend like a cannibal tribe on a landing party of slave raiders. As the raiders multiply, the body's defense system accelerates its production of phagocytes and rushes them in increasing numbers to the battle. We know how rapidly microbes reproduce, and so the issue of the battle depends on whether the defending cannibals can gobble up the raiders faster than they multiply. Many of the white cells are killed in the battle. Their bodies, the bodies of the enemy microbes, and the tissue cells the microbes have damaged are gathered up within the infected area in the white matter we call pus. Eventually this debris of battle is absorbed, or it finds or creates a drainage route out of the body.

The phagocytes may not succeed in halting the microbes, and the multiplying invaders may break through their quarantine and spread to other areas. Here they will run into the body's next line of defense, the lymphatics. These are vessels like the blood vessels, a circulatory system like a pale shadow of the arteries and veins, carrying not blood but the colorless lymph. This is a body fluid like the fluid that bathes all the cells and tissues, but with some of the special properties of blood plasma. In fact, it is the lymph and lymph tissues that supply the plasma with its particular immunizing constituent, gamma globulin.

At certain points along the route of the lymph vessels, for example, in the neck, the armpits, the inner sides of elbows and knees, are the lymph nodes, small glandlike bodies made up of lymph tissue. Each of these nodes acts as a trap for the invading microorganisms, catching them in its netlike structure and holding them for the phagocytes to destroy. If the battle is on a fairly large scale and the lymph nodes become overloaded, they become enlarged and knotty and we have "swollen glands."

This holding operation is only part of the defensive system centered in the lymph tissue. The nodes themselves are manned by a cellular army, different from the phagocytes. These cells, called lymphocytes, are produced in the nodes and other lymph tissue, for example, the tonsils and the spleen. When the infection spreads, the lymph nodes release gamma globulin from their lymphocytes. This is part of the process, not yet entirely understood, by which the defense system produces the antibodies of immunity against disease.

WATCHDOGS OF IMMUNITY

The body's power to build up immunity is both wonderful and baffling. Antibodies, as they have long been called for lack of a more exact name, are chemical defenses. They have been classified according to the way in which they combat the microorganisms of disease. One group, the antitoxins, act as antidotes, neutralizing the poisons that the microbes release into the body. The second group, the agglutinins, clump the microbes themselves together, making it easier for the phagocytes to destroy many at one time.

Unlike the phagocytes, the roving cells that attack every sort of intruder, the antibodies are selective. The body produces a particular antibody in response to the presence of a particular microbe, and that antibody is effective only against that microbe. Thus diphtheria antitoxin will not neutralize any poison except that of the diphtheria bacillus, and the antibodies that combat the measles virus will have no effect on the virus of mumps.

Some antibodies, once produced, never entirely disappear. If the body's defense system has ever manufactured them to fight off a particular microorganism, they remain permanently on guard against that enemy's return. An individual may not remember whether he has ever had the measles, but his body remembers. Let the same virus gain entrance again, and the antibodies sleeping in his blood awaken at once. At the signal the body immediately begins to produce more of the same antibodies for the emergency.

No other microorganism can awaken these particular antibodies except the one against which they were originally produced. But to this one they automatically respond. This enduring immunity, which may last a lifetime, is one of the body's finest defenses, and it is also one that men have learned how to invoke artificially, with heartening success.

Vaccination is a most familiar medical term. Large numbers of American children are vaccinated against smallpox in infancy and again at the time they reach school age. Our government requires a certificate of vaccination of citizens returning from travel outside the country. It is an old and rather an odd word; its derivation—from the Latin word *vacca*, a cow—reminds us that this gentle domestic animal, besides giving us milk, also freed us from one of the dread scourges of mankind by the simple coincidence of sharing the disease with us, but in a mild form.

Today the word vaccine is used for other immunizing preparations, for example, the Salk vaccine against poliomyelitis. The original vaccine was against smallpox; it was in fact the virus of the bovine version of the disease. In the pleasant farmland of the west of England, the good country physician, Dr. Edward Jenner, learned from the dairymaids that once they had had cowpox they no longer needed to fear smallpox, and in 1796 he demonstrated that an attack of the mild disease did indeed immunize against the dangerous one. He inoculated a farm lad with cowpox and then deliberately tried to infect the boy with smallpox. This demonstration and others that followed it were totally successful, and vaccination began a new era of preventing disease by artificial immunization.

Dr. Jenner's method was new, but the principle of courting a disease in order to gain immunity was many centuries old. People had long observed that those who recovered from smallpox almost never were stricken by it a second time. George Washington suffered a severe case of smallpox in his youth while on a visit to Barbados with his brother, and ever afterward he was able to travel where his high destiny called him, unharmed by the terrible killer of his time.

People also knew from experience that the same disease, which in one epidemic left thousands of dead in its wake, in another year came in so gentle a form that nearly all its victims recovered. Thus when the opportunity came to have the disease in its milder version, many people daringly exposed themselves to it, hoping to gain safety for the rest of their lives.

The next step was a primitive and rather dangerous form of inoculation with matter taken from a pustule on the skin of a person recovering from smallpox. Most often the virus was weak and the attack was consequently mild, but it could be fatal or leave severely disfiguring scars. Nevertheless the custom was followed for centuries in China and India, and early in the eighteenth century the British ambassador's energetic and literary wife, Lady Mary Wortley Montagu, had her own children inoculated while in Constantinople and persuaded many of her friends in England to follow her example.

Today we consider it routine to plant sentinels of immunity against diseases that once were fatal, such as diphtheria and tetanus and whooping cough, number-one killer of the very young. As the immunity of a population is increased, the once terrible microorganisms of each of these diseases are driven from their favorite habitat and gradually lose their power to do us harm. Now we may hope that poliomyelitis will soon be on the list of diseases conquered by immunization and, in time to come, the microscopic enemies of man may be sent to languish, perhaps to perish, in exile from human tissues which need never again harbor them.

All this will be the triumph of scientific medicine. But its cornerstone will be the body's own incomparable defense, its self-created antibody sentinels that never forget their microscopic foes.

PART II

ORGANS AND SYSTEMS

5

THE PUMP WITH THE
BUILT-IN MOTOR

To no organ of the body has such flattering court been paid as to the heart. It has been romanticized, glamorized, personified, glorified, endowed with emotions, insight, even with intelligence and speech. "The heart has its reasons," we say, and "You must do as your heart tells you."

Primitive tribes ate the heart of an enemy to gain his courage, and not only primitives but sophisticated ancients believed the one was the seat of the other; the very word *courage* comes from the Latin word *cor* for heart. Even today we use the two interchangeably, as in the song, from a recent Broadway success, about what a baseball player needs: "You gotta have heart." Most of all, the heart is synonymous with love.

Physicians will admit on occasion that a patient "died of a broken heart," well knowing that the heart itself was not medically involved. They mean—and we never miss their meaning, couched in symbol though it is—that the patient lost interest in living, that the mysterious psychic and biological level within him, the will to live that so often pulls an individual back from the brink of death, in this instance failed. The vitality of the organism ebbs away although every organ may be healthy, including the heart.

Lore and symbol have their logic, and there is a logic to the symbolic aura that glows around the heart. It is the only one of our internal organs that we can actually feel and even hear at its work. We are aware of its pulsations, and by our very mythology of the heart we acknowledge the accuracy with which it reflects our mood. We feel it beating quietly and steadily when we are tranquil, thumping in fright or suspense, pounding strongly when we gather our forces for a dangerous or difficult task. Sometimes it seems to flutter, sometimes to race; sometimes it seems heavy and sometimes light. There are moments when we are sure it leaps into the throat or plummets to the pit of the stomach.

We know that these sensations we ascribe to the heart come from other sources. Obviously tissues do not change in weight only from emotional provocation; happy or sad, the adult human heart continues to weigh about a pound. Nor does it change its position in the body. It neither leaps nor drops, but remains safely cushioned between the lungs, resting on their resilience as though on a soft balloon, within the strong springlike bars of the rib cage.

What does change is its beat, and this changes in both rate and output. It may jump from a normal 70 or 80 per minute to 150 or even 180 in an athlete making his best try for a score. It accelerates when we are in the grip of strong emotion. The emotion, as we well know, is in the brain, not the heart, and the heart does not even have any direct nervous connection with the conscious part of the brain that experiences emotion. It responds, as do all the involuntary mechanisms of the body, to the prompting of the autonomic nervous system, whose connections with the emotions are in the hypothalamus of the old, primitive brain. It responds, too, to the adrenalines that pour into the blood stream under the stimulus of any excitement.

The heart is neither a thinking nor a feeling organ. It is nothing more or less than a muscle. But it is a very remarkable muscle, equipped to do a sustained, lifelong job of pumping. With its two sets of chambers and valves, exquisitely synchronized to each other, it is also an unmatched and probably unmatchable pump.

It needs no glorification or romanticization. In its own terms of muscle power and function, the heart is hard to describe as anything short of a miracle.

THE MUSCLE

Virtually all the muscles in the body belong to one of two types of contractile fibrous tissue: either they are the striped muscles of the skeleton, made up of bundles of long tough fibers that move our bones and joints, or they are the smooth short-fibered tissue of inner organs such as the digestive tract and the blood vessels.

The heart, unique in so many ways, is unique also in the nature of its muscle tissue. It fits into neither one nor the other category of muscles; it is something between or a combination of both. Its fibers are somewhat striated like those of the skeletal muscles, and it shares the skeletal muscles' power of quick contraction compared with the rather sluggish response of smooth muscle. But it also has the smooth muscle's inherently rhythmic action and its tireless power. Its connections are not with the voluntary but with the autonomic nervous system that governs the smooth muscles throughout the body. Thus it combines the virtues of both kinds of muscle tissue for its unique function.

It has, besides, some virtues peculiarly its own. Its fibers are not insulated from each other, but instead they branch off into slips or bridges connecting each fiber with its next neighbor, so that any stimulation spreads with extraordinary swiftness through the entire muscle. In the human heart, as in mammals generally, a tiny area of this muscle has even developed into a specialized kind of tissue, halfway between muscle and nerve, that performs as an independent nervous system. This muscular band, connecting the auricles with the ventricles, is called the bundle of His, for the German physician Wilhelm His, Jr., famous son of a famous physician father.

One small mass of this tissue in the wall of the right auricle is believed to generate the rhythmic contraction of the muscle, in other words the heartbeat, and it is called, consequently, the pacemaker. This tiny node sends a wave of excitation, apparently electrical, throughout the heart; at the apex or tip of the heart the impulse diverges to right and left, keeping the beat synchronized on both sides. This is the impulse that maintains the characteristic slow basic rhythm of the heartbeat.

The working capacity of the heart is very nearly incredible. Imagine lifting a thirty-five-pound weight, say a packed suitcase, to a height of two feet once every minute; you would be putting out seventy foot-pounds of energy per minute. That is an approximation of what the heart does: it propels more than ten pounds of fluid with enough power to lift it seven feet in the air, every minute of the day. To match it, you would have to lift that thirty-five-pound suitcase the same two feet in the air 1,440 times without stopping. That is the heart's ordinary daily work load.

In actual fact the heart only has to pump its load about as high as you have been lifting your imaginary suitcase, the two feet or so from heart to head. The additional power is to keep the blood moving along the tortuous pathways of the circulatory system and back again through the veins.

You can prove to yourself how superior the heart muscle is to any ordinary muscle by clenching and unclenching your fist rhythmically in time to a slow count. At what point do the muscles in your hand protest, then ache, and finally quit? You will not be able to make them work again until they have had some rest.

You have been clenching your fist on comparatively unresisting air, but the heart muscle clenches on a rather thick fluid and drives it out into the arteries against the pressure of the blood that already fills them. Try the same experiment with a soft rubber ball or a handful of salt or sugar, and your fist will be attempting something closer to the task of the heart muscle. With the more resistant material to clench on, your hand will probably tire even sooner than it did the first time. Yet the heart is able to clench on a chamber full of fluid faster than once a second. Furthermore, it does not stop at the count of thirty but goes on pumping day after day, year in and year out, for as long as you live.

FORM AND FUNCTION

The Valentine outline of twin curves meeting in a bow at the top and a point at the bottom is a pretty picture and suitable for framing in lace, but it bears no likeness to the working organ. The heart is not dainty, but it is handsome in its rugged efficiency. Its actual shape is that of a bulky cone, somewhat asymmetrical, with its base at the top and its apex pointing downward and to the left. About one-third of its bulk lies to the right and two-thirds to the left of the mid-line of the body. It is surrounded by a double layer of thin membrane with a film of fluid between the layers, and around this again a tough fibrous outer membrane which goes on to join with the outer coats of the great blood vessels. Cushioned softly against the lungs, the heart lies close to the sternum or breastbone in front and on the upper surface of the diaphragm.

The heart contributes some twelve ounces to the body's weight; the brain and the liver each weigh four times as much. An elephant's heart weighs about forty-eight pounds and beats between two and three times a minute. The hummingbird that you may see sometimes, poised like a helicopter above a flower while its wings flutter almost too rapidly to be seen, has a heart that weighs one one-hundredth of an ounce and maintains the almost unbelievable rate of 2,000 beats per minute.

With its beat of between seventy and eighty per minute, the one-pound human heart pumps the entire five-quart contents of the blood vessels once through the system every sixty seconds. In strenuous exercise it may pump the blood seven or eight times around the circuit, moving forty quarts of fluid, every minute. Most of this accelerated circulation is for the muscles, including the heart muscle itself, which needs a full quart of blood to supply its oxygen and sugar fuel and carry away its wastes during periods of intense physical activity.

Compared with the demand of the skeletal muscles for increased supplies of blood during activity, the demands of other parts of the body are modest. The digestive system needs only a quart of extra blood to digest a hearty meal. A hot day calls for rather more than that to be sent to the skin for cooling. The brain does its work with virtually no extra blood supply; we can do the hardest kind of thinking and yet the heart is not required to accelerate its pumping, unless the mental effort is accompanied by anxiety. Fear, even of the shadowy variety engendered in the mind, sets up an accelerated heartbeat.

So responsive is the powerful heart muscle that, when we want to know its basal pumping rate, we have to put not only the body but the mind, too, into a state of serene relaxation. Thus it is all the more amazing that there is no nervous connection at all between the heart and the thinking brain and that it can function on its own even without stimulation from the autonomic nervous system with which it is connected. With its inherent power of rhythmic contraction, and its own self-regulating built-in motor, the heart is just about the most independent organ in the body.

THE FOUR-ROOM HOUSE

In structure the heart is like a two-story house with four rooms, two above stairs and two below. The rooms are divided from each other in a curious way. The only entrances to the house are into the two upstairs rooms, and the only exits are from the two downstairs rooms. Furthermore, the two sides of the house do not communicate with each other at all. To go from one side of the house to the other it is necessary to travel all the long way through the body's circulatory system or the somewhat shorter route through the circulatory system of the lungs. It is as though you lived in one side of a semidetached dwelling and had to drive downtown and clear around the city to visit your neighbor next door.

This may be inefficient as housing, but for a pump that is keeping two separate circulatory systems going in perfect synchronization, it is hard to imagine a better job of engineering. The two systems, one through the lungs and the other through the body, are quite independent of each other; conceivably each could have its own pump. But the heart powers both systems with a single motor, a single set of fueling and electrical connections, a single timing device, and—most satisfactory of all from an engineering point of view—a single expenditure of energy that sends the fluid coursing powerfully through two separate circuits at each stroke of the piston.

A look at the illustration on page 69 will make clear how the two circulatory systems are co-ordinated in the heart's two separate sets of chambers. The two upper chambers, the auricles, are the receiving chambers. Here the blood can only enter. It can leave each auricle in only one direction, downward into the ventricle on its own side. The ventricles, the two lower chambers, are the real power units of the pump. The auricles, with somewhat thinner muscular walls, exert a mild contraction lasting about one-tenth of a second at the beginning of the heartbeat, which speeds their contents downward into their respective ventricles. The ventricles complete the pumping cycle by sending the blood out into their separate systems. For this part of the heartbeat the ventricular systole, which takes three or more times as long as the auricular systole, the ventricles are equipped with considerably thicker muscular walls, and the left ventricle, which powers the body's circulation, is more muscular than the right, which pumps the blood to the lungs.

The blood on its twin courses must enter and leave the heart twice in a single complete circuit, first through one and then through the other set of chambers. To follow the blood on its

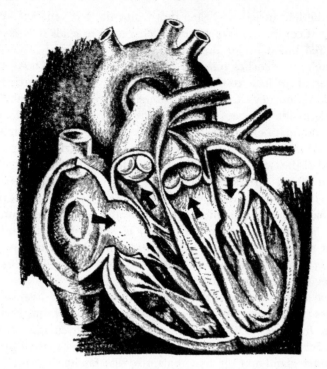

journey we might begin with the right and smaller ventricle, the pumping station for the shorter pulmonary system. The blood at this point in its course is venous; that is, it has been carried through all the parts of the body, through every limb and organ, giving up its load of oxygen, and has been returned to the heart via the veins. It is de-oxygenized, bluish in color, and ready to take on a new load of oxygen. It is also loaded with the body's gaseous waste, carbon dioxide, which it must dispose of at the same time it takes on its oxygen supply.

With the next beat or contraction of the heart's muscular wall, the right ventricle ejects this venous blood into the pulmonary artery and sends it coursing through the branching blood vessels in the lungs. There the red blood cells, filing through their capillaries, can drop their carbon dioxide loads and pick up the vital oxygen.

Back goes the blood, now bright red with oxygen, to the heart. But this time it goes to the entrance on the other, the left side,

into the left auricle and then down into the left ventricle. With
the next contraction the powerful left ventricle sends this oxygenated red blood under pressure into the body's great artery and
through its branches into the furthest reaches of the body from
the top of the head to the tips of fingers and toes. Returning from
this long journey, it re-enters through the receiving chamber on
the right side and goes down and out again on the short loop of
the pulmonary circuit to replenish its oxygen. Thus it completes
its double cycle. In the body's resting state it makes a complete
round of the twin circulatory systems in less than one minute.

The blood carries far more than oxygen. It carries nutrients
extracted by the digestive system from the food we eat. It carries
the many complex chemical products of the body's own manufacture, hormones, enzymes, antibodies, as well as the salts and the
water that are essential to all our functions. It also transports a
variety of chemical wastes. Some of its load goes only short distances, like freight on a local line.

One such local line is the portal circulation of the liver, which
carries the nutrient products of digestion absorbed from the walls
of the intestines. This is the largest subsidiary circulating system.
Another is a portal system—a very short one—shared by the
pituitary gland and the hypothalamus, that fascinating small center in the old, primitive brain that still holds many secrets, especially of our most powerful emotions. There is a possibility that
this tiny portal circulation provides the one connection between
our emotions and our system of endocrine glands which are, as
we know, extraordinarily responsive to emotional states.

The heart necessarily has its own circulation, by way of the
coronary arteries. Except for this, the pump's own fueling and
waste-removal system, the local lines do not go through the central pumping station but branch off from and rejoin the main
line at their own junctions. Only the lungs, which breathe for all
the body's community of cells, share with the body's general
circulatory system the direct pumping power of the heart.

ONE-WAY TRAFFIC

Despite the fact that it propels the blood through two separate
systems, this central pumping station suffers no traffic confusions.
The blood can go only in one direction. The heart maintains its

one-way traffic system by virtue of a set of valves which, like their mechanical counterparts in an engine, regulate the passage of fluid through the pump. They open and close in response to the pressure of fluid on one or the other side of them, but when they open it is in only one direction.

There are two of these valves within the heart itself, opening from auricle to ventricle on each side. On the left side is the mitral valve, which gets its name from its twin cusps or leaves of tissue, somewhat resembling a bishop's miter. On the right, the larger tricuspid valve has three cusps or leaves.

Both the valves function in the same way: when the pressure of blood in the auricle is higher than that in the ventricle, the leaves of the valve are pushed downward to open the passage between the chambers and allow the blood to flow through. The rather gentle contraction of the auricle, at the beginning of the heartbeat, hurries the flow along. With the eddying of the blood as it fills the ventricle, the leaves of the valve flutter upward to close the passageway, and when the ventricle contracts, the pressure on the ventricular side of the valve shuts it firmly. The leaves of tissue are slender and quickly responsive to the pressure of fluid, but they are supported from below by a sturdy set of tendons with muscular attachment, like guy ropes, which hold the leaves firm against the considerable pressure generated by the ventricular contraction and prevent the valve from opening inward into the auricle.

Thus, with each systole or contraction, the blood can go only in one direction, and that is outward from the heart, into the arteries, the pulmonary artery on the right and the body's great artery, the aorta, on the left. Here, too, there are valves, one in each arterial exit from the ventricle, with the same three-leaved structure and the same one-directional opening. Only the guy ropes are absent, for the great pressure here is outward and the closing of the valve is enough to prevent a return flow during the diastole or relaxed phase of the heart's pumping cycle.

One more set of valves contributes to the one-way traffic system; these are the venous valves, distributed through the system of veins that convey the blood back to the heart. By the time the blood reaches the veins, it has lost its pressure and a good deal of its velocity. It has slowed up on its way through the capillary field, and it no longer has the constant propulsion of the heart's pumping action behind it, as it does while it is flowing through the arteries. Also, in upright two-legged animals like ourselves, the blood must travel a good part of its return journey against gravity. And so we find that the large veins of the legs and abdomen are fitted with valves that open only toward the heart and thus prevent the blood from pooling in the lower part of the body. In the next chapter we shall discover other mechanisms that help it on its way against gravitational pull.

6

THE RIVERS OF LIFE

FROM OUR VANTAGE POINT today it is hard to believe that the course of the blood through the body was unknown until nearly the middle of the seventeenth century when Dr. William Harvey, citizen of London and royal physician to James I and Charles I, published his revolutionary book, *Essay on the Motion of the Heart and Blood in Animals*. Nearly another century passed before the Reverend Stephen Hales tied a mare to a gate, inserted the windpipe of a goose into her thigh artery (he had, of course, no rubber tubing) and connected it to a glass tube. When the column of blood in the tube rose to a height of nine feet he had demonstrated beyond doubt the principle of arterial blood pressure.

Dr. Harvey traced the course of the blood through the pulmonary circulation from the right to the left side of the heart and argued that the blood journeys from arteries to veins by way of smaller vessels. Numerous forerunners had prepared the way for him with observations of one or another detail of the circulatory system. But his contemporaries found it difficult to give up an image of the circulation that had been unquestioned for some fifteen hundred years, ever since Galen had described it in the second century, with all the authority of the leading physician of Imperial Rome.

For the centuries that followed him, Galen had said the final word when he declared that the liver was the central organ of the system, manufacturing blood out of food material brought to it in the portal vein from the intestines. He conceived the blood not as circulating but as ebbing and flowing like a kind of tide in the veins, while the heart served only to refine a small part of the blood by exposing it to blood received there from the lungs, where it gained a life-giving essence, the pneuma, from the air. Clearly he was trying to name an essence in the air that was essential to life and trying also to relate it to the blood. The discovery of oxygen and its importance to living matter had to wait for the French scientist Antoine Lavoisier in the eighteenth century.

Since the days of Harvey, a host of medical scientists have followed the pathway he pointed out, and precise techniques and instruments have replaced the Reverend Mr. Hales's windpipe of a goose. By the end of this chapter the reader of this book will be an expert on the heart and circulatory system by comparison with these honored pioneers.

In the body's community the cell is the ultimate consumer, comparable to the individual in the human community. The individual's daily need for food, fuel and the materials of life is met by a vast distribution system of roads, railroads, and shipping. If he lives in a city, another system of sanitation, sewage, and waste disposal carries away his garbage, rubbish, and excreta. In the body's community the circulating blood performs both the distribution of supplies and the removal of wastes, and the heart takes the place of locomotives, trucks, and ships by providing the motive power for the system.

We have millions of miles of roads in our country to supply foodstuffs to our one-seventh of a billion people. In the body one-tenth of a million miles of "roads" carry the necessary nourishment to some thirty trillions of cells. The total length of the arteries, veins, capillaries and the subsidiary lymphatic vessels is somewhere between 60,000 and 100,000 miles. The body's five quarts of blood make a complete circuit of this system once every minute; in the course of twenty-four hours the system has carried 7,200 quarts of blood through the body.

THE OUTWARD JOURNEY

The great artery, the aorta, receives the rich arterial blood from the heart's left ventricle and carries it, under pressure, on the first lap of its long journey. This great conduit, about an inch in diameter, sends its first branch out a short distance from the heart to supply the head, neck, and arms. It turns downward through the chest and abdomen, sending further branches to the major organs, the bones, muscles, nerves and skin. The liver, pancreas, and spleen receive large offshoots, as do the stomach and intestines. The arteries to the kidneys are large enough to carry a quart of blood per minute to these organs. In the lower part of the abdomen the aorta itself branches into two large iliac arteries, from which subsidiary arteries supply the pelvic organs and the buttocks muscles, and the femoral arteries continue down through the thighs and legs.

The large arteries have a smooth inner lining, a middle layer of elastic tissue, and an outer covering containing supporting tissue and the blood vessels needed to supply their own tissues—for, curiously enough, blood vessels also need a blood supply, and the walls of all but the capillaries are too thick for them to exchange nutrients and waste with the blood that flows through them.

The blood courses through the branching arterial system with a continuous pressure behind it; the rhythmic thrust of the pump is felt in pulsations all along the line. As the arteries divide and subdivide into ever thinner branches their walls also become progressively thinner, losing their elastic tissue and retaining mainly muscle tissue of the smooth type.

The finest branches, the arterioles, are highly muscular and responsive to the contracting and dilating impulses from the autonomic nervous system, thus controlling the supply of blood to tissues as it is needed. They widen in the digestive tract walls, for example, when a meal is being digested and in the muscles when physical work is going on.

The quick responsiveness of the arterioles in the skin is essential to the body's temperature control system. When we are too warm their muscular walls relax and allow increased blood to flow through the skin, cooling the body by evaporation, and when we are chilly the walls contract, keeping the blood mainly closer to the center of the body and away from the surface. They are equally responsive to emotional stimuli; it is the arterioles in the face and neck that cause us to blush. Usually at such times we wish we had conscious control of those tiny vessels and could keep a cool countenance in an embarrassing situation.

The blood rushes along the great arterial conduits; its speed through the aorta is three-fifths of a foot per second when we are at rest and even faster than that when we are active. As the blood spreads through the branches its speed diminishes; even though the bore of the vessels becomes steadily smaller the number of them is multiplying, and there are more and more channels through which the same volume of blood is flowing. By the time the blood reaches one of the many capillary beds, the velocity of its flow is reduced to half a millimeter, about two one-hundredths of an inch, per second. This slowing down is comparable to the slowing of a river current when it empties into a larger body of water, a sea or a lake. Indeed, the capillary system, into which the blood spreads at the end of each set of arterioles, has been called the capillary lake.

THE CIRCULATION'S CLIMAX

The capillary lake—or rather the chain of many lakes, ponds, and pools of capillaries that spreads throughout the body—is the peak of the whole circulatory system. In each of the body's organs, in muscles and brain, lung and intestine and gland, in the quick of the fingernails and around every hair follicle of the skin, are these exquisitely fine tubes. Each capillary is about the width of a single blood cell; the average diameter is ten microns. Twenty-five hundred of them laid side by side have a combined width of only one inch.

Through the spreading fields of these tiny tubes, the blood, with its vital burden of oxygen and nutrients, spreads like a film. It is kept within the circulatory system by membranes as fine as a spider's web. Through these membranes the molecules of oxygen and carbon dioxide, the amino acids of protein, and the sugars of carbohydrates pass back and forth in an orderly way. So also do the body's own chemical products, the essential mineral salts, and molecules of water.

The red blood cells go by in single file like a continuous line of microscopic freight cars or rather like tiny barges on a steadily flowing canal, each one delivering oxygen and gathering up its capacity of carbon dioxide while passing among the body cells. The red blood cells perform the same process in reverse as they make a similar circuit through the lungs. The pores in the cob-webby capillary walls are large enough to permit these minute exchanges of molecules between the blood and the cells and yet small enough to keep the blood itself intact with its necessary complement of cells.

In certain organs the pores are of special sizes to allow specific molecules to pass through and bar the way to others. Each organ takes its necessary nutrients and also whatever special chemicals it may need for its work: the thyroid gland captures iodine from the passing blood to use in its particular hormone. Taking what it requires, the individual cell of each organ and tissue at the same time gives up to the blood its own products and its wastes.

In at least two instances the capillary walls are curiously reinforced by barriers against chemicals that might be harmful to specialized tissues or disturbing to their environment. The brain has such a barrier, and so has the placenta that nourishes the growing infant in the womb.

This quiet but continuous flow of blood through the capillary lakes is undramatic and even anticlimactic compared with the beating of the heart. Nevertheless it is the true climax of the heart's impressive functioning. If, like the scientists of an earlier day, we assumed a constant guiding purposefulness in our biological universe, we might say that the capillary system is the purpose of the circulation, that the entire system, heart and all, was designed for just this end. Since Darwin, with his theory of evolution, drew back the curtain and revealed our long biological history, we have accepted the evidence of many sciences that whatever purpose there may be, it does not necessarily manifest itself so explicitly as in the design of a biological structure.

All the more magical, then, is this structure that has developed down the eons of evolution, changing and elaborating and refining out of an unimaginable sequence of adaptations and mutations. Each change that hindered survival spelled its own doom, and each that was advantageous was carried forward as the species in whose genes it occurred prospered and multiplied.

Only with the service of such a system as the circulation, to carry supplies and wastes, could the cells of organisms develop into more and more specialized structures and emerge at last as the human body. In the vital exchange, molecule by molecule, between blood and body tissues across the porous web of the capillaries, the whole magnificent mechanism of the heart and circulatory system accomplishes its life-sustaining function.

THE RETURN AGAINST GRAVITY

From the capillaries the blood must be gathered again and returned to the heart. And so we find the tiny capillary vessels emptying into slender veins which in turn empty into larger ones until the whole volume of the blood is once more collected and flowing toward the right auricle of the heart in two great veins, the superior vena cava from the upper part of the body and the inferior vena cava from the lower. The branching veins parallel the arterial system, and the diameter of the great veins is about the same as that of the great arteries.

The veins, carrying blood which has lost much of its pressure and velocity in the capillary fields, have walls that are far thinner and less muscular than the arteries and with the middle layer of elastic tissues scarcely developed. The veins also run closer to the surface of the body, though usually on the protected inner sides of arms and legs and trunk, and on the backs of hands and feet rather than on the palms and soles. We can trace their bluish lines down the inner side of the arm and wrist, along the back of the hand and even into the fingers.

To bring the blood back to the heart from the upper body presents no problem in an erect biped; it is more or less a matter of gravity. With the valves in the great veins guiding the flow in only one direction, as we have already noted, we can safely stand on our heads, but it is not a comfortable position for too long a time.

The blood from the lower part of the body must make its way back to the heart against the force of gravity, and for this the two-legged animals, man and the apes, have a well-developed set of mechanisms which in most quadrupeds is nowhere near as efficient. When we stand erect, the muscles of the belly and the legs tighten and exert a pressure on the veins which, thanks to the one-way venal valves, can milk the blood only in one direction and that is upward, toward the heart. When we breathe, the downward thrust of the diaphragm contributes powerfully to this milking pressure on the veins. If the leg muscles are kept still during a long period of standing, the flow of the blood upward through the veins does in fact slow down, with the result that the volume of blood available for pumping upward into the brain is likely to be inadequate. This accounts for the curious phenomenon of strong young men fainting when they are kept standing too long at attention in a military formation. The same thing happens in crowds watching a parade or other spectacle. If it is a hot day and blood is also being deflected toward the blood vessels of the skin, fainting may well become epidemic. Actually the faint is a self-regulating mechanism; it lays the victim out flat and automatically overcomes the effects of gravity on the blood in the veins.

The blood has lost most of its pressure on its return to the heart, as we have mentioned. Its velocity is another matter. It has lost velocity, too, on entering the capillaries, but as it collects from the wide-spreading capillary fields into the amalgamating conduits of the veins it begins to pick up speed again, and it comes into the heart at last at almost the same velocity it had when it was ejected. Thus scarcely more time is spent on the return journey than on the outward one and, as it is sent out again, this time through the pulmonary circuit, it is once more proceeding under the powerful head of pressure generated by the heart.

DEMAND AND SUPPLY

How the circulatory system manages to deliver the blood supply where it is needed is one of its many miracles of co-ordination. The pressure generated by the heart, and so necessary for getting the blood around through its twin circuits, also contributes to this matter of local demand and supply. Pressure can be compared to voltage in electricity. When there are a good many electrical appliances at work in the house, there will be enough current for all of them as long as there is high enough pressure, or voltage.

The organs and systems of the body vary tremendously in the sheer quantity of blood they require. The needs of the brain are steady; it demands very little more when it is working than when it is resting. Most demanding are the muscles; physical exertion of a really high order may speed up the circulation to eight times its resting rate. The body's thermostatic system, as we have noted, depends upon a shift of blood to the skin for cooling and into the interior for warming. The digestive system demands its extra supply, up to a quart, to digest a meal.

The way in which we increase the water supply to an upper story is enough like the working of the circulation to provide a simple analogy. We may have to get a better pump—that is, increase the water pressure by adding power. If the pump already has enough power, we put in larger pipes. Once we have the pressure and the volume, all we have to do is open the faucet, and the water flows into the tub.

In the body the volume of blood remains fairly constant at about five quarts. To get the supply where it is needed, the pipes —that is, the blood vessels—change their caliber, and if necessary the pump increases its output.

All this happens automatically, in response to the dilating and contracting impulses that pass along the blood vessels from the autonomic nervous system. The same system accelerates the heartbeat when an increased demand on the blood supply requires more pressure and a more rapid turnover of blood. The muscles express their demand by means of a chemical signal. An increase in the products of combustion, such as carbon dioxide, stimulates the co-ordinated action of dilating blood vessels and accelerated heart rate, as well as accelerated breathing to increase the supply of oxygen and hasten the disposal of carbon dioxide. The arterioles and the capillaries open wide, and an increased volume of blood rushes into the widened vessels.

When a large supply of blood is shunted to one part of the body, necessarily the vessels elsewhere are not going to get as much. Indeed, the autonomic system co-ordinates the constriction of blood vessels in certain areas with the dilatation in others. The sympathetic nerves which accelerate the heart and increase the blood supply to the muscles also constrict the vessels in the abdominal viscera, while the parasympathetic nerves, which expand the visceral blood vessels, have an inhibiting effect on the more violent physical functions.

We sometimes feel chilly after a big meal, when blood is diverted from the vessels in the skin to help in the digestive activities, and we have little inclination to play tennis or chop wood on a full stomach. It is just as well to heed this wordless body wisdom, for the intestines have priority when it comes to blood supply, and the muscles will be scanted. Athletes eat lightly, if at all, before a contest; the ethereal ballerina dines like a hummingbird, although after the performance she may sup like a stevedore.

The brain requires a constant supply of blood, with little variation, and this is a real challenge to the circulatory system. Each time we shift from the horizontal to the vertical position, the quantity of blood in the brain would alter except for the action of two important nerves. One of these is in the aorta, and the other is in the neck, at the carotid sinus, the point where the carotid artery separates into two branches on its way to the head. Between them, these two nerves regulate the blood pressure so that it will not get either too high or too low. A rise in blood pressure, pressing on these nerves, causes a reflex slowing of the heart and dilatation of blood vessels to lower the pressure. Conversely a fall in blood pressure reduces the impulses and the effect is to raise the pressure by acceleration of the heart and constriction of blood vessels.

These inbuilt regulators thus adjust the pressure to whatever position we are in. As we jump out of bed in the morning, the mechanism immediately goes to work to raise the arterial pressure. It makes its adjustment when we bend down to tie our shoelaces and again when we straighten up. If for some reason it is a little slow, we tend to feel lightheaded and dizzy for a moment. This may happen, not through a failure of the sinus and aortic nerves, but because we have suddenly stood up from a position in which the veins of the legs have been constricted—a squatting position, for instance—and the return of venous blood to the heart has been temporarily slowed. Thus the blood supply is, for the moment, inadequate to meet the urgent summons of the regulating mechanism. Usually it takes only a moment for the pressure of the leg muscles to push the venous blood upward, and the pressure in the arteries going to the brain is once more correct for the upright position. Like other such vital mechanisms in the body, the carotid sinus reflex usually works so quickly and smoothly that we are not aware of it.

THE VITAL FLUID

So far this chapter has concentrated on the marvels of a circulating system that gets the blood around to every one of the body's cells. It is time now to see just what that vital fluid is, that it should merit such an extraordinary mechanism for its transport.

When you cut your finger, the thick, smooth fluid that flows from the cut looks homogeneous, all of one piece. But if it stands in a test tube for a while it separates into a clear amber liquid, the serum, and a mass of red and white cells and platelets. The serum fills rather more than half the tube, and the cells and platelets make up the remainder.

The blood fulfills many functions in the body, but its first and most vital function is to carry oxygen to the tissues. This is the task of the red blood cells, and we shall see in the next chapter, on respiration, how they do this by virtue of their hemoglobin and its curious affinity for oxygen. About twenty-five million million red cells dance and tumble along the conduits of the circulatory system. In a single drop of blood that oozes from a pinprick, 150 million red cells find space to move around, almost as many cells as there are people in the United States.

The red cells are tiny, less than one three-thousandth of an inch in diameter, and they have, besides, a curious shape. They are disks, concave on both sides, with the result that they have an enormous surface area, considering their size. This has its virtue when they come into the capillaries of the lungs and have to pick up their loads of oxygen in less than a second, and again in the capillaries of the organs when they must release their oxygen as rapidly to the body tissues. Tiny as they are, the aggregation of red cells in the lungs has 1,200 square yards of surface to expose to these swift exchanges of molecules. The red-cell population of one-fourth of the body's blood is present in the lungs at all times.

The body's red cells are born in the bone marrow. Originally they are equipped like other cells with a nucleus, but by the time they are released into the blood stream as mature cells, ready to do their work, they no longer have a nucleus which would enable them to reproduce themselves. Some biologists question whether the mature red cell can be considered a cell at all because of this lack. They prefer to define it as a transport mechanism for oxygen.

However we define them, the tiny disks turn and tumble through the blood vessels, and when they come into the narrow capillary tubes their flexible concave membranes bend and twist in the cramped passageways. They are tossed in the swift currents within arteries and veins, pushed and crowded against blood vessel walls; red cells are constantly suffering destruction from the sheer mechanical hazards of the circulatory system. They also seem to have a limited span of life, for reasons that we do not know. In any case, a red cell lives approximately 120 days. Every second more than five million of them perish, and new cells are being manufactured and turned into the blood stream at about the same rate.

During prenatal life the liver and spleen contribute to the manufacture of the red cells; from birth on, except when the body is under unusual stress, the task is taken over by bone marrow and cartilage, and bone marrow is by far the major producer. A little more than half a pound of it can provide 250 billion red blood cells a day. The sternum or breastbone, the ribs, and some parts of the long bones, vertebrae and pelvis contain this highly productive variety of reddish-gray, spongy matter, actually a network of blood vessels and connective tissue, in which are nested almost uncountable numbers of red cells in all stages of growth.

When the oxygen content of the blood falls too low, the production of new red cells in the bone marrow is accelerated. This is one of the adaptations the body makes—for example, to high altitudes. Another source of these cells in an emergency is in the spleen. This curious organ, situated behind the lowest left front ribs and above the left kidney, is a reservoir of blood with a high concentration of red cells. It squeezes out a small quantity of its reserve blood in gentle rhythmic contractions of about two per minute; in response to a low oxygen content in the blood it contracts more forcibly, increasing the volume of circulating blood and its red blood cell population at the same time. This happens on a hot day and during physical exertion or strong emotional excitement, as well as at high altitudes. As a defensive mechanism it goes into action when there is severe bleeding and also when carbon monoxide poisoning destroys the oxygen-carrying power of the red cells.

The spleen, like the liver, also produces scavenger cells that clear the blood of aging red cells and dispose of the debris. Most of the precious iron of the cells' hemoglobin is stored in the liver and used in the synthesis of new hemoglobin. The thrifty mechanism allows only about one two-hundred-fiftieth of the body's iron to escape each day, and this is easily restored by the iron in our ordinary diet.

The white cells in the blood number only about one to five

hundred red cells. Some are manufactured in the bone marrow like the red cells, possibly from the same parent cells. They function mainly as shock troops to fight infections in the body.

These white cells, or leukocytes, present a good many mysteries. They seem to belong to a kind of freebooter or buccaneering variety of cells that arise in various parts of the body such as connective tissue, lymph nodes, the spleen, even in the liver and lungs. They are large—some are gigantic, compared with most other blood cells—and very active. As we have seen, they possess the extraordinary power of devouring invading bacteria and even foreign particles such as dust and carbon. They gather around the site of an inflammation or infection in great numbers. The physiologists' name for this system of free-floating scavengers and defenders is the reticuloendothelial system.

Finally, floating in the blood, are the platelets, tiny fragments of protoplasm which may have broken off from giant cells in the bone marrow or may be remnants of red blood cells that have disintegrated. Their origin is still debated, but not their function, which is an important one in the coagulation of the blood.

The clear amber fluid, the plasma, that carries all these active cells is a bit more than 90 per cent water. In it are dissolved small amounts of oxygen and carbon dioxide in addition to the loads of these gases carried by the red cells. It also transports the enzymes, antibodies, internal secretions and hormones contributed by the various organs. It carries organic products such as urea and uric acid, ammonia and the amino acids of protein metabolism, and it carries the necessary inorganic salts—sodium, calcium, potassium, phosphorus, iron—and the trace elements; the list of them, needed only in tiny quantities but needed nevertheless, is long.

Most important in the plasma are its own proteins, which form about 7 per cent of its volume. There are three—serum albumin, serum globulin, and fibrinogen. They contribute to the blood's viscosity and significantly to the osmotic pressure that regulates the volume of the blood. The fibrinogen is essential in blood coagulation. The serum globulin, one of the products of the spleen and lymph nodes, has as one of its three fractions the gamma globulin that contributes to the body's immunity from many infectious diseases.

THE GHOSTLY CIRCULATION

An almost invisible circulation more or less follows the circulatory system of the blood along part of its route, and that is the lymphatic system. It takes its fluid from the blood plasma, a certain amount of which is given up through the capillary walls, and it has virtually the same constituents as the plasma though in different concentrations. It carries white cells, but of red cells it has very few or none at all.

The lymph capillaries, called the lymphatics, spread like a shadow of the blood capillaries through the tissues, and like them they feed into collecting vessels and finally into two large lymph ducts. Their flow is rather like a tide than a current, since they do not share the pumping action of the heart.

Small nodes of lymph tissue occur at physiologically strategic points in the lymph vessels: in the armpits, the elbows, the groin, the inner side of the knees, along both sides of the neck and behind the ears, and some are deep within the tissues and the viscera. They manufacture lymphocytes, part of the roving system of scavenger and defense cells that we mentioned previously, and also serum globulin, which is one of the three proteins of the blood plasma. Most of all, the lymph nodes act as filters for disease bacteria, which are devoured by the defense cells within the nodes as well as at the site of infection. Thus the lymphatic system, shadowy subsidiary of the pulsing blood, makes its significant contribution to the body's protection from hostile invaders.

The study of blood chemistry is comparatively young; much of what we know today we owe to the constantly improving techniques of microscopy and to new instruments and techniques such as superspeed centrifuges, electrophoresis, and paper chromatography. In every era medical science has had to wait on invention and technical advance. In our time techniques and scientific knowledge are advancing together at a breath-taking pace. Most of what we have been able to say of the blood in this chapter has been learned in this century. And probably we have glimpsed up to now only a fraction of what we may someday know of the fabulous fluid that flows through our arteries and veins.

7 | TWENTY TIMES A MINUTE

THE MOST OBVIOUS difference—and yet the most astonishing—between ourselves and the water-dwelling creatures who are the ancestors of us all is that we can breathe air. We have only to watch the newly caught fish gasping out his life on the deck to be freshly confronted with this enormous fact. The fish, like us, must breathe to live; that is, he must have oxygen. Yet, out of water, he dies for lack of it, even though the air that surrounds him is full of the life-sustaining gas.

We can dive deep into his element, or fly high into the element of the birds, and still live. We can walk about on the good earth and lift our heads in the sunshine. We can talk and laugh and sing, build cities and expand our ways of living with the creations of hand and brain. We can do all those things that are singularly human, thanks to some ancient grotesque creature who dug blindly into the mud of a drying watercourse in the youth of the world.

That curious ancestor of ours was able to cling to a spark of life, even as the water drained away, by virtue of an oddity in his equipment that enabled him to take oxygen out of the air. Somehow, by a happy genetic accident, he had developed a primitive lung. We know his direct descendants as the lungfishes, the Dipnoi, which have both gills and lungs.

Through the uncounted millenniums the evolving species of air breathers found further adaptations to their dry environment. They could not live out of water by their lungs alone. The exquisite chemistry of the living cell still needed its surrounding sea; the body's community of organs and systems must have such specialists as the kidneys to purify and reconstitute this inner sea in which alone our metabolic functions can go on. Each new human life is still conceived and spends its first nine months of growth within the mothering sea that fills the womb. The species might have been obliged to return and lay its eggs in water if it were not for another happy genetic advance, the amniotic fluid in which the embryo of the mammals can float in blissful prenatal security with all its vital needs supplied.

We are still essentially water dwellers. Thanks to the many wonderful adaptive mechanisms we possess, we can carry our watery environment around within us, inside our skins. And thanks to our lungs and their power to take oxygen from the air and transfer it to our blood, we are free to wander over earth and oceans, to delve in the deeps and soar to the heights, even someday to explore the universe beyond the enveloping atmosphere of our small home planet. Perhaps a gill-breathing fish could devise a space ship; perhaps on some other planet there are water dwellers who have done so. With us it was necessary to emerge from the sea before we could develop the inventive hand and brain, and for this we must thank our tireless air-breathing lungs.

If we did nothing but rest, never calling upon our lungs for more than a minimum supply of oxygen, we would still need 300 quarts of oxygen every day. In a single minute of ordinary activity half a pint of oxygen has to be transferred from the air to the blood, and for this half pint the lungs must process about five quarts of air every minute. An athlete running a race at sea level breathes as much as 120 quarts of air a minute, and if the track meet is being held in the mountains, his lungs will have to do even better than that to keep him in the race. And they can, with training, meet some astonishing demands. We use our lungs normally at only a fraction of their working capacity.

THE VITAL TRANSFER

Every living cell must breathe: that is, every cell needs oxygen for its vital metabolic activities. Every cell must also get rid of its carbon dioxide, the gaseous waste of its metabolism. In the simplest animal forms each cell gets its oxygen for itself out of the surrounding environment and gives off its carbon dioxide in the same way. In the more highly developed organisms a special mechanism makes the exchange of oxygen and carbon dioxide with the environment on behalf of the entire body, and a carrier fetches the oxygen and carries away the waste for all the cells. The carrier is the blood in its circulatory system, and the mechanism that does business with the outer atmosphere is the respiratory system with its key organs, the lungs.

From its very portals this system is specialized for its task. The air comes down the corridors of the nose, the pharynx, the larynx, and the trachea or windpipe, and into the bronchial tubes which branch off into the twin lungs. Most other passageways in the body—the digestive tract, for example, and the blood vessels— are composed of muscle only. But the corridors of the respiratory system must be kept open at all times for the vital exchange with the atmosphere. And so we find that, unlike those of other passageways, the muscular wall of the trachea is braced. It has a series of C-shaped cartilages holding it firm at the front and sides. A strong membrane made of elastic fibers connects the open ends of the cartilage rings across the back and stretches from one ring to the next. The two main bronchial branches have the same sturdy construction, and the smaller tubes branching off from them carry thin plates of cartilage, at irregular intervals, that stiffen their walls to some extent.

The system of bronchial tubes branches out into smaller and smaller bronchioles, a millimeter and less in diameter, like a tree putting out thinner and thinner branches and finally its slender twigs. The twigs end at last in clusters of air sacs like bunches of grapes; there are 750 million of these alveoli, as they are called, in the lungs. And here, in these hundreds of millions of tiny air sacs, is the actual point of transfer. Here, through the thin membrane of a network of capillaries, the air and the blood make their exchange of oxygen and carbon dioxide.

We know from the previous chapter on the circulatory system that the lungs have their own circuit, a separate loop of blood vessels leading out from and back to the heart. As this pulmonary circulation proliferates through the lungs it divides into a network of capillaries that have a surface area of about 1,000 square feet, fifty times the area of the skin and about the same as the floor space in an average American home.

This vast lacy surface of thread-thin capillary walls spreads what amounts to a film of blood 1,000 feet square, of a depth of only one blood cell's diameter. This thousand-foot film is exposed to the air in the alveoli of the lungs, with only the thinnest of membranes between.

THE MARCH OF THE RED CELLS

As we breathe in and out we tend to picture our lungs as a pair of hollow elastic bags, like balloons, filling and emptying by turns. To be sure, they are elastic, but they are far from hollow. They are filled with interlacing networks of bronchioles and air sacs and the slender filaments of the capillaries, carrying blood. Through the capillaries march the red blood cells in single file, exchanging their carbon dioxide for oxygen. In normal activity each one of them has just one second to drop its load of carbon dioxide and pick up its load of oxygen. During physical exertion it has only about one-third as much time as that.

The red blood cell coming into the lungs is like a man in a hurry with something he wants to get rid of—the carbon dioxide —in one hand while he picks up something he wants—the oxygen —with the other. Naturally the cell has neither hands nor wishes in the matter. What the cell has is a remarkable chemical affinity for oxygen and a remarkable ability to pick it up, carry it in loose combination with the iron in the cell's hemoglobin, and relinquish the oxygen on demand to the body cells that need it.

The exchange of the two gases between the blood on one side and the air on the other side of the membrane is accomplished by means of a phenomenon called diffusion. Only the name of this phenomenon is comparatively unfamiliar; the phenomenon itself is as familiar as your morning cup of coffee. It is by diffusion that the sugar you put in your coffee spreads throughout all the coffee in the cup. Even if you did not stir the coffee the sugar would sweeten it all; it would merely take a little longer. The molecules of sugar spread from where they are thickest to where they are thinnest, until they are evenly diffused throughout the fluid.

It is the same with the air in the air sacs and the blood in the capillaries: the air has more oxygen and less carbon dioxide; the red cells have less oxygen and more carbon dioxide. The carbon dioxide molecules automatically migrate from the red blood cell through the thin, porous membrane into the air in the air sac, while the oxygen molecules cross from the air to the cell. Another way of explaining this is in terms of differences of molecular pressure: the molecules are pushed out by the higher pressure of their kind on one side of the membrane or pulled out by the lower pressure on the other. When the molecular pressure on both sides of the membrane is equalized, the exchange is completed. Another word for this diffusion across a membrane is osmosis.

The blood plasma picks up a small amount of oxygen in simple solution by this method. But it is the hemoglobin of the red blood cells, with its peculiar ability to take on a massive oxygen load, that carries most of the oxygen we need. If we had to depend upon the plasma alone for our oxygen, we would have to have nearly sixty times more fluid than we have circulating through the body, 300 quarts of blood instead of our present five, about five times the bulk of all our solid tissues. Imagine the bloated monsters we would be and the effort it would take merely to move such a mass. Except for our efficient hemoglobin, we would never have a ballet dancer or a basketball player among us.

The red blood cells, having made their swift transaction, proceed on their way through the circulatory system, leaving most of their carbon dioxide for the lungs to get rid of. This the lungs do, and very smartly, but not by the simple method of breathing it out. Curiously, we do not breathe out a lungful of used air and breathe in a lungful of fresh each time we take a breath. We exchange only about one-sixth of the air in our lungs under ordinary circumstances.

What happens is that the air sacs—the alveoli—exchange carbon dioxide for oxygen by the same method as they make their exchange with the blood cells—that is, by diffusion. The new air coming in takes on carbon dioxide so that it will contain an amount equal to that in the air already in the lungs and gives up oxygen until this, too, is equal in both the new air and the air already in the lungs. This principle of diffusion is as commonplace in the body's many processes as it is in the organic and physical world about us.

WORKING THE BELLOWS

The lungs inflate and deflate some sixteen to twenty times a minute. Their elastic tissue allows them to expand and contract like balloons, but they do not have the muscle to do the job by

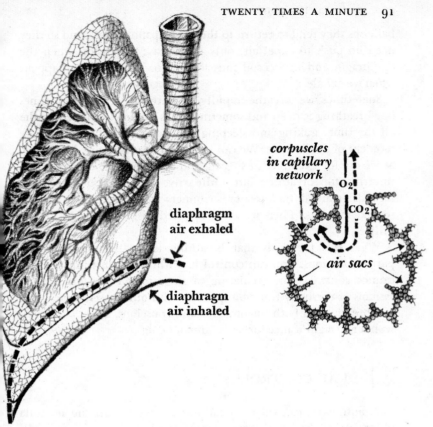

corpuscles
in capillary
network

O_2

CO_2

diaphragm
air exhaled

air sacs

diaphragm
air inhaled

themselves. They are like a pair of bellows, which someone has
to pump.

The chief muscle on the pump handle is the diaphragm, and
the pumping action is not pushing the air out but pulling it in,
in other words, expanding the lungs so that they will fill with
air. The diaphragm, the great dome-shaped muscle that forms
the floor of the chest, does this by contracting, flattening itself
downward, and thus enlarging the chest cavity. The ribs are
pulled up and outward by the action of the intercostal muscles,
narrow but powerful muscular strips between the ribs that expand and contract the rib cage; we have twenty-two of these muscles on each side. Thus the whole chest expands in all directions.
The lungs stretch wide, and the air rushes in. This is what happens when we inhale.

The reverse action comes about through the elasticity of the
lungs. When they are pulled out and filled with air, like rubber

balloons they tend to return to their unexpanded size. And so they need no push to expel air, only the release of tension when the diaphragm and intercostal muscles let go. This is what happens when we exhale.

Sometimes we breathe rapidly, sometimes slowly; sometimes our breathing is deep and sometimes it is shallow; but we breathe all the time, waking and sleeping; we stop breathing only at the moment of swallowing. We can voluntarily control our breathing, as we do, for example, in singing and speaking. We can even voluntarily stop breathing but, ordinarily, only for about forty-five seconds; trained underwater swimmers can extend the time to several minutes. Then we are compelled to breathe again, willy-nilly.

What this means is that breathing is partly automatic and partly conscious. You can control it, within certain limits, as you cannot control your circulation or digestion. These other great systems of the body function quite beyond our consciousness. But our breathing is both unconscious and conscious, a fact which has wonderful significance for us as human beings.

DUAL CONTROLS

The automatic control of breathing is centered in the medulla oblongata of the brain. From one particular group of nerve cells in the medulla, rhythmic impulses go down the spinal cord to the phrenic nerve, which controls the diaphragm, and to the intercostal muscles. But it appears that this small spot in the medulla is not alone in managing this complex and vital function. There are at least two other nerve centers in the medulla concerned with respiration, and there are chemical and reflex signals that control them in turn.

The chemical controls of breathing are mainly dependent on the level of carbon dioxide in the alveolar air, that is, the air in the air sacs of the lungs. The response is so extremely sensitive that if the carbon dioxide in the air sacs increases only two-tenths of 1 per cent, automatically we are moved to breathe faster and usually more deeply than we normally do. Even so slight an excess of carbon dioxide in the lungs causes us to double the amount of air we take in per minute until the excess is eliminated. If we are breathing air that has as much as 5 or 6 per cent carbon dioxide, our breathing becomes very nearly violent, and this in spite of the fact that with every breath we are getting air that is more than 90 per cent oxygen. So it is not lack of oxygen but excess of carbon dioxide to which we have this instant and powerful reaction.

If the situation is reversed and we deliberately breathe a normal mixture of air as deeply and quickly as we can for a minute or so, then we have the unusual experience of not having to breathe at all for almost as long as a minute. Laboratory volunteers, who have made this experiment with air containing a very high percentage of oxygen, have stopped breathing for as long as seven or eight minutes at a stretch.

In other words, by forced ventilation—or voluntary overbreathing—we can give the alveolar air such a balance of oxygen versus carbon dioxide that we simply do not require any exchange with fresh air for a while. We would think it was the more-than-normal supply of oxygen that makes it unnecessary to breathe, but another step in the experiment shows that it is the less-than-normal supply of carbon dioxide that does the trick. For example, if the air with which we do our voluntary overbreathing contains more than a normal percentage of carbon dioxide, say 4 or 5 per cent, then it makes no difference how quickly and deeply we breathe for the minute of the experiment. We have to go right on breathing when we go back to normal air, as though we had not made the extra effort at all.

What happens when we overbreathe normal air is that the carbon-dioxide content of the air in the air sacs is greatly reduced, and the blood cells passing by along the capillaries give up more of their own carbon dioxide load than they would ordinarily do. It is as though the alveolar air sucked carbon dioxide from the blood to bring up its own low carbon dioxide pressure; here we have a graphic illustration of the principle of diffusion, or differences in molecular pressures.

As long as the situation continues, and the blood cells are circulating with less carbon dioxide than usual, the blood passing through the respiratory centers in the medulla does not give them the chemical signal that sets in motion the reflex nerve impulses to the diaphragm and the intercostal muscles, and we have no compulsion to breathe. The instant the effects of our overbreathing experiment have passed off and the carbon dioxide level of the blood returns to normal, the autonomic system goes back into action. The respiratory nerve centers respond, the nerve impulses go out, and whether we will or not we have to breathe.

Want of oxygen does make us breathe faster and more deeply, without a rise in the carbon dioxide level, as we can observe when we get up to altitudes of 10,000 feet or higher. There is another control center in the neck, a tiny structure attached like a twig to the carotid artery, close to the carotid sinus. This little mechanism, called the carotid body, has receptor nerves that respond to the oxygen and carbon dioxide content of the blood. As far as we know they do not contribute to the control of breathing under ordinary circumstances, but they seem to become involved when we get into the thin air of high altitudes. Possibly this is another of the many instances in which the body has second- and even third-line mechanisms which may take over a function in an emergency.

Breathing into a paper bag to get over a case of hiccups—or singultus, the physicians' name for those uncomfortable spasmodic contractions of the diaphragm—is an old folk remedy, certainly a good deal older than our knowledge of the respiratory system's sensitive controls. Our grandmothers knew that it worked, but today we know how it works. What it does is to take advantage of the medulla's nervous response to the carbon dioxide level in the alveolar air as this signal is conveyed in the blood. Breathing into a paper bag simply has the effect of cutting off the normal exchange with the surrounding atmosphere. The air in the bag, after a few breaths, has an increasingly high carbon dioxide content; consequently so does the alveolar air, and finally the blood. In response, the respiratory centers in the medulla call for stronger and deeper inspirations, regularizing the contractions of the diaphragm and eliminating the spasm.

So much for the involuntary or unconscious control of our breathing. It seems elaborate enough to take care of just about everything. Yet we exert voluntary control over our breathing every time we speak or sing, whisper or shout. A swimmer times his breathing with his strokes, and a good athlete in any sport manages his breathing in relation to his muscular co-ordination. A batter takes a deep breath just before he swings at the ball and expels it as he swings; so does a golfer or any well-co-ordinated individual making a powerful muscular effort. You hear the piano mover grunt on an expelled breath as he lifts the piano onto his dolly. A marksman holds his breath while he aims and fires; the least breath may spoil his aim by causing his arm to waver if only by a hair. You learn to hold your breath when you are snapping the shutter of your camera, and for the same reason, unless you are using a high-speed action lens.

You find yourself holding your breath when you are moving on tiptoe, trying not to waken a sleeper, or when you are carrying a glass filled to the brim and trying not to spill it, or when you are performing almost any task requiring the co-ordination of fine muscles, like threading a needle.

Considering that our life depends upon our breathing, it is remarkable that we have as much conscious control over it as we do. Our automatic controls keep us breathing, fortunately, whether or not we are paying attention, or we would not be able to go to sleep. If we had only automatic controls, we could not perform many of our most highly developed acts of skill. Nor would we be capable of those most human forms of expression, laughter, song, and speech. (Animals make their sounds by the same physiological mechanisms, but the controls are instinctual or reflex rather than voluntary, as we shall see later.)

Probably our survival, or rather the survival of our evolutionary forebears, also depended upon a thousand unforeseen adaptations and co-ordinations in attack and defense that were more skillfully managed with the breath held or expelled at will. And so we have the wonderful gift of dual control, part voluntary, part automatic, of the very breath of life.

PROTECTIVE MECHANISMS

The lungs are the most exposed of our internal organs. Twenty times a minute, more or less, they suck in indiscriminately from the surrounding atmosphere a gaseous mixture, along with whatever foreign particles happen to be floating in it and at whatever temperature it may happen to be. But our lungs are not so vulnerable for all that; indeed, they have some remarkable protective devices.

We can safely breathe air that is many degrees below our normal body temperature, because on its way through the nasal passages it is preheated by a large supply of blood, circulating like hot water in a radiator, giving off warmth through the thin mucous membrane that lines the respiratory tract. We can breathe very dry air because this same mucous lining is always moist and the air picks up moisture as it passes.

Dust, soot, and bacteria are present in some degree in almost any air that human beings breathe, but the system is equipped to filter out great quantities of this alien matter with a barrier of cilia, tiny threadlike growths that line the passageways to the bronchial tubes like a fine fuzz. These catch not only foreign particles but also mucus produced by the respiratory passages themselves; the movement of the cilia is always toward the outside, and thus they push the interfering matter out into the nostrils. Particles that are too large for the cilia to dispose of are irritating enough to stimulate a sneeze or a cough.

Sneezing and coughing are reflexive acts in response to stimulation of nerve endings in the respiratory passages. In both the basic muscular action is the same: first we take in a short breath and then we expel it forcibly. The blast should dislodge the irritating particle; if it fails the first time, then the reflex is repeated and we sneeze or cough again until the invader is ejected.

A cough is the end result of stimulation of specific nerve endings of the vagus nerve, the principal nerve of the parasympathetic system of involuntary nerves. Usually a cough originates with an irritation in the larynx or trachea, but it may also come from nerve endings in the lungs or the membrane that surrounds them. In a cough the larynx closes and a column of air under high pressure forms within the lower air passages. Then the glottis, the trap-doorlike opening in the larynx, suddenly opens and the air under pressure escapes explosively, generally carrying with it the offending particle.

This is what happens, violently and often embarrassingly, when in the midst of our most animated dinner-table conversation a morsel of food or a drop of liquid goes down the wrong way. The timing of the swallow and the supposedly simultaneous closing of the respiratory passage need only be thrown off by the merest fraction of a second, and we burst into a spasm of violent choking coughs that bring blood rushing to the head and tears to the eyes. We cannot control the spasm; we go right on coughing, red-faced and weeping, until the unwelcome stray that took the wrong turning is finally expelled.

The stimulus for a sneeze comes not from the air passages in the throat but from those in the nose, where, presumably, the irritation is lodged. In a sneeze the glottis remains open, but at the beginning of the reflex the tongue automatically rises up against the soft palate and blocks the passage of air through the mouth. The blast is thus forced through the comparatively narrow nasal passages, and if it does not clear them the first time we are likely to sneeze and sneeze until it does. Pressure on the upper lip where it joins the nasal septum can cut off the nervous reflex and stop the sneezing, but the sneezy tickle goes on until we dislodge the offending substance by blowing the nose.

Sneezing and coughing, especially coughing, can also be set off by psychological causes. Any actor or public speaker of experience knows that a wave of coughing going through the audience is a signal that he has lost his hearers' attention. Sneezing is often, as we know, an allergic reaction, as witness the many hay-fever sufferers; but allergies have an emotional as well as a physiological basis, and the nasal congestion and consequent sneezing may occur from an emotional cause without the irritating pollen or the hair of a dog or cat being present at all.

Even more markedly psychological is the long gape-mouthed inhalation, the yawn, and its counterpart, the sigh, which is a prolonged exhalation. Probably the yawn as a physiological phenomenon has to do with a need to liven up a weary, drowsy, or bored mind and body by accelerating the exchange of oxygen and carbon dioxide between the blood and the lungs, and thus send a more stimulating mixture through the body. An animal waking from a nap characteristically yawns, stretches, and is then ready to go about his animal business.

Among human beings the yawn seems almost entirely psychic in origin. Nothing is more infectious; we may yawn for no reason except that we see someone else yawn. You are probably tempted to yawn even while you read this paragraph about yawning.

The sigh is also largely psychic; we sigh in relief after a tense experience, or to unburden ourselves of an emotional weight of grief or anxiety. Physiologically, the deep inhalation and the prolonged exhalation, often vocalized, serve to relax muscle tensions.

OXYGEN DEBT AND OXYGEN WANT

A track athlete running at sea level can breathe fifty times a minute, sucking in 120 quarts of air in that short space of time. Even with this extraordinary respiratory capacity, however, he is likely to collapse, panting and gasping for breath, at the end of a sprint; speed swimmers not infrequently suffer nausea and vomiting when the race is done.

Every newspaper reader is familiar with the look of anguish, even agony, on an athlete's face as he crosses the finish line. A British physician who happened also to be a gifted sculptor, Dr. R. Tait Mackenzie, once made an extraordinary record of these tormented faces of athletes at the moment of supreme effort, in a series of sculptured heads—the mouth pulled wide, the lips drawn back from the teeth in a near-snarl, the forehead ridged over narrowed eyes and the brows drawn upward in that circumflex angle that we recognize instantly as an expression of pain, anxiety, or grief; nineteenth-century writers on physiognomy named it the "angle of sorrow."

In these young men in prime physical condition, both the look and the anguish it expresses are fleeting, but the agonized moments are real enough as the whole organism strains to squeeze out the last ounce of power against a desperate insufficiency of oxygen. Virtually every athlete, no matter what his sport, has experienced that moment when his lungs seem near to bursting with the effort to get enough air. And then, mercifully, if the race or other feat is one of the longer and necessarily slower ones, he slips into the new gear that we call "second wind," and he can go on smoothly and easily with almost no feeling of strain.

These two curious phenomena that we experience in athletic exertion provide a good illustration of the remarkable interrelation between the lungs and the blood. In the short, hard sprint the lungs cannot possibly supply, or the blood cells pick up and carry, enough oxygen for the sharply increased muscle metabolism. The muscle tissue cannot even absorb the needed oxygen that rapidly. For the hundred-yard dash the muscles need about six quarts of oxygen in a little more than ten seconds; the world's record for this event is actually under ten seconds. In that brief space of time, even with respiration and circulation working at their peak, the body tissues can absorb only about a quart of oxygen, in a large, healthy man perhaps two quarts. The runner could do almost as well if he held his breath from starting gun to finish line.

What happens is that the muscles do their work and the body goes into debt for oxygen for the emergency. Lactic acid, the waste product of muscle metabolism, accumulates, and when the race is run the panting, gasping athlete takes in enough air to complete the metabolic cycle of reconverting the lactic acid to glycogen. If he has made a really strenuous run or other effort, his oxygen debt may come to as much as fifteen quarts.

The "second wind" phenomenon occurs in a prolonged muscular effort. As the muscles use up oxygen at an increased rate, the athlete's breathing becomes deeper and more rapid, the heart accelerates and enlarges, and the blood pressure rises so that the blood is circulating more rapidly, making the transfer of oxygen and carbon dioxide ever faster both with the air in the lungs and with the muscle tissues. On the long pull this speeding up of respiration and circulation, together with the dilation of blood vessels which increases the actual quantity of oxygenated blood carried to the muscles, becomes equal to the muscles' oxygen need, and a balance is established. The athlete who has made a marathon run or a distance swim, or played a match of tennis, will be tired but he may not be panting at all—unless he has finished with a sprint and incurred an oxygen debt at the very end.

It takes only a moment's thought to realize what an advantage this power of going into oxygen debt must have given to any species that possessed it. Our progenitors did not run races for trophies, whether on two feet or four. But they often had to run swiftly to spear their prey or else to save their lives; the ability of the muscles to deliver the extra ounce of strength or speed, regardless of oxygen supply, must often have made the difference between eating and being eaten. And the power to jog on over hundreds of miles in search of game, with lungs and heart and blood vessels co-operating smoothly and tirelessly to supply the muscles with their full measure of oxygen—this surely meant survival in a world in which the struggle for survival was more often desperate than not. We know from fossil evidence that our Old

Stone Age ancestors, those great hunters the Neanderthal men and the gifted Cro-Magnons who left us their handsome cave paintings, covered Europe from one end to the other on their hunting trips.

Thus they survived and passed on to us the wonderful lung-blood-muscle mechanism that makes athletic heroes. Even habitual chair sitters and automobile riders can enjoy its benefits in the tennis and swimming season, and if they keep in condition they can enjoy it even more. It is, like most body mechanisms, an inborn gift that improves with use.

Like physical exertion, the thin air at high altitudes also makes for hard breathing, but for quite a different reason and with very different consequences. When there is just too little oxygen in the air, no matter how deeply or quickly we breathe, the red blood cells are not able to get up to their normal oxygen saturation of about 97 per cent. Between 8,000 and 10,000 feet the breathing becomes perceptibly difficult and the rather disagreeable symptoms of mountain sickness may begin to appear: headache, nausea and vomiting, or perhaps a lightheaded, illusive exhilaration.

At 15,000 feet, ordinarily stable and sensible people may become boisterous, pugnacious, or unreasonable and stubborn; they may laugh, cry, explode into outbursts of temper, wild hilarity, or recklessness. At 30,000 feet there is not enough oxygen to support human life; on the lofty slopes of Mt. Everest, which is nearly that high, it was oxygen hunger that robbed many early climbers of reason and judgment, gave them hallucinations, and all too often lured them to their death. Only portable oxygen tanks made it possible for Sir Edmund Hilary and his Sherpa guide, Tenzing, to master the terrible peak.

Airplane travel at 18,000 feet and above is possible only because air is pumped into the cabins, keeping the pressure at about the equivalent of an 8,000-foot altitude. Even that would not be adequate if the passengers had to do heavy work while aloft; fortunately they are asked only to sit quietly in their seats.

The ceiling for human labor is 19,000 feet. Indians working in the Andean mines at that altitude move slowly, and their respiration and circulation are adapted to the low oxygen content of the thin air. Anyone else suddenly transported to that altitude would almost certainly collapse. An air traveler from a low altitude who lands at 8,000 feet is uncomfortable; some visitors to Mexico City find themselves breathless with even mild exercise unless they remain there long enough for the body to make its adjustments. Performing artists on concert tour, especially dance companies, have to reckon with the beautiful city's altitude. A wise precaution that many of them take is to insert a few extra days into the tour at this stop.

The principal adaptation that the body makes to high altitudes is an increase in the number of its red blood cells; more of them are needed to carry oxygen to the tissues since each one of them carries less than the normal load. A high-altitude dweller may have one and one-half times as many red blood cells as people living at sea level.

Although the roof of the world is not possible for human beings without mechanical aids to respiration, birds and other wild life exist in that rarefied atmosphere, and some birds which normally live at ordinary altitudes can fly very high indeed. The condor, the great bird of the Andes, flies well above that range's highest peaks. Airline pilots have seen Egyptian geese soaring at 30,000 feet. How these high-flying birds pump oxygen remains a puzzle to scientists.

WORDS AND MUSIC

The human species shares its vocal ability with a good part of the animal kingdom. Even the ocean is by no means the silent world it was long believed to be. Fish grunt, squeal, bark and mew, and the aquatic mammals, the whales and porpoises and sea cows, have an extensive vocabulary of sounds. Some animals sing at mating time; the love song of the wolves has been beautifully described. The birds, however, are the master vocalists. Some of the more accomplished songbirds practice their turns and trills by the hour until they have perfected their refinements on the basic song of their species.

The mechanism by which they and we produce vocal sounds is roughly the same as that of an organ pipe or a reed instrument such as the clarinet or oboe. In the musical instrument a reed and a column of air are set to vibrating by the air we blow or pump into it. In the throat the vocal cords, equivalents of the reed, vibrate as the air is blown across them from the lungs. Chest, throat, mouth, nose, and the sinuses and bones of the head are the resonating chambers and sounding boards that magnify the sound and give it its quality or timbre.

The larynx or voice box with its vocal cords is amazing for its apparent simplicity; we can only marvel at the astonishing variety of sounds that can be produced with it. It is nothing more than a cartilage-walled chamber with a pair of membranes stretched across it from front to back.

Set at the top of the windpipe (or trachea), just below the root of the tongue, is a small bone, the hyoid bone, and below that is a cartilage shaped like the bow of a boat pointing forward. Below that in turn is another, ring-shaped cartilage, the cricoid. Within the bow-shaped cartilage, called the thyroid cartilage because of its location, are two thin-edged bands of membrane, the vocal cords. They are fastened closely together at the front end, in the very bow, and they stretch back to separate anchorages in two other tiny cartilages, called the arytenoids. These in turn are attached to small muscles which can rotate the arytenoid cartilages to swing the vocal cords away from each other toward the walls of the larynx or toward each other so as to leave only a small space between them.

Ordinarily the vocal cords lie apart, each one against its own side of the larynx, and as we breathe, the air passes between them and we make no sound. We whisper without using the vocal cords, by framing the words with lips and tongue. But when we want to make a sound—to talk, shout, sing, laugh or cry—the little muscles turn the arytenoid cartilages around and the vocal cords are brought close together, into the center of the larynx and into the column of air being expelled from the lungs. The air, forced through the opening between them, sets their edges vibrating, and the vibrations create the sound waves that we call the voice.

Each of us has a specific and individual voice, and what makes it recognizably individual is its characteristic combination of pitch, loudness, and timbre. Loudness depends on how hard we blow out against the cords; some people habitually use less breath and some more, but we all vary the volume of air depending on the circumstances. We use more breath to be heard in a noisy place or across a distance, or when we are excited or want to express ourselves emphatically. When we really want to shout or bellow, without even thinking about it we take a deep breath before we blast away.

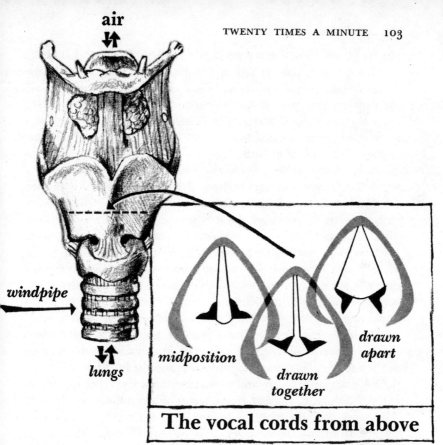

air

windpipe

lungs

midposition

drawn together

drawn apart

The vocal cords from above

diagrammatic view

Timbre is a complicated blend of effects. It involves the size and shape of all the bones and chambers from head to chest and how we "place" our voices in them. Some people get most of their resonance from the head bones, some talk mainly through their noses, and some specialize in deep chest tones.

Pitch is determined by the length of the vocal cords, their thickness, and their tension, which together fix the frequency of their vibrations. In the violin family of stringed instruments the strings of each instrument are all the same length but they differ in thickness—or weight, in some cases—and tension. In other instruments, such as the piano and the harp, thickness and tension are still involved, but the most apparent difference is in the graduated lengths of the strings, from long ones for the low notes to short ones for the high.

The same principles apply to the voice. Children, smaller than adults in every dimension, have short, thin vocal cords and high voices. Women on the average have smaller throats and shorter, slenderer cords and therefore higher voices than men. Boys' voices change at puberty when their chests and throats and all their dimensions grow to adult size, and their vocal cords accordingly become thicker and longer. The change is so startling that it seems to come overnight; actually it takes a bit longer than that, as does their spurt of growth.

Cords of the same length also change their pitch within a somewhat narrow range according to how tautly they are stretched. You tune a piano or violin or any stringed instrument by tightening or loosening the strings; the greater the tension, the higher the note. We ourselves control the tension of our vocal cords to some extent. We can speak high or low, within the range of the voice (how well we stay on pitch when singing, however, depends not only on control of the vocal cords but also on the exactness of our hearing). Singers, actors, and trained speakers— and some who are untrained but naturally gifted with a wide vocal range—can cover quite a span of both pitch and timbre, thanks to their highly developed skill in controlling the tension of the cords, the placement of the voice, and the breath.

Our voices also go up and down involuntarily, reflecting physical, psychological, and emotional states or a combination of them. The voice goes up with excitement, fright, or joy, or a state of tension from any cause, unless it is voluntarily controlled; when the individual is tense, the vocal cords, too, are stretched taut. If you have ever tried to keep your voice from showing excitement or alarm, you know that you have had to make a conscious effort to relax those tiny muscles in your throat. You are not aware of the muscles, as you are of your biceps when you deliberately flex it; all you do consciously is think about pitching your voice lower, and the message goes to the proper muscles by nervous pathways which are voluntarily controlled even though we are not conscious of them. Conversely, the voice goes down in pitch automatically when we are relaxed, lazy, weary—or apathetic or low-spirited— because in those states the whole body is in a low state of tension and so are the vocal cords.

Our animal cousins can make a great variety of sounds, and some of the birds are very clever at imitating other birds and even mimicking the human voice. Animals bark, growl, and snarl. They have mating calls and warning calls and comforting or admonitory mother sounds that they make to their young. All these sounds are involuntary; that is, they are instinctual, reflexive responses to specific stimuli. The animal would make them even if there were no other living creature to hear. Your dog barks at a stranger not to warn you that someone is coming but because he is responding reflexively to an unfamiliar scent, voice, or footstep. Your parrot or parakeet imitates your voice whether or not you are there to speak to him. A human being makes the same kind of involuntary vocal response when he cries out in pain or fear or joy or sudden surprise.

The sounds of laughter and weeping are peculiarly human, and no animal except a human being is capable of true speech. Only man is gifted with the marvelously complex co-ordination of brain and voice and facial muscles to form words and communicate ideas. And only the human infant, of all the living creatures in the world, plays at making sounds, babbling all the possible vowels and consonants of all the possible human languages, until he learns to listen to and repeat the particular sounds of his own particular people and so becomes a participating member of his branch of the family of man.

All the fabulous tools of speech, from the tiny muscles of tongue and lip to the slender branching nerves and the mysterious associative centers of the thinking brain, would be of no avail if it were not for the breath that gives them sound. The same breath that sustains life also provides us with that precious instrument of our common humanity, the voice with which to speak with one another.

8

THE FOOD CONVERTER

THE DIGESTIVE SYSTEM is one of the world's true wonders. Its structure has been investigated by thousands of scientists. Our growing knowledge of its relationship with the psyche is one of the foundation stones of psychoanalysis and of psychosomatic medicine. It has been the subject of millions of printed words. Its functions and malfunctions have created entire industries, and its workings occupy the thoughts of uncounted citizens. With all this, its deceptive simplicity still frustrates all our efforts to understand it.

To people in other countries, Americans appear obsessed with the thirty or thirty-two feet of continuous hollow tubing that runs from lips to anus. Our native alimentary canal, down which passes the world's most abundant diet, seems subject to every kind of ill, real and imaginary, that anxious fears and Madison Avenue fantasy can conjure.

The concern of Americans begins, like the digestive tract itself, with the mouth, which the toothpaste and mouthwash industries insist must be cleansed, purified, deodorized, and put into a state of green grace by the magic of chlorophyll, before either success or love can be achieved. The food may get safely past the pharynx and the esophagus, only to land in the stomach and in trouble. Row after row of patent medicines are guaranteed to save us from the consequences of hasty meals, angry meals, indigestible meals, or meals that are just too big. On goes the food—and the obsession—through the small and large intestines and finally into the rectum where the digestive process is given a final blessing by the laxative industry, with breakfast foods and dozens of preparations designed to impose a mythical "regularity" on the system whatever the cost to its normal functioning.

Along with all these well-meant attentions, the long-suffering alimentary canal must absorb a good deal of the stress of our emotions, our psychosexual development, and our interpersonal relations from childhood on.

That is why the digestive system is a true wonder. It is so rugged, so perfectly automatic, that it goes on with its work no matter how we harass it, with only now and then a protest in the form of constipation, diarrhea, flatulence, sometimes an ulcer, or the constellation of vague and indefinite ailments whose first causes usually originate far from the digestive tract itself. Tough, resistant, and resilient, it copes with an extraordinary variety of groceries, beverages, pills and powders, and it manages somehow to extract from the confusion the essential nutrients to keep our bodies fueled. For this it has an assembly line of special devices, some mechanical, some chemical, tuned to perform their successive tasks on the food as it travels down the tract.

THE INNER WALL

The task of digestion is to convert foodstuffs for the body's use. This it does by physically breaking down, churning, diluting and dissolving the food, and by chemically splitting its molecules into simpler compounds that can be absorbed into the blood. Physiologists speak of the alimentary canal as being outside of the body, a curious notion which appears to contradict observable fact. What they mean is that even when we have eaten a fine full meal and feel thoroughly well fed, as long as the food is still in the digestive tract it might as well be on the table. We have enjoyed gastronomic pleasures and have sensations of inner comfort, but we are not really fed—that is, the body is not nourished —until the nutrients pass through the intestinal wall into the blood.

The alimentary canal is like the outside of the body in another way, too. It is protected throughout its length by the mucosa, or mucous membrane, a lining that is soft but remarkably tough. This permits all manner of things to pass safely by, without suffering harm itself or allowing them to penetrate its walls and do harm to the vulnerable organs and cells beyond.

Indeed the membrane is astonishingly able to resist its own chemistry. It can dissolve beef, bone and gristle, and animal and vegetable matter that is far tougher than the membrane itself. It can digest animal stomachs and intestines—tripe and sausage casings. We would have to boil our food in strong acids at 212° Fahrenheit to do with cookery what the stomach and intestines do at the body's normal temperature of 98.6°.

In the stomach, for example, the gastric juice as it comes from the glands has a high concentration of hydrochloric acid, between 0.5 and 0.6 per cent. Hydrochloric acid, as we know, is corrosive enough to dissolve metal, and the gastric juice disposes of a hard-boiled egg in a few minutes. Apart from the astonishing fact that living cells can secrete such a powerful mineral acid without harm, what keeps the gastric juice from disposing of the stomach as readily as it does the egg?

The scientists used to believe that the digestive organs resisted their own powerful chemicals simply by virtue of being living tissue, but laboratory tests have proved that this is not so. The boa constrictor's stomach is apparently busy digesting the live dinner even while the snake is still in the act of swallowing it.

One part of this puzzle, at least, appears to be solved: it has been discovered that the lining of the stomach produces not only the powerful acid but also ammonia, an equally powerful alkali, and thus protects itself from its own chemicals. The lining of the intestine may one day reveal a similar secret.

The continuous wall of the digestive system acts as a barrier to keep undigested food and the chemicals of digestion away from the delicate inner organs and systems of the body. It also must act as a sieve, to allow the nutrients through, or else we would never be fed at all. Another of the wonders of this lining is that it is very choosy about what it will and what it will not pass—or absorb—and its rules change according to the location.

The stomach wall will allow alcohol, some mineral salts and some water to go through, as well as some glucose and other simple sugars if they are in a sufficiently strong concentration. The large intestine absorbs mostly water.

The small intestine's wall is the busy one: through it pass most of the body's nutrients, but they do not merely slip through, as through the holes in a sieve. The intestinal wall works at its absorption task; it sucks up some nutrients first and then others. Glucose, for example, the form in which the body cells use their carbohydrate fuel, is absorbed most readily and actively, and then the other simple sugars, galactose and fructose, in that order. The amino acids of protein probably go next. The fats, first broken down and then resynthesized, are the slowest to be absorbed.

All this processing and absorption, a series of operations following one after the other in a prescribed order, requires a long surface of mucosa, just as continuous processing in a factory requires a long conveyor belt to carry the stuff of manufacture from its raw material stage through all the necessary operations to the finished product.

We might be justified in saying that the inventors of continuous processing in manufacture were not really very original, for the body developed the same system in its earliest stages of evolution, many millions of years ago. In our thirty or thirty-two feet of alimentary canal each one of us possesses a tube-shaped, specially lined, private conveyor belt. Figured in terms of area, we have a great deal more inner than outer skin: the mucosa of the small intestine alone has about five times the area of the epidermis that covers our bodies from top to toe, curves and folds notwithstanding.

Not only the lining but also the walls of the canal are of rather special construction. They are muscle tissue of the smooth type, and here we see with particular clarity the value of smooth muscle with properties that the skeletal or striped muscles, for example, the biceps, do not have. Smooth muscle can keep up a steady sustained tonus, or contraction, and on top of this it has the power of rhythmical contractions—peristalsis—like a series of waves running down its length. The long tube of the digestive system, sometimes narrow and sometimes wide, can hold its tonus and carry on its peristaltic contractions indefinitely. For all this work it uses up only a negligible amount of energy. And—most remarkable—it never becomes tired.

Another peculiarity of the stomach, incidentally of the urinary bladder and to a lesser degree also of the intestines, is the way it stretches and contracts. When we have gone for some time without eating and the stomach is empty or nearly so, the muscle wall pulls together and the hollow inside virtually disappears. When the stomach is full, however, the walls automatically adjust to the distention without strain.

What happens, apparently, is that the muscle fibers are not themselves stretched when the stomach is distended. Smooth-muscle fibers are very short compared with those in striated muscle, and they are placed in crisscross layers instead of bundles. To stretch, the fibers simply slide over one another until they are not in layers but in a line; the wall loses thickness and gains area, like a rubber balloon when it is blown up. The way the fibers pull out is rather like the jointed zigzag device of a collapsible gate such as we put across the top of a stairway to keep the baby from falling downstairs. This powerful, tireless, elastic muscle wall is one of the working tools for the mechanical task of digestion, propelling the food along the canal, churning and mixing it with the digestive juices as it goes.

THE GATEWAYS

We have talked about the inner skin of the digestive tract and about the muscle wall that surrounds the skin, or mucosa. On the mechanical side the digestive system has a series of devices, gateways that open and shut automatically. Since we are speaking of a canal, we may also speak of these gateways as locks. Like the locks of a canal, they hold the traffic back under certain conditions, while under other conditions they permit it to go ahead, and they may even close behind it so that it cannot go back again but only forward.

They are of different kinds, these locks or gateways. The first set is at the back of the throat, where there are two entrances, one to the digestive system and the other to the respiratory system. The entrance to the respiratory tract is actually a passageway or corridor leading from the nasal passages to the pharynx, the larynx, the bronchial tubes and the lungs.

This corridor is necessarily kept open at all times for breathing; the one exception is the instant when we swallow. Then two doors close: one of them, the soft palate, rises up and seals off the nasal passages; the other, the epiglottis, shuts over the larynx, or rather the larynx is lifted by the muscular action of swallowing so that it comes close up to the epiglottis and is covered by it while the food goes by.

We usually take a short breath just as we get the food to the back of the throat and into the pharynx, and then we stop breathing while the automatic second step of swallowing goes on. As we noted in an earlier chapter, when our timing is off for some reason, some bit of food or fluid literally goes down the wrong way, and the presence of solid or liquid matter in the respiratory tract immediately sets up the reflex of coughing to get it out of there.

The right way down is, obviously, into the esophagus, the first length of the digestive canal. The upper part of the esophagus in man is composed of striated muscle, not smooth like the rest of the digestive tract, and the food goes down that part of the tube quite rapidly, although not so rapidly as in a dog's throat, in which the esophagus walls are of striated muscle all the way. Then comes the second canal lock, called the cardiac sphincter because of its location in the general region of the heart.

A sphincter is a circular muscle which contracts to close and relaxes to open a gateway. The cardiac sphincter, at the gateway from the esophagus to the stomach, draws together to close the passage in response to stimulation by the sympathetic nervous system, which generally operates at times when active functions are going on. It opens in response to the vagus nerve, part of the parasympathetic system, which is largely concerned with digestion. The cardiac sphincter opens at the approach of food, and the food is swept on into the stomach by the peristaltic waves.

The next gateway, the pyloric sphincter, opens from the lower part of the stomach into the first section of the small intestine, the duodenum. This sphincter is open most of the time, closing only for a moment each time a peristaltic wave passes over it. But since the stomach is a wide place in the canal—wide enough, indeed, to be considered not a tube at all but a vessel—and since it also has a J-shaped curve at its bottom, the passage of food through the pylorus is automatically slowed up until the consistency of the food is such that it can flow through the narrow opening into the intestine, which is also very narrow. Fluids pass through the stomach and into the intestine with little delay, but solid food must be reduced almost to a fluid state to go through, and the foods that go most rapidly are those that are most easily liquefied, the carbohydrates. Meats go more slowly and fats, for chemical reasons, slowest of all. It takes between three and four and one-half hours for all the ingredients of a mixed meal to pass the pyloric sphincter.

At the junction of the small and large intestines is the ileocolic sphincter. Its name means simply that it connects the ileum, the lowest portion of the small intestine, with the colon or large intestine; actually it connects with the cecum, the first portion of the large intestine. This is an especially efficient one-way valve, allowing food to go from the small to the large intestine, but preventing the contents of the large intestine, with its normal bacteria, from seeping back to the small intestine where they might be harmful. The two branches of the autonomic nervous system, the parasympathetic and the sympathetic, collaborate to open and close the valve.

The final gateway is the anal sphincter, and in the first year or so of the child's life this sphincter opens and closes involuntarily. The distention of the rectum by accumulating feces sets up nerve impulses from the rectal wall to a center in the sacral region, the lowest part of the spinal cord, and a reflex impulse travels back to the anal sphincter to open the anus. A higher nervous center for the anal sphincter is in the medulla oblongata, a part of the brain which is not yet connected with the conscious brain at birth but develops these connections during early childhood. Thus, as the nervous system matures, the control of the anal sphincter becomes voluntary. This is why toilet training begun too soon cannot succeed; a baby cannot be responsible for controlling its anal sphincter until the nervous connections for voluntary control are developed.

ALCHEMISTS OF DIGESTION

If we are amazed by the mechanical arrangements of the digestive system, how much more bedazzled must we be by its chemistry. Man is by nature omnivorous. He does not dine exclusively on grass like the herbivores or on steak like the carnivores. He indiscriminately consumes both grass and steak, vegetable and animal food. And, being man, he eats not only for nourishment but also for pleasure, and out of an insatiable curiosity about every detail in his environment.

Most other animals, encountering some unfamiliar substance, sniff it, paw it, and if it turns out not to be recognizably edible they usually end by leaving it alone. Not man. It is not enough for him to touch and smell. From the beginning of time, or at least his time on earth, he has also tasted everything that came his way. He has even, incautiously, swallowed it to discover what interesting effects it might have on him.

Long before the Egyptians began to write down the 700-odd drugs and medications for which they knew a purpose, prehistoric man had sampled just about every natural substance—vegetable, animal, mineral—that he stumbled on. He discovered poppy seeds that made him sleep and banished his aches and pains, mushrooms that made him dream dreams and see visions, herbs that made him vomit or defecate, that gave him a stomach-ache or relieved him of one. He made concoctions that gave him the strength and courage to kill his enemies, and others that accomplished the same purpose more efficiently when slipped into his enemy's beer.

And it was, in fact, beer; even in the mud-daubed huts of the prehistoric men who first cultivated the soil, the delightful results of allowing grain to ferment and then drawing off the juice had already been discovered. Where they came upon grapes they learned that that juice also, when allowed to ferment, made a fine heady draught. When the milk from their cattle stood too long and turned sour they discovered cheese, and when the cream rose and thickened they discovered they could make butter. Some peoples, the Tibetans, for instance, still prefer their butter rancid. The Romans, great gourmets that they were, prized a sauce that they made from fish entrails set out to putrefy in the sun. Medieval physicians prescribed arsenic and antimony for many ills. Chinese apothecaries today still sell ground-up dinosaur bones as medicines of great potency.

There is no accounting for tastes, and men have tasted everything. Looking back at our ancestors' gastronomic daring, we must admit that we, today, are arrant cowards about what we will put into our mouths. Our sole claim to venturesomeness is in our pharmaceuticals; we are still willing to try anything that comes in a capsule.

All these gambles with food and drugs our digestive system has taken pretty much in stride, or men would not be, still and increasingly, populating the earth. For our ability to cope with all manner of alimentary adventures we can thank the silent microscopic chemists of the digestive tract who manage either to convert what we offer them into food or eliminate it as waste. Drugs, to be sure, get by them; so does alcohol, which is only partially to be classified as food, also the caffeine in coffee and the nicotine in tobacco. These substances are also dealt with in the body, and fairly successfully if we serve them up in moderate doses.

The chemists of the digestive system might rather be called alchemists; so slyly do they perform their conversion processes that we know only a fraction of what there is to know. Except for one or two specialists not within the digestive tract itself—the salivary glands, the pancreas, also the liver—they are all part of the fabulous lining of the tract, little clusters of gland cells of enormous variety, dotted along the mucosa in strategic positions, carrying out the chemical process of breaking down food molecules by orderly stages. The stomach alone has thirty-five million of these gland clusters.

These alchemists do their work by way of a group of substances that they produce and send out into the digestive tract at their appointed stations. We call them enzymes, a word that means literally "in yeast," and we also call them ferments. Chemically most of them are quite complex proteins. We know what they are made of and what they do. But how they do what they do is still something of a puzzle to us.

Each of them has its particular task: one variety of enzymes, the ptyalin in saliva, will split only starch molecules; the pepsin of the gastric juice will work only on protein; the lipase in the pancreatic juice is effective only with fats. In the act of splitting other molecules, the molecule of the enzyme itself appears to remain unchanged; it does not, as far as we know, combine chemically with the stuff on which it has its effect. Nor does it begin the chemical reaction that ends with the breakdown of the food molecule; other processes do that.

What the enzyme does is speed up the action. In its presence, the food molecule is broken down and reconstituted at a greatly accelerated pace. And it seems that this speed is essential, for when for some reason a particular enzyme is lacking, things can go very wrong indeed. Some of the deadliest poisons we know are poisons simply because they combine with certain enzymes, thus destroying their digestive effectiveness.

Enzymes are not limited to the digestive system. They appear throughout the body, in great numbers and variety; the energy production of each cell depends upon its enzymes. Every kind of metabolism—which means virtually every activity of the body—requires its particular enzymes, and the cells make the enzymes for their own use. Plants also manufacture and use enzymes in their metabolism, and we have learned to use enzymes in many manufacturing processes.

We say that the enzyme acts as a catalyst. An English chemist of another generation, Sir William Bayliss, compared a catalyst with the oil that speeds a metal object down an incline. The oil does not combine with either the metal or the material of the incline, nor does it start the object going down; but it does accelerate the descent. How this analogy can be translated into chemical terms to explain the functioning of the enzyme, neither Sir William nor any of the scientists who have since struggled with the problem has been able to tell us.

The digestive system's alchemists produce other chemicals besides enzymes, among them the hydrochloric acid of the stomach. For their work they need plenty of fluid—water, as we shall see in a later chapter, is essential to all the body's chemical reactions—and this is one reason why we traditionally take a beverage with our meal and the antelope and the tiger both make for the water hole after they have dined.

And finally the digestive system produces hormones, which we generally—and inaccurately—think of as exclusively a product of the endocrine glands. A hormone is a messenger, an exciter, produced somewhere in the body and usually having its effect on another part of the body. The stomach is believed to produce at least one hormone, and the intestines produce more.

APPETITE JUICE AND HUNGER PANGS

Like a national capital expecting a state visit from a foreign monarch, or like the innkeepers and shopkeepers everywhere in Europe as the American tourist season approaches, the alimentary canal begins to make its preparations well in advance. The sight or smell or even the thought of food sets the salivary and gastric juices flowing.

By the time the first mouthful pops into the mouth the reception committee of digestants is waiting not only in the mouth but in the stomach as well. The more appetizing the food, the greater the advance secretion. Ivan Pavlov, the Russian physiologist, was so struck by the response of the stomach to these psychological stimulants that he named the gastric juice "appetite juice." Other scientists give this preparatory excitement the importance of a first phase, the "psychic phase," of digestion. The second they call the gastric phase, and the third is the intestinal phase.

The reception committee can also be discouraged, as well we know. The prospect of an unappetizing meal, or of a meal in unattractive surroundings or disagreeable company, inhibits the gastric juices. So do emotions that may have nothing whatever to do with the meal itself; worry, irritation, anger, and fear are powerful inhibitors. These psychic spoilsports actually cause the stomach to blanch. Conversely, the expectation of a pleasant meal makes it flush in warm anticipation, as the glands get busily to work and the capillaries widen to bring in an extra blood supply for their activity.

All these psychic preparations are part of the phenomenon of appetite, which is dependent on memory and associations; it is a conditioned response that develops out of experience. Hunger, on the other hand, is physiological. A newborn baby experiences hunger but probably not appetite. When a meal is overdue we have a hollow feeling in the pit of the stomach—actually from the duodenum, that part of the small intestine just beyond the stomach. We may even experience hunger pangs, the spasms of the stomach's contractions when it is empty; laboratory volunteers have swallowed balloons connected with a recording apparatus to measure the spasms.

Hunger is not merely a local sensation in the stomach, however. The need for nourishment is a body-wide metabolic condition. There is a part of the brain where changes in nourishment, occurring in its own cells along with all the other body cells, could be a hunger signal. The hypothalamus, as we shall see when we come to consider the nervous system, is that part of the brain that regulates many other unconscious body functions; it is the main center of the autonomic nervous system and also of primitive emotions such as rage and fear. Certain cells in the hypothalamus are apparently specialized to note a falling off in the rate of sugar consumption; they have been named glucoreceptors, meaning that when their sugar consumption slows down they react in some way that passes on the information. This is the best we can do, so far, to explain the still mysterious hunger mechanism.

The same theory is offered to explain thirst. For a long time thirst was believed to be a local sensation of dryness in the mouth and throat. But while a thirsty man gets some relief out of rinsing his mouth and gargling, he still has the sensation of thirst.

The physiologists have suggested that a signaling system like that which provokes the sensation of hunger probably exists for thirst. This would mean that like the glucoreceptors that register the slowing down of sugar consumption in the cells, other cells (called the osmoreceptors) register the changes in the osmotic pressure of the blood when the balance of salt and water changes. When we come to discuss the kidney, we will find that there are such signals regulating the release of water by way of the urine. It is therefore reasonable to assume that the same or a related system regulates the incoming water supply and signals the need for water by the sensation of thirst.

Although hunger and appetite are separate phenomena, appetite depends to some extent on the physiological state of the stomach, and hunger most certainly is an appetite whetter. But it is possible to have the illusion of hunger: an alcoholic drink before a meal, or the first few mouthfuls of the meal itself—perhaps in the advance form of canapés or cocktail snacks—sharpens up the tone of the stomach so that even if we are not metabolically hungry we feel hungry and enjoy our food all the more.

THE ROUTE

Having read the travel literature and the guidebook, we might now follow the food on its journey through this interesting region of the body's geography. The first stage of the journey, in the mouth, we know quite well. Indeed, we enjoy it and consciously work at the mechanical reduction of the food with teeth, tongue, and jaws. Here the taste buds give us our gastronomic pleasure in what we are eating, and the olfactory buds in the nose contribute their sensations of savory fragrances. Meanwhile the salivary glands, three separate pairs of them, pour their secretions into the

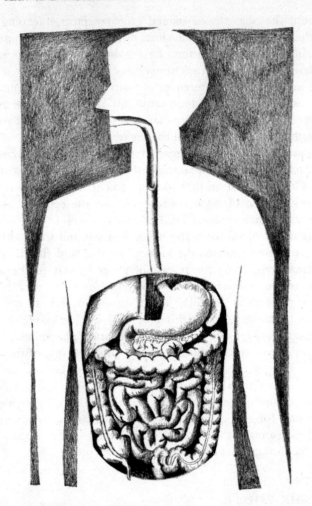

mouth from under the tongue, inside the lower jaw, and up in front of the ear lobe. Their juices soften and lubricate the food and dissolve some of it (or we could not taste it) and they also begin the conversion of starches in the food to sugar by the action of their enzyme, ptyalin.

The saliva also moistens the inside of the mouth, the tongue and the teeth, so that they can articulate, and it rinses and cleans them after the food has departed on the next stage of its journey. The saliva contains a natural bacteriocide, lysozyme, which is quite as effective a germ killer as the much-advertised drugstore prep-

arations for the purpose, and it has the advantage of being manufactured on the spot when needed.

We are aware of the food while it is in the mouth, but once the
tongue pushes it to the back of the throat and we swallow, we
know it no more. There is no sensation the rest of the way, and
there is nothing we need to do. The digestive system does it all
for us from this point on.

If you tilt your head back as far as it will go, there will be a
straight line of descent from throat to stomach, a fact that makes
sword swallowing possible. (Contrary to his name, the sword
swallower's art lies in *not* swallowing. If he allowed the muscles
to contract, the results would be unfortunate!) Nevertheless, we
do not depend upon gravity to get our food down to our stomachs. We could eat quite as well, although perhaps not so comfortably, standing on our heads, as grazing animals virtually do.
The food is propelled onward, as we have noted, by the rhythmic muscular contractions, the peristalsis, of the esophagus walls.

In the stomach the peristaltic motions are still stronger, and
they come at the rate of three per minute, churning, liquefying,
and mixing the foods with the gastric juice. In the juice are the
enzymes pepsin, rennin, and lipase, a secretion called mucin
which coats and protects the stomach lining, and hydrochloric
acid. Together the pepsin and hydrochloric acid begin the splitting of the proteins in the food, and the rennin acts upon milk in
the food so that the pepsin can also work on its proteins. The lipase in the stomach is a rather weak fat-splitting enzyme, able to
act only on fats that are already emulsified, such as those in cream
and the yolk of egg; more powerful lipase is available in the intestine, where most of the fat digestion takes place. Both the lipase and the rennin in the gastric juice are of more use to babies
than adults, because of the predominance of milk in the infant
diet.

The average adult stomach holds one and one-half quarts.
When it is full, the little valve at the bottom of the esophagus,
the cardiac sphincter, closes quietly, indicating, "No more." If we
ignore the signal and stuff more food in, it remains in the esophagus and we feel—and literally are—full.

The stomach reaches its peak of digestive activity nearly two
hours after a meal and may empty in from three to four and one-
half hours; a really heavy meal takes some six hours to pass

through the pylorus into the small intestine. Food leaves the stomach in the form of chyme, a thick liquid mixture like heavy cream, ready for the real work of digestion.

The small intestine is so called only because of its diameter, which is a little more than a half inch. Actually it is not very small, with a length of 22 feet; its deeply folded and irregular lining has an absorptive surface of about 106 square feet, approximately the size of the floor in a small bedroom. Its coils are in almost constant motion, the peristaltic waves churning, mixing, and moving the food slowly along the tract.

The duodenum, a C-shaped curve, is the first and widest part; its name, coined by a physician of ancient Greece, refers to its length of "twelve finger-breadths" or about ten inches. Into it flows the pancreatic juice, with enzymes for breaking down starch, protein, and fats; the intestine produces hormones that stimulate the pancreas to secrete its juice with its vital enzymes. Into the duodenum the bile duct also empties its bile, which emulsifies fats and thus prepares them for the action of the fat-splitting enzymes.

Around a sharp bend from the duodenum is the jejunum, the longest portion, and beyond that is the ileum, the last and narrowest section of the small intestine. Along this whole length the molecules of carbohydrate, protein and fat are broken down into the sugars, amino acids, fatty acids and glycerine that are the building blocks of the body's own chemistry. All along the way, too, the lining of the intestine is busy absorbing these nutrient compounds as rapidly as they are produced. The bulky parts of the diet, such as vegetable cellulose, and any other unusable materials continue to travel along at the urging of the powerful muscular waves, until they reach the next gateway and are emptied into the large intestine.

Along the five and one-half feet, approximately, of the large intestine, the liquid waste is gradually drained of its water, which is reabsorbed into the body through the intestinal walls. Here the waste is formed into the fairly solid feces and pushed down into the rectum for eventual excretion. This stage takes anywhere from ten to twenty hours. The thoroughness of the digestive process is evident in the fact that nothing useful to the body remains in the excretion, which consists of bacteria, cells cast off from the intestines, some mucus and such indigestible substances as celery fibers, fruit peel, and seeds, the bulk that keeps the excretory system in tone.

Thus ends the digestive process—a parade of molecules of every description, proteins broken down into thirty different parts, starches and sugars, fats taken apart and put together again in new molecules, iodine, iron, copper and numerous other minerals in minute quantities. All have been extracted from our daily food, decomposed and recomposed, screened and selected. Finally, in the slender muscular coils of the small intestine, those of value have been absorbed through the versatile walls into the body fluids, to nourish its tissues, fire its millions of cell furnaces, and provide the essential materials for the fabulous chemistry of life.

9

THE CHEMICAL WORKSHOP

Aʙᴏᴜᴛ five thousand years ago a very imaginative people, the ancestors of Father Abraham in ancient Mesopotamia, considered the liver the most important organ of the body, the seat of the soul and the center of life. They mapped and charted its anatomy, and when they sacrificed an animal to their god it was the liver they scrutinized, believing that the god spoke to them through this singular organ.

Never since then, except for Galen's teaching, has the liver been held in such high esteem. Indeed as late as a generation ago writers of texts on the human body had little to say about it except that it provided bile for the digestion.

Today we once more recognize the liver as a most extraordinary organ, even though it is not quite what the Mesopotamians or the Romans believed. It is not romantic like the heart or deep and mysterious like the brain. Yet it has a number of claims to uniqueness: it is the body's master chemist, also the fuel storage and supply office, housekeeper, and poison control center. In its unspectacular way it is about as hard-working an organ as we have; if we chose to list them we could put down some five hundred separate functions that it performs.

Most astonishing of all are its regenerative powers. Other organs are self-regenerative to some extent, but the liver can rebuild itself virtually from a fragment. Like a plant that puts up new shoots from the merest bit of root stock, the liver may lose or wear out almost all of its cells, but as long as it has a few left it simply makes more. It is potentially immortal.

Dome-shaped, thick-bodied and rich in blood, the liver is about one-fortieth of the body's weight. If we were to draw its outline diagrammatically in straight lines instead of curves, it would resemble a right-angle triangle with its short leg pointing downward along the right side of the body, its long leg extending horizontally to the left and somewhat overlapping the stomach, and its hypotenuse running diagonally downward from left to right. Put your right hand over your lower right ribs with your fingers pointing straight across, and your hand is roughly covering your liver. Its upper surface is anchored to the diaphragm so that it moves with this muscle when you breathe.

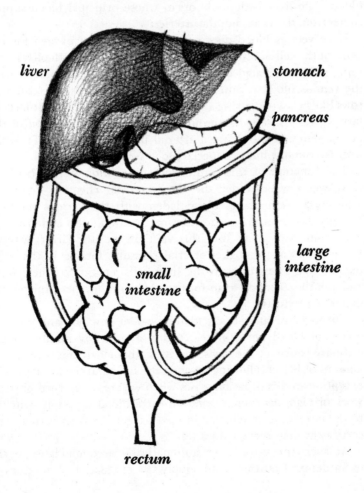

liver

stomach

pancreas

large intestine

small intestine

rectum

LIVER ODDITIES

The liver is an oddity among the major organs in being almost entirely of one texture. Except for certain scavenger cells, all the liver cells are identical, and each one of them can perform all of the liver's multiple functions. The liver is odd in another way: it has its own private circulation system, called the portal system, and this is remarkable, too, in being mainly a circulation of venous blood. The liver is the only organ whose principal blood supply comes from the veins, not the arteries.

Since venous blood does not contain sufficient oxygen for the work of the cells, there is a special artery that runs to the liver, carrying well-oxygenated blood under high pressure to mingle with the venous blood within the liver. The liver cells are strung in rows like beads on a string and between the cords or rows run capillarylike vessels, called sinusoids. In these vessels the blood of the portal vein and the rich red arterial blood are pooled. Thus the liver has not one but two special blood supplies.

The function of this roundabout circulation system becomes clear when we consider the liver's crucial chemical activities. The portal vein brings blood laden with the various products of digestion from the gastrointestinal tract and also certain products from the spleen. Into this vein the hepatic (liver) artery's blood comes at the higher arterial pressure, forcing in the extra oxygen that is essential to the liver cells' energy for their work and for the chemical transformations that they perform on the digestive products.

Through this private circulatory system flow one and one-half quarts of blood per minute. During almost any minute in the ordinary course of the day's activities, about half the body's total amount of blood is flowing through the liver and the kidneys. The exception to this situation arises when we are doing hard physical work or vigorous exercise, and an extra blood supply is switched to the muscles to provide additional oxygen for their activity and carry away their increased wastes.

At such times the liver automatically accommodates to the extra demand on the blood supply. Its circulation diminishes as soon as action begins in the muscles; in a matter of seconds the amount of blood in the liver may drop by a pint, even as much as a quart. The liver's own blood vessels contract to a smaller bore and thus help to reduce the blood supply; but pressure from the diaphragm and the contracting abdominal muscles also seems to be part of the mechanism that reduces the volume of blood in the liver during muscular activity.

With the accelerated breathing and tightened belly muscles of physical exertion the liver apparently gives up blood like a sponge, increasing the general supply in the body, and when breathing slows down and the muscles relax, like a sponge this curious organ expands once more and soaks up all the blood it requires for its labors.

THE BILE FACTORY

Best known of all the liver's functions is its secretion of bile. For this the liver cells are arranged like a series of well-planned factories, each on a dock between two waterways, one to bring the raw materials and fuel, the other to carry away the finished product. Each row of cells, or liver cord, has its sinusoid on one side, where the pool of portal and arterial blood provides the chemical stock pile. On the other side the cells discharge their tiny separate loads of bile into a thread-thin canal, which drains into a larger channel and this in turn into a larger one until the supply of bile collects in the main duct. It continues along in this duct to the gall bladder, where it is stored in concentrated form until it is needed for digestion.

The bile, a clear yellow or orange-colored fluid, is a combination of salts, fatty acids, pigments, and other components suspended in water. Its significant function is in the digestion of fats. By the action of its organic salts, the bile emulsifies the fats —homogenizes them, like cream—in the intestines so that they can be acted on by the intestinal and pancreatic fat-splitting enzymes, the lipases. Without this action they would be about as digestible as cold lard. An incidental effect of the bile salts is to activate the pancreatic enzyme to an efficient job of fat splitting.

The bile salts preside over the absorption of fat into the body, and this they do by a neat chemical sleight of hand. First they

combine with the fatty acids into compounds which have the property of passing into cells in the intestinal wall, something the fatty
acids alone cannot do. Once in, the bile salts part from the union,
leaving the fatty acids to combine with glycerin, another product
of fat digestion, to form neutral fat, which is then absorbed into
the body systems in various ways. The bile salts meanwhile return
to the portal blood and go with a new batch of raw materials to
the liver; they go on again, via the liver cells, into the bile to repeat their fat-digestion tasks. The circulation of the bile salts,
while not a unique phenomenon, is as pretty a sample of chemical
efficiency as there is anywhere in the body.

THE EVER-READY STOREHOUSE

As a food-supply center, the liver can store up to 20 per cent of
its weight in glycogen, the body's form of stored sugar, and 40
per cent in fats. Furthermore, it is not merely an inert storehouse
but a busy converter and regulator as well.

Glucose is a simple form of sugar that constitutes the body's
cell fuel. It comes into the liver by way of the portal blood as one
of the products of digestion. The liver cells convert it into glycogen and convert it back to glucose, when necessary, to keep up a
steady level in the blood. This is ordinarily a quiet, continuous
process in response to the releasing action of insulin from the
pancreas. In emergencies the liver cells work at top speed under
the prodding of adrenaline from the adrenal glands, supplying the
blood with increased quantities of fuel for the muscles. Another
thrifty cycle like that of the bile salts then occurs: lactic acid, the
main waste product of the muscles' use of glucose, comes back into
the liver by way of the blood and is reconverted to glycogen there
for further storage or use as the case may be.

As the body's principal glucose supplier, the liver is sometimes
called upon to turn other substances besides sugar—that is, carbohydrate—into this essential fuel. The liver cells can make glucose out of the amino acids of protein, and recently it has become
clear that they can even make it out of fat.

This chemical laboratory also works the fat-sugar system in reverse: when we eat a rich, starchy meal and top it off with a lush
sweet dessert we may be giving the liver more than its 20 per cent

of sugar to store. The consequence is that the liver cells convert everything over that limit into fat and send it for storage to other parts of the body. This is the saddest physiological fact of life for people with an overweight problem and a sweet tooth.

Besides its work with carbohydrates and fats, the liver is a builder of body proteins. Proteins, as we know, are the substance of living tissue; protoplasm is made up of an uncounted number of protein compounds. They are chemically very complex indeed, and a molecule of body protein—that is, a protein substance produced within the body for one of its own chemical processes—is of giant size, as molecules go. The liver cells have the unique ability to pass these giant molecules back and forth through their own walls without damage in the course of building and delivering them. This is a feat equivalent to pushing around a fleet of battleships.

It is no news to anyone that we need proteins in our food in order to survive and that a good, wholesome diet is rich in proteins. Each of the body's organs and cells uses this valuable material in one way or another. The liver is a specialist in making certain protein substances that are essential in the body's blood plasma.

Two of these liver products, fibrinogen and prothrombin, are necessary for blood clotting, the body's defense against loss of blood. A third is serum albumin, which, with the other serum proteins, helps to regulate the volume of blood and tissue fluids in the body.

Among the many substances that the liver converts and regulates is cholesterol. To what extent this substance is connected with the health or otherwise of the heart and arteries we do not yet know. What we do know is that the liver passes it back and forth from the bile to the blood and maintains it at a certain level in the blood plasma.

And finally the liver serves as a storehouse of certain vitamins: A, which is used by our eyes to make the substance necessary for night vision; D, which is essential to the normal growth of bones and teeth in children and regulates calcium and phosphorus metabolism in adults; and B_{12} which after a long search turned out to be the mysterious specific antianemic factor that made liver and liver extracts the miraculous cures for the formerly incurable, and inevitably fatal, pernicious anemia. B_{12}

comes into the body in adequate amounts in any good diet and is absorbed with the help of an enzyme in the gastric juice. The liver is not responsible for the absorption of the vitamin but only for storing and releasing it into the blood stream as it is needed for the blood-forming function of the bone marrow.

POISON, POLLUTION, AND PEST CONTROL

Besides the liver's many activities in the production, storage, and delivery of vital substances to the body, it also has some important protective tasks in policing the circulation and getting rid of undesirable elements.

The liver's position in the body cavity, especially in the circulatory system, is strategic for police and sanitation work. All the blood that has passed through the digestive system must go through the liver before it returns to the heart, thence to the lungs to be reoxygenated, and out again to the rest of the body. As we have seen, this blood is carrying all the nutritive products of digestion, the raw materials from outside that are needed by the organs and systems for their work. The liver processes some of these raw materials, stores some, lets some go through.

Mingled with these nutritive substances are a good many others; some are merely clutter, some are potentially poisonous, and some are downright dangerous. The liver straddles its blood-vessel gateway, from the digestive system into the body, like a police roadblock across a main highway, checking the qualifications of everything that goes by. The various kinds of undesirable elements in the traffic are picked out and dealt with, each according to its kind.

First there is the removal of clutter, the sheer picking up and disposing of worn-out cells. Besides supplying some of the vital fractions of the blood plasma, the liver also keeps up a continuous housekeeping supervision of the red blood cells. Through subtle chemical reactions, it sorts out cells that are ready for disposal, extracts the iron and globin (a body protein) from the hemoglobin molecule, and stores some of the iron. What is left is the porphyrin, a pigment which is a product of living matter; some other porphyrins are the chlorophyll of plants and the brown coloring matter in eggshells. The liver adds the porphyrin to its bile, and it is this pigment that gives the bile its greenish yellow or yellowish orange color.

Then there is the liver's pest control function: bacteria that get into the blood from the digestive tract are picked out and destroyed.

Particularly lively is the work of poison and pollution control. In the process of digestion some powerful poisons are quite normally produced in small amounts, and they come to the liver in the portal blood. If these substances were to be injected into the body's circulation, they would act like deadly poisons. Yet day in and day out, at almost any time after we have eaten, the liver is routinely purifying them out of the blood.

The kidney filters out unwanted substances and excretes them in the urine. The liver does its purifying by taking a poison right into camp: it may destroy the toxin outright or combine it with another substance and turn the resulting harmless compound over to the kidneys to be excreted. Chemists call this process conjugation.

The liver does this not only with poisonous products from the digestive tract but also, oddly, with sex hormones. As we shall see when we come to discuss the endocrine glands, a certain amount of female hormone is normally produced in males and male hormone in females. When the level of this opposite sex hormone in the blood goes above a certain point, the liver takes up the excess, combines it with a sugar and sends the end product on to the kidneys for disposal. When the liver is damaged by disease and can no longer inactivate the female hormone, then a male patient may develop swollen breasts.

Finally, the liver polices the proteins that have passed through the digestive system. As we know, the body builds its own cells and its many essential protein substances out of the animal and vegetable proteins that we take in with our food. In the course of digestion, each of these foreign protein molecules is broken up into its separate components, or amino acids, and these are carried in the blood to the various tissues, each tissue taking the particular ones that it requires. Not all of these amino acids are usable in the body, and the liver passes on them as they go by. Those which are not usable it de-aminates: that is, it takes out the nitrogen.

To appreciate this function in the liver we might stop and consider nitrogen for a moment. This element, harmless and inert in our atmosphere, is the very stuff of living matter. It constitutes 15 per cent of all proteins, and protoplasm *is* protein. Every living thing, from man to the tiniest invisible virus, is essentially protein.

Now there are three common substances in food, all essential to the body, that in the course of metabolism can be converted into the strongest possible acids: sulphur, phosphorus, and nitrogen. The acid that forms from nitrogen is, of course, nitric acid, and when it is mixed with hydrochloric acid it is powerful enough to dissolve gold. But in its de-amination process the liver routinely lifts the nitrogen out of the amino acid molecule—removing the fuse from the bomb—and neutralizes it by converting it into an inert compound called urea, then sends it harmlessly on to the kidneys, taking a heavy load from the body's acid-neutralizing system.

FEEDING THE LIVER

To keep this hard-working organ going takes a good supply of foods; as the gardener says of some of his plants, the liver is a heavy feeder. What it needs, however, is not quantity but quality, a diet with enough proteins and vitamins. The liver of an alcoholic, we now believe, is damaged not so much by the excess of alcohol as by the lack of these essential foods. The confirmed alcoholic eats little and what he eats is generally lacking in solid nutrients, and so his liver is suffering from vitamin and protein starvation. Among some primitive peoples, the Bantus, for example, a liver ailment develops with the exotic and nearly unpronounceable name of kwashiorkor. Recent studies of this disease have traced it to the severe lack of protein in the diet of these peoples, and some investigators see a resemblance between this and the alcoholic's liver damage.

What the liver needs in the way of food to keep it healthy is nothing fancy, just the familiar well-balanced diet of meat, fish, eggs, and vegetables—a good supply of proteins and vitamins. People who have little animal protein but a good supply of carbohydrates in their diet, for example, the rice eaters, enjoy the benefit of another protective device that enables the body to make the most of its protein intake. Physiologists call this the *sparing effect* of carbohydrate on protein metabolism.

So many of the liver's tasks end by passing on the waste products to the kidneys that these organs begin to sound like a garbage-disposal plant. That they are far more than that we shall see in the next chapter.

10

THE GREAT PURIFIER

THE BODY, a multi-function chemical plant, has wastes both liquid and solid which it must eliminate. Some wastes it eliminates through the lungs, some through the skin, some through the anus. But its major eliminating process is a masterly scientific performance unmatched in any industrial or laboratory operation that we know, and its end product is the urine.

The urine is the difference between pure, wholesome blood coursing through our body tissues and blood contaminated with dozens of useless and even poisonous chemicals. In the course of a year the kidneys, each about the size of your fist, filter 73,000 quarts of fluid, enough to fill 384 average bathtubs brimming to the drain. They eliminate 2,000 pounds of chemicals, a full ton of solid material, during an average lifetime.

Imagine, if you can, a filter system small enough to carry in your hands, which can put out with equal efficiency a flow of twenty quarts or more of fluid in a day or a mere trickle. Those are the extremes of performance—from a beer-drinking contest to the extreme heat of the desert or the boiler room of a steamship on a tropical run—which the kidneys are perfectly capable of delivering.

Probably the people best able to appreciate the kidneys, apart from physicians, are engineers and mechanics, for these organs are the ultimate in filtering devices. Each human kidney is equipped with one million individual filter units, yet it is compact enough to fit in the palm of your hand. Each kidney is capable of filtering 1,700 quarts of viscous fluid a day. It scans selectively at least fifty different chemicals dissolved in the fluid, reabsorbs the ones that are needed in the body and filters out the others. Even if it were possible to build a mechanical kidney of the same tiny dimensions, no man-made pump would last seventy years or more and never once shut down for cleaning or repairs.

This is the kind of filtering marvel that only an engineer's mind, perhaps, can fully appreciate. The same principle operates, as every mechanic knows, in the oil filter of an automobile. The housewife makes use of it in its simplest form with her strainer or colander, or when she pours water into any version of the drip or filter coffee maker. The water seeps down through the ground coffee beans, extracting the coffee solubles, and the filter allows the coffee-laden water to drip through to the lower part of the vessel but keeps the coffee grounds behind. This is, mechanically, what the kidney's million filter units do as they filter out the waste materials from the blood. But there the similarity ends. No comparison can do the kidneys justice; no filter that we know accomplishes what the kidneys do in the course of a day.

SOCIAL OUTCASTS OF THE BODY

There was a time when physicians believed they could learn everything there was to know about a man's health by looking at, smelling, and even tasting his urine. A woodcut of one of these uroscopists, dated about 1574, bears this inscription:

"I am a doctor of medicine. From the urine I can determine what illness plagues a man, whom I can help with God's grace, through a syrup of prescription which counteracts the malady."

By the time the artist Jost Amman produced this portrait the uroscopists were already being ridiculed for their claims, but through the Middle Ages it had been one of the great specialties of the oldest and, for a time, the most distinguished medical school in Europe, the school of Salerno in Italy which was founded before the ninth century.

In Shakespeare's exuberant day urine was still a polite subject and the kidneys were treated with respect as the seat of courage and quality. A man might say of another whom he admired, "He's a man of my kidney." By Victorian times the excretory function and the sexual function were both beyond the bounds of propriety, and the kidneys, associated with one and believed also to be connected with the other, shared their banishment. To add to the confusion, urology became a medical specialty embracing both kidney and venereal disease.

H. L. Mencken noted sardonically that the heart, lungs, and brain were always socially acceptable, but not the kidneys. When one of the present authors became a specialist in kidney disease, twenty-five years ago, the urologist shared the kidney's low estate. But to a physician who happened also to be a graduate engineer, who had studied every kind of industrial filter and even designed one for use in papermaking, the kidney was the most beautiful organ in the body. Some of the finest minds in medicine had also been attracted to this remarkable organ, as he later discovered, no matter whether it was a social outcast to the public.

In less than a generation all has changed, and the kidney has come into its own as a triumph of the long, toilsome process of evolution. Without some mechanism like the kidney, we now know, living creatures could not have crept out of the warm ooze and survived. Only with the kidney, to purify the blood and maintain the delicate balance of the body's internal environment, was it possible for life to become transformed, as Dr. Homer W. Smith has neatly put it, "from fish to philosopher."

A MILLION FILTERS

Put your hands on your back over the two lowest floating ribs; beneath your palms will be the kidneys, set deep in the abdominal cavity and protected by the heavy layer of the back muscles. In a human adult each one weighs about six ounces; even together they weigh less than the heart. A mouse's kidney is barely visible, an elephant's weighs about sixteen pounds. Yet the nephrons, the kidney's fabulous filter units, are just about the same size in mouse, man, elephant, giraffe, boa constrictor, or any other animal.

There are a million of these nephrons, as we have mentioned, in each human kidney. Each nephron has two major parts, a slender convoluted tube or tubule, and a sphere-shaped vessel. Inside the spherical part some fifty separate capillaries cluster, each one bent into a short loop. Through these marvelously tiny capillaries flows the blood, and as it flows, a part of its water, salts, and all the substances with small enough molecules pass through the capillary walls. The blood cells and those plasma proteins we mentioned as being contributed by the liver, the serum albumin, prothrombin and fibrinogen, with some others of their kind, remain behind.

The capillaries are contained within a capsule, and the water and substances filter through the capillary walls into the capsule, which drains into the tube-shaped part of the nephron. Through this tubule, making one long hairpin bend and two sets of convolutions, flows the filtrate from the capsule. On the way substances of value to the body are restored to the blood that is now flowing through a capillary network woven through the tubules. Back into the blood through the walls of the tubule capillaries go glucose, sodium chloride, vitamin C, the nutrient amino acids, and probably other essential materials. By the time the blood has reached the end of the tubule journey, it has regained 98 to 99 per cent of its water and all its cargo of solubles still useful to the body.

Left behind in the tubule are urea, uric acid, and other protein wastes, together with acids, salts, some yellow pigments, and excess quantities of trace metals. All these combine to form urine. Under ordinary conditions the urine itself changes from alkaline to acid, and on it goes to the collector tubes which empty into the bladder, to wait until the signal for excretion is given.

These exchanges back and forth through the capillary walls take place by way of the most minute adjustments in blood pressure and osmotic pressure. They are carried on along miles and miles of microscopically fine tubules leading from the million filter units, winding through their loops and convolutions around the capillaries and providing surface for their many chemical activities.

Just how tiny are these filter units, with their capillaries and their miles of winding tubules? Every generation invents new tools that provide a new look at the workings of the body. In this generation one of the most exciting experiences was the new look at the nephron through the eye of the electron microscope. Until this instrument was invented, the best magnification possi-

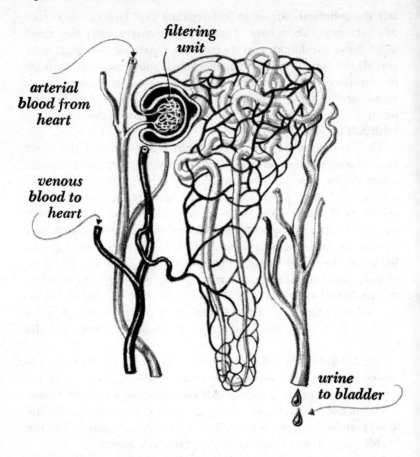

ble was 2,000 times. The first electron microscopes increased this to enlargements of 57,000 times, and the latest ones magnify up to a half-million times.

The old optical microscope showed little of the exquisitely detailed structure of the nephrons. Today's electron microscopes reveal tiny openings in the capillary walls through which the water and dissolved materials appear to pass. Investigators had previously predicted the size of these pores by studying the different molecular diameters of those compounds that appeared in the urine and those that did not. They guessed that the pores would be smaller than the diameter of the red cells and plasma proteins which do not pass out of the blood into the urine through the filter membranes. By actual measurement the prediction has been proved correct. But the real excitement is to see at last the structure of each one of the million tiny filters that do the vital task of purification for the body.

THE KIDNEYS AND THE INNER ENVIRONMENT

For most of us the daily excretion of urine comes to about one and one-half quarts. Yet every day the kidneys draw off from the blood about 180 quarts of water, screen it, remove the impurities, and return it to the blood.

How much water they return and how much they excrete, how dilute or concentrated the urine will be, depends in the first place upon how much fluid we take into our bodies. But it also depends upon other factors, some of them obvious—like the weather, or the amount of physical exertion we do—and some that are of great chemical subtlety. The kidneys are not merely a waste disposal mechanism. They have a major role in maintaining the chemical equilibrium of the body's inner environment.

Water is the body's life fluid; the blood, which we ordinarily think of in those terms, is 80 per cent water. The level of water in the blood and the body tissues must be maintained, come heat or cold, come wet or dry. On it depend all the chemical functions of the cells, all those delicate adjustments of chemical tension that determine what shall and what shall not pass through a cell or capillary wall. The entire osmotic system of the body's chemistry depends on these balances.

Fortunately the balances are not rigid; there is a wonderful flexibility about the body in all its functions. It can adapt itself to many rapid changes and to extreme conditions of many kinds for periods short or long. The kidneys are sensitive to these demands, and they contribute vitally to the adjustments.

Is it a hot day? The kidneys restore more water to the system, and more is available for cooling the body by evaporation through the skin. Conversely, in cold weather we either cut down on our fluids or else we urinate more copiously—usually we do both— since the body is losing less moisture through the skin and the kidneys are correspondingly taking more out by way of the bladder.

Is there a hard job of physical work being done, or a good game of tennis being played? More water is needed to keep the body temperature normal while millions of little cell furnaces are going full blast in the muscles, turning fuel into energy; this is the water that gives us the familiar sensation of getting up a good sweat. Again the kidneys respond, taking less water out of the body in the urine, leaving more for these other needs.

The kidneys may also take less or more water for urine, depending on our diet. A balance of salt and water must be maintained in the body regardless of how much salty food we eat or how much fluid we drink.

Let's say that at dinner you have soup, coffee and other liquids adding up to a quart, and in the evening, in one way and another, you drink two or three quarts of beer or other beverages. You have added nearly eight pounds of water to your body weight, yet next morning you will weigh just about the same as usual. The kidneys have managed to get rid of it all.

They do not manage to keep the water balance unaided. There is a messenger, in the form of a hormone sent out by the pituitary gland through the blood, that stimulates the tubules of the kidney's filter units to reabsorb more water into their walls from the urine as it is flowing by. When this hormone does not arrive in the blood, the tubules let the water pass but continue to reabsorb sodium chloride. Another hormone, this one from the cortex of the adrenal glands, also has the effect of increasing the amount of salt but decreasing the amount of potassium that is reabsorbed into the blood. This is one of the more subtle reactions to stressful situations, as we shall see when we discuss the endocrine glands. It is also the basis for one of the side effects of the use of cortisone, the adrenocortical hormone used as medication, in which undue amounts of salt and water are retained in the body.

Another chemical function of the kidney is to steady the acid-alkaline balance of the body fluids. It is elementary chemistry that, in order to neutralize an acid, you pour in a base or alkali; vinegar—acetic acid—is neutralized with bicarbonate of soda, and you can see the chemical reaction going on as the mixture fizzes.

Urea, as we have seen, is the neutral end product of the taming of nitrogen, which might otherwise become converted to nitric acid. The liver attends to this, and it is not the kidneys' concern. But sulphuric acid comes to the kidneys, from the metabolism of sulphur in eggs, for example, and phosphoric acid comes from the phosphorus in milk and cereals. Our high-standard

American diet, rich in meat, eggs, milk and cheeses, tends to produce an excess of these acids, and there is a limit to the degree of acidity—and of alkalinity—that the body tissues will tolerate. The excess acidity must be reduced.

Now the most readily available substances to neutralize these acids are the alkaline sodium compounds that are plentiful in the body fluids. But to use the body's sodium in this way would seriously alter the internal environment, and it is one of the kidney's chief functions to forestall precisely this kind of event. Ammonia, however, is also a strong alkali. And so we find the kidneys producing certain enzymes that convert amino acids, coming from the liver, into ammonia. Thus to keep the body's acid-alkali balance without disturbing its salt balance, the kidneys have their own ready supply of antacid available. They can produce ammonia, and they are able to produce it in larger or smaller amounts as needed.

Recent investigations indicate that the kidney's ammonia-producing function is also a factor in the production of red blood cells. And this again reminds us how the work of the kidney dominates, indeed determines, the very nature of the blood.

Thus steadily, tirelessly, the kidneys maintain the internal environment on which the life of land-dwelling creatures depends. The brain sleeps, the muscles rest, the digestive system loafs between meals. Even the heart and lungs may idle at a reduced pace. But the kidneys continue to work over the blood that serves them all, weighing and measuring and balancing its composition, taking out a little more of this, putting back a little more of that, and always conserving the water content that keeps our bodies functioning.

Every drop of blood filters through the kidneys many times a day. In the end our bodies are not what we put into them but what our kidneys keep.

It is worth noting that the kidneys alone, of all the visceral organs, do not develop from the innermost layer of cells in the embryo from which grow liver, pancreas, lungs, stomach, heart and intestines. They grow from the middle layer, along with the blood vessels, and blood, as well as the muscles and bony skeleton.

And so, knowing what we know of them today, we can no longer think of the kidneys merely as a way station for excreta along the digestive tract. We see the kidneys in their highly evolved, mammalian form as a giant step, perhaps a crucial one, in the long groping struggle of life from salt water to fresh water, to the mud of drying rivers and swamps, and at last to independence on dry land. If it were not for the kidneys, we would not carry within our skins a replica of our original, biological, salt-water environment. We could not maintain our cells in that hothouse climate, with its controlled chemical balance, in which alone they can survive. We could not walk about in that strange element, air.

In fact, if it were not for our mammalian kidneys, we might all still be swimming about in the warm salty sea.

PART III

TEXTURE AND
TAPESTRY

11

ORDINARY STAR-STUFF

ONE OF our lively minded scientists, the astronomer and cosmologist Harlow Shapley, in a recent book turned his eyes momentarily downward from the vast heavens to the tiny earth and its inhabitants and commented that man is made of "ordinary star-stuff."

So he is. But in man this ordinary star-stuff is woven into the most extraordinary human stuff.

The star-stuff to which Dr. Shapley referred was that list of basic elements, ninety-two of them, with which most of us become familiar in an introductory chemistry course somewhere along the educational route. Man, never content to leave nature as he finds it, has managed to manufacture a few more in this nuclear age: neptunium, plutonium, americium; curium, which is named for the Curies, Pierre and Marie, who discovered radium. Then there is berkelium, for Berkeley and the university where it was discovered, and californium for the university and the state. Three more have been named for Einstein, Fermi, and Mendeleev. All the new elements are at the heavy end of the scale, following after uranium, the heaviest element found in nature.

Wherever the astronomer probes—on the nearby moon, the neighboring planets, our life-giving sun, or the farthest galaxies beyond the Milky Way—he finds no other elements besides the original ninety-two. And some of the commonest of these make up the body of man. Living matter is an entirely new tapestry compared with matter that is lifeless, yet it is all embroidered from the same elements that make our mountains and rivers, our sea and sun and all the suns that light our skies at night. So far as we know there are no other substances in the universe.

And, as Dr. Shapley notes, the stuff of stars is simple compared with the organic chemistry even of a humble caterpillar. The elements combine to make an altogether different texture when they become part of living matter.

In the sun the most complex unit is apparently an atom of helium, the second element, in which four hydrogen nuclei are fused together. Ninety per cent of the matter in the universe is made up of naked atoms of hydrogen, the first element and, as we believe, the raw material of creation.

But in the body we have substances in which as many as 25,000 atoms are combined, and in very specific ways, to make a single molecule. A variation of even one of these atoms, or merely of its position in the molecular structure, may make a significant difference in the substance and how it performs in the body's chemistry.

The white of an egg is one of these complex materials woven out of common elementary particles, ordinary star-stuff. The hemoglobin that spurts out when you cut yourself is composed of molecules, each one of which contains about 3,000 carbon atoms, 4,800 hydrogen atoms, 870 of oxygen, 780 of nitrogen, plus 8 of sulfur and 4 of iron. The numbers are approximate, but we know that the atoms are there in those proportions, nearly 9,500 of them clinging together in a precise design in each molecule of hemoglobin. They are all ordinary atoms, but the molecule they make is not in the least ordinary. It is a particle of living matter and it serves to sustain life, a function for which it has properties not found in the ordinary stuff of stars.

WHICH ELEMENTS FOR LIVING MATTER?

As life was developing there was a choice of the ninety-two earthly elements out of which it might be built. Some were automatically unusable; the radioactive ones, for example, would not do for building since they destroy life as we know it or alter it with sudden mutations so that vital activities cannot proceed in a reliable way. Other choices are not so obvious. Why did calcium and phosphorus come to be the elements that form the body's hard skeleton, rather than silicon, equally hard, that occurs in stones?

We can conjecture that all the possible elements were sampled in the course of evolution, and those remained that proved useful or at least not harmful. There may well be vestiges of one or another substance in the body's chemistry that have been left over from earlier evolutionary stages, like the appendix among the organs. Perhaps there are some that merely continue to go along without ever having had any particular usefulness. We know that in the evolutionary process nature is only relatively efficient, not absolutely so. Many mutations come and go that appear to have no particular significance.

Where we find the significance of the elements woven together to make living matter we are awed. From our tiny planet the vastness of space is impressive. But within each one of us is a molecular world, mysterious, full of marvels, and containing the secret of life itself.

The astronomers calculate that the conditions for life may be found out there, billions of light years away, on planets like our own warmed by suns like our own. They calculate that life may actually exist on perhaps a hundred million planets. What limits the possibilities to merely a hundred million is the combination of conditions necessary for life as we know it. The elements of life are virtually everywhere.

THE INVISIBLE WORLD PERCEIVED

It is not hard to believe in the universe of the astronomers, despite its vastness. We can see fragments of it. We see the nearby stars at night with our own eyes, and with even an amateur's telescope we see their numbers multiplied by millions. We see our own Milky Way and we see photographs of galaxies and nebulae discerned by the mammoth eyes of the great telescopes.

All this is not too enormous for the imagination; however little of it is visible to us, it is enough to help us see beyond to the invisible. We are sensate creatures, and we rely on our senses to bring us evidence of the world around us.

The molecular world is harder to imagine. Men have learned to explode atoms, but no one has ever seen an atom. The largest molecules are barely microscopic. So we cannot rely on our eyes to tell us about the molecular world.

But if it is beyond our vision, it is present to other senses, and in the most familiar everyday ways. We smell the flowers in the garden, the exhaust from the car, the tobacco in the pipe. Do we ever ask ourselves what constitutes an odor? We put salt in the soup and sugar in our coffee. Do we wonder how the salty taste becomes diffused throughout the bowl and the sweetness throughout the cup?

Children sometimes ask about such mysteries. One of the present authors first became acquainted with the world of molecules during his childhood, by way of the sugar in his father's cup of tea. He loved the sweet taste, and he wondered what became of the lump. He experimented by dissolving the sugar in water. The sugar disappeared but the sweetness remained, and it was spread all through the water; every part of the water was equally sweet. Could one get the sugar back again out of the water? One could boil away the water, perhaps. One did—and there, sure enough, was the sugar. It was no neat white cube at the bottom of the pot, to be sure, but a sticky caramelized mess. Yet it was unmistakably sweet, unmistakably sugar.

If the sugar was there all the time, then it must have broken up into smaller and smaller bits, so small that they could disappear in the water and leave it as clear as pure water with nothing in it. Other substances did not work that way. Soil from the garden darkened the water and eventually settled to the bottom. Oil rose and formed a film on top. Apparently these did not break up into small enough bits to spread all through the water and remain that way. Sugar, salt, and vinegar did. They could not be seen but they could be tasted. They were there, present to one sense if not to another.

This is still the simplest way to grasp the concept of molecules, by the way they have of making mixtures. Some substances break up into such small particles that they make a true solution; that is, they break into the smallest individual units of which they are composed, small enough to be diffused through the solvent and remain diffused even when they are left standing. Sugar, table salt, salts generally, and acids have this property of dissolving into their smallest particles, their molecules, in water. Other substances, like oil or garden soil, make what we call suspensions. A lump of clay will break up into small enough particles to cloud the water, but not small enough to mingle with the water molecules and remain mingled with them.

Both these kinds of mixtures are all around us and also within our bodies. Solids are diffused in liquids, liquids in liquids, gases in gases and liquids. Soda pop is a solution of sugar, a solid, and carbon dioxide, a gas, in water. If perfume is spilled in one corner of a room it can soon be smelled throughout the room; the volatile liquid has released molecules of the scented stuff in gaseous form, and the gas has diffused through another gas, or rather a mixture of gases, the air. It is the molecules of perfume that we smell, striking against the olfactory buds in the nose. On the other hand, medicines that are labeled "shake well before using" are not solutions but suspensions.

THE THIRD MIXTURE

A third kind of mixture is vastly more important in living matter than these. It is one in which the substance breaks up into molecules too large to form a true solution, yet small enough not to settle to the bottom or rise to the top. This is a colloidal suspension, or solution, or it is called simply a colloid; the word comes from a Greek word meaning glue, because it is sticky. It is a mixture of molecules midway between a suspension and a true solution.

Protoplasm, the stuff of living matter, is a colloidal solution of many complex substances carried in water. It might not be too far-fetched a metaphor to say that the whole human body is a colloidal solution. The solution varies in density from tissue to tissue: bone tissue is 20 per cent water, brain tissue is 85 per cent water. That is pretty watery, considering the hard work it performs; it is not much more solid than a jellyfish, which is about 95 per cent water.

Living matter was born in the sea; it left its native home for another environment, but it still carries the sea within as an internal environment. One speculation is that the mineral salt content of our bodies is the same as that of the sea in the Cambrian age of the earth's past, the age when life first crept up on the land and survived there. The sea today has a slightly higher concentration of salts than our bodies, a little more than 1 per cent compared with the body's nine-tenths of 1 per cent.

THE SMALLEST PARTICLES

A molecule is the smallest particle of a substance that has all the properties of that substance. A brick wall is all made of bricks, and for all essential purposes, one brick is like another. In the same way, every molecule of a particular substance is like every other molecule of the same substance, made of the same atoms in the same combination.

Every molecule of water, for instance, is made of two atoms of hydrogen and one of oxygen, H_2O as the chemists write the formula. When the molecules divide into their component atoms, we no longer have water, but hydrogen and oxygen, both free to combine with other atoms to make other substances.

When the molecules of a substance break up or change in any way, we say that a chemical reaction has taken place. Sometimes the change is no more than a recombination of the same atoms in a new relationship, or the addition or subtraction of one or several atoms. When its molecules are changed, even by an atom, the substance itself has changed.

Substances can undergo other changes which do not involve changes in their molecules. Water constantly undergoes such changes in our everyday life. It becomes ice, a solid, or it becomes steam, a vapor. Its molecules may spread so thinly in the air that the water is invisible. But it is still water, whether we pry a solid cube of it out of the ice tray, or pour it from a glass or pump it in and out of our lungs as part of the air we breathe. It has undergone physical changes, but not chemical ones. It is still composed of the same undivided molecules; each one of its smallest particles is still the same parcel of two atoms of hydrogen and one of oxygen, snugly bound together. Not until the molecule itself has changed does the water change into some other substance, or several others, which will behave chemically in new ways.

How do atoms combine into molecules in the first place, and in these very specific combinations? This question takes us into a world newly opened to exploration in our time, the world where chemistry and physics meet.

The atoms of the different elements differ from each other in size and weight and also in the number of subatomic particles of which they are made. We picture the structure of an atom as an infinitesimal replica of the solar system, with the nucleus playing the role of a sun, and particles revolving around it, planetlike, in their orbits.

The orbiting particles are electrons, each having a negative electrical charge, and they are more or less balanced by positively charged particles in the nucleus, the protons. It is the number of these particles, the protons, carried by each atom in an element that gives the element its atomic number in the periodic table. All the known elements in nature have their numbers in the table; they march down the list in order from hydrogen, which is 1, to uranium, which is 92.

Atomic weight, which we have mentioned once or twice, runs parallel with but is not the same as atomic number. Hydrogen's number is 1, but its weight in the standard table is 1.008; uranium's is 238. The atomic number of an element does not vary, but its weight does. And this brings us to a third kind of particle in the atom, the neutron.

Neutrons join the protons in an atom's nucleus. They have no electrical charge but they add to the atom's weight. Atoms within the same element may have more or fewer neutrons than the standard, and so their weight may be a little more or a little less. Ordinary hydrogen has only a single proton in its nucleus, but in "heavy hydrogen" (another name for it is deuterium) there is a neutron in the nucleus of the atom along with its regular proton. Because of the addition or subtraction of neutrons we have uranium 235 and 239 as well as 238.

These are the isotopes. Their name means literally "same place," indicating that, although the atoms vary in weight, they still occupy the same place in the table of atomic numbers. The isotopes of an element have the same chemical properties, but because of the variation in their weight and also, in some cases, because they are radioactive, they can be detected. This makes them invaluable as tracers in biological and other research.

THE CHANGING ELEMENTS

Only a generation or so ago we still believed that the elements were unchanging and unchangeable, that the atoms of which each element was composed were identical with each other, and that atoms were the final indivisible particles of all matter. Our concept of the world and indeed the world itself has altered since the physicists broke into the supposedly unbreakable atom and discovered how changeable it is.

Not only has man learned to change it. It changes constantly in nature. The very heart of an atom, its nucleus, is changeable. At sufficiently high temperatures four hydrogen nuclei combine to form an atom of a new element, helium. This is atomic fusion. It happens in the fierce temperatures of the sun; it is, in fact, the principal source of energy that keeps the sun and stars shining. And we know now how to make it happen, although by doing so we may destroy ourselves and all our works.

Theoretically, all the elements in nature evolved by the development of atomic nuclei from the simplest one, that of hydrogen, into increasingly complex structures, an evolution like that of life itself. This is why hydrogen, the element with atomic number 1, which still constitutes most of the matter in the universe, is called the raw material of creation.

Today we can imagine that ordinary star-stuff has followed the same evolutionary pattern as has the stuff of life, beginning with simple patterns and organizing into ever more and more complex ones, on the vast scale of the universe as in the evolution of living forms from the amoeba to man. We can believe that atoms of hydrogen, spread thinly over the enormous void of space, gathered together into galaxies and suns and solar systems, each with a life cycle of its own. All this is not too unlike the evolution of living species, as we have reconstructed the pattern from the fossil records of the rocks. It is not too different from man's own history, and the evolution of his societies from tribe and clan, isolated and unrelated one to another, to today's intricate and interrelated social structures in which no members—except for a few remaining islands of primitiveness—any longer exist totally independent of and unaffected by the others.

Just so the atoms, we now believe, evolved, not necessarily one from the other in the order of the atomic table, but perhaps in separate series or family groups. In the radioactive elements we see the reverse process going on, the nuclei disintegrating from more to less complicated structures. The Curies, in discovering the mysterious powers of radium, also discovered that when its powers were exhausted it was nothing but a lump of lead. Now we know that uranium disintegrates to radium, and thence to a lead isotope, in what is called the uranium disintegration series. This natural disintegration of certain elements or their isotopes occurs at measurable rates of speed, and this fact has given geologists and archaeologists a new tool—carbon dating—in fixing the age of fossils and artifacts that they dig out of the earth.

Peering into the nucleus of the atom has led us on a considerable journey into time and space. Coming back to the atom itself, we find that it undergoes changes even in its ordinary, everyday chemical reactions.

These changes are nowhere near so sensational as the nuclear changes. They do not transform the atoms from one element into another. We are dealing now not with the nuclei of atoms but with those orbiting particles, the electrons.

We find that atoms, in their chemical encounters with each other, gain and lose electrons. This is how they form bonds with each other in various combinations. And these combinations are the molecules.

THE GREGARIOUS CARBON ATOM

When atoms of the same element combine, we have a molecule of that element; the oxygen we breathe is mainly composed of molecules of two oxygen atoms each, O_2. Sometimes after a thunderstorm we recognize the peculiar odor of another form of oxygen molecule, ozone, O_3, which is made up of three atoms that cling together for a while after an electric spark has passed through the air. It is an unstable molecule, which soon loses its extra atom and subsides into the stable molecule of O_2.

When atoms of different elements combine, what we have is a compound. In the molecular world of living matter what we find are mostly compounds. With all their diversity, they are mainly compounds of a few very versatile elements. These are the elements that give and take electrons more readily than others and enter into many kinds of molecular relationships.

Carbon is one of those that can readily give or take. It is also a very abundant element in nature. Its availability, coupled with its readiness to share electrons with atoms of its own and of other elements—what chemists call its covalent properties—leads it into a great variety of molecular marriages. An entire science, organic chemistry, is devoted solely to the compounds in which gregarious carbon plays a role. Whole colonies of carbon atoms may join up in a chain or ring formation in a single molecule, each one holding atoms of other elements in the molecule.

The carbon in lead pencils, coal, and diamonds is the same as the carbon in our bodies, as far as atoms go. But in the molecules of living matter it makes infinitely more marvelous molecular tapestries than in any inanimate variety of star-stuff, even the most perfect, glittering diamond.

THE VITAL PARTNERSHIP

Carbon's most intimate partner in the body is hydrogen. Carbon atoms and hydrogen atoms have a powerful affinity for each other. In every important compound involved in life processes, whatever else is there, carbon and hydrogen are bound to be there too, and usually tied closely to each other.

This is so not only in the carbohydrates, whose name tells us that both elements are there, but also in the fats and the vast array of proteins that the body uses as cell tissue, enzymes, and hormones. When carbon and hydrogen part from each other in the body's chemical activities, it is most often to combine with oxygen: the hydrogen to form H_2O or water, the carbon to form CO_2 or carbon dioxide.

These two are the simplest and most common waste products that result from the body's chemistry. We are excreting them all the time, the gas through our lungs in breathing, the water through our lungs and skin by evaporation, the invisible perspiration that we give off even at rest and in comfortable temperatures.

The ability of these elements to combine with oxygen, the gas that supports life as we know it, is one of the two qualities that make carbon and hydrogen so essential to living matter. The other is their combustibility. We shall see the importance of this second property when we come to discuss how the cells of the body "burn" the food we eat with the oxygen we breathe—that is, how they transform food and breath into the energy that moves muscles and supplies power for thinking.

GIANTS OF THE MOLECULAR WORLD

Carbon and hydrogen, combined separately with oxygen, form the common molecules of carbon dioxide and water. But together, carbon and hydrogen are the foundation of the most magical of molecules. These are the giants of the submicroscopic world, the molecular aggregates or macromolecules.

Nothing so remarkable as these molecules exists in ordinary star-stuff, not even on the most brilliant star or the most dashing comet. The stuff that stars are made of is simple inorganic material; it is lifeless and has always been so. In nature only living matter or matter that has been alive embraces these great molecules; wood and leather, sponge and coral have them but the sun and Betelgeuse do not. With the help of a new science, developed within our generation, men are able to make these molecules synthetically; the science is polymer chemistry (polymer comes from a Greek word meaning "many parts") and its products, which we know today in many forms, are plastics.

All living matter, from lichens to Sequoias, from bacteria to whales, is alive by virtue of its macromolecules. In nature living tissue constructs these complex molecules and also breaks them down in the process we call metabolism. Starches and sugars in our foods are of this complex molecular structure. Many of the substances in the chemistry of living things are not polymers, however. Glucose, the sugar to which all our food is eventually reduced for the cells' use, is a comparatively simple molecule as organic molecules go: $C_6H_{12}O_6$, six atoms each of carbon and oxygen and twelve atoms of hydrogen.

Carbon is the basic building unit of all these organic compounds. The biochemists sometimes write formulas in series for these substances, sequences of symbolic letters and numbers like the one above for glucose. Or they make structural formulas, diagrams of how the atoms are linked together. The shape of the molecule as shown in these diagrams is in every case significant. Recently, for example, an antidote was developed for certain poisons, affecting the nervous system, which the newspaper headlines refer to as "nerve gas." An experimental team succeeded in placing one single atom of oxygen within the molecule of another substance, in exactly the right spot to counter the noxious gas. The right spot, in this instance, was determined in hundred-millionths of an inch.

Often the significant difference between one and another of the body's many proteins lies merely in the position of certain atoms or groups of atoms in the molecule. Chemical reactions take place on the surface of the protein molecule. Hence the actual configuration of the molecule determines how it will perform in a chemical reaction, or even whether it will react at all.

CARBON STRINGS AND RINGS

Carbon lends itself to these structural elaborations which bring now one and now another set of atoms to the surface of the molecule. Some substances have carbon atoms strung out in a row, a long skeleton or string of beads on which other atoms or atom groups may hang. Sixteen carbon atoms line up one after the other to make the underlying structure of a molecule of one of the fatty acid compounds. In other compounds the carbon atoms combine in a ring. This we find in cortisone, the hormone produced by the cortex of the adrenal glands, and in the sex hormones. In all these compounds each carbon atom is linked to the next, and each has one or more hydrogen or other atoms attached to it.

Since carbon dioxide is the familiar waste product of breathing, for a long time it was assumed that carbon was combining directly with the oxygen in the air that we inhaled. Now we know that a far more elaborate process takes place in which the hydrogen of glucose is "burned" away, so to speak, leaving the carbon and oxygen to combine and be disposed of by way of the lungs.

About 96 per cent of the body is made up of these three elements plus one more, nitrogen. Nitrogen is ordinarily 15 per cent of any protein—the white of the egg you had for breakfast, the steak you enjoyed at dinner, or the biceps muscle you flex to lift your arm. It is essential to the body for growth and repair of tissues, for the enzymes that preside as catalysts at the successive stages of metabolism, for hormones and many other secretions.

THE HARD STUFF OF BONES

Two more elements, as we mentioned earlier, are used in the body in significant quantities, calcium and phosphorus. Without the hard compact material that they form together we would have no bony structure to hold our body's shape or support our organs. We could not stand or sit or walk; we could only flow like molasses.

No matter how powerful our muscles, we could not lift a mouthful of food to our mouths without the leverage of our bones. We could not make a swift or a precise movement, let alone a strong one, without the firm anchorage that the bony skeleton provides for our moving parts. Nor could we chew a mouthful without that other, even harder material, the calcium phosphate that forms our teeth. Tooth enamel is the hardest material in the body; it is almost pure calcium phosphate.

How the elements change their personalities, depending upon the company they are in, is most astonishingly revealed in the case of phosphorus. We have mentioned that the chemical behavior of a substance alters with any alteration in its molecule. We can take this statement a step farther: the elements—that is, the atoms—of which a molecule is composed do not change substantially between one compound and another. They do not themselves become transmuted from one element to another, as they do in nuclear alterations. What changes their behavior is the relationship they form, in each instance, with other atoms of their own and of other elements.

Phosphorus is a striking example. This Jekyll-Hyde element lies like a stone in our bones and teeth. Combined with calcium in the simple molecule of calcium phosphate, it resists all sorts of chemical attacks from the foods, fluids, and on occasion the powerful medicines we put into our mouths. But, uncombined with calcium, in the tiny energy-producing dynamo, the living cell, phosphorus becomes a power generator of extraordinary intensity. It is still phosphorus, still the same element composed of the same atoms. But in the alchemy of life processes these same atoms of phosphorus enter into different molecular relationships—chemical bonds—and their behavior is transformed from the lumpishness of phosphorus in bones and teeth to the lightning of the cell dynamos. In the biochemical formulas, the shorthand record of the metabolic story, the energy-rich phosphorus bond has its own symbol indicating the point at which, like a high-powered electric line, it kicks into the metabolic cycle.

TRACES OF STAR-STUFF

The body uses a few other minerals; though the essential quantities are small, in the form of inorganic mineral salts they are indispensable to life. Iron we know best as a component of the red blood cells; it also occurs in certain of the enzymes. Sodium and potassium, with calcium, have to be maintained in a particular balance in the blood and cells for many functions, the most dramatic of which is the heartbeat. Magnesium has a special connection with the activity of the brain and nerves.

In even smaller amounts some other elements are essential; we call these the trace elements. How small is a trace? Of iodine, without which the thyroid gland cannot function normally, we get along if we take in as little as two ten-thousandths of a gram a day (0.0002 gm.); of manganese, important in the cell enzyme systems, three ten-thousandths; of copper, a lack of which is like iron deficiency in the blood, one one-thousandth of a gram (of iron we need just fifteen times as much, 0.015 gm.). Zinc is present in some enzymes, molybdenum in some others. Cobalt is needed for manufacturing blood; we get it in vitamin B_{12}. Cadmium is found in the kidneys in high concentrations; why, we do not yet know.

Fluorine has been the subject of much controversy among the city fathers: should it or should it not be added to municipal water supplies? The evidence is clear that it offers considerable protection against dental caries.

Strontium may also be essential, though not the radioactive isotope, strontium 90, which occurs in nuclear fallout and which, unlike other radioactive isotopes, is not so accommodating as to be unstable and subside to a harmless form in a short time. Vanadium, barium and, according to some, a little bit of arsenic may be essential. Eventually we may find that all the ninety-two elements that go to make the earth, the sun, and the stars are needed in some way in the tapestry of human stuff.

Thus in our bodies we knit together the incredible vastnesses of space. And we knit together time as well. With each breath we take into our bodies a thousand million million million atoms (10 to the 21st power, for the mathematically minded) of oxygen. These atoms of the life-giving gas in our earth's atmosphere are virtually indestructible. And so it may well be that in some of the oxygen you breathe today there may be the same atoms that coursed through the blood of Washington, of Da Vinci, of Caesar and Cleopatra, of Cheops the pyramid builder, perhaps of the first man who lifted his gaze upward at night and wondered about the stars.

Turning the eyes of the mind inward where the eyes of the body cannot see, we can now follow the stuff of stars as it is transmuted into human stuff, in that microscopic powerhouse, the living cell.

12

THE LIVING CELL

GAZING OUTWARD into space and inward into the molecular world, scientists marvel at the complexity of the universe and the majestic forces that move it. They wonder at the variety of forms these forces have produced, the nonliving and, even more, the living. They ask, How did life begin? How does it maintain itself? How does it perpetuate itself? And finally—or perhaps the first question of all—what is it?

Each of these great questions obviously involves hundreds and thousands of lesser questions on which all the branches of biological science are constantly speculating, investigating, experimenting. The answers to most of them lie in the microscopic unit of life, the living cell.

Men had to wait for the invention of the microscope to see with their own eyes that living matter was not a pulp, a mass, or some sort of continuous homogeneous fabric, but was made up of individual units, each of them performing the essential functions that kept life living. The seventeenth-century English scientist Robert Hooke, an astronomer and mathematician as well as a biologist, was one of the first men who saw these units, and he named them cells because that is what they look like, the tiny individual compartments in, for example, a honeycomb.

All living things are composed of cells: plants and animals, molds and men. An adult human being is composed of thirty trillion cells, an amoeba of only one. Living cells bear only a general resemblance to the cell of a honeycomb, in the sense that each is a tiny, walled-in area; in their great diversity they are diverse also as to shape. Those of the skin and eyeballs are shaped like scales, those inside the nose and throat are columnar, and under the scale-shaped stratified cells that line the mouth are cube-shaped cells. Muscle cells are long slender fibers; nerve cells with their extensions are still longer, some of them several feet in length, and they may also be elaborately branched. Bone cells are oval, and the red blood cells are tiny disks like coins floating in the blood.

THE SPECIALISTS

The higher an organism stands in the evolutionary scale, the more various and specialized are the cells of which it is composed. In man, as in mammals generally, virtually all the cells of the body's population are specialists of a high order. Cells of the mucous

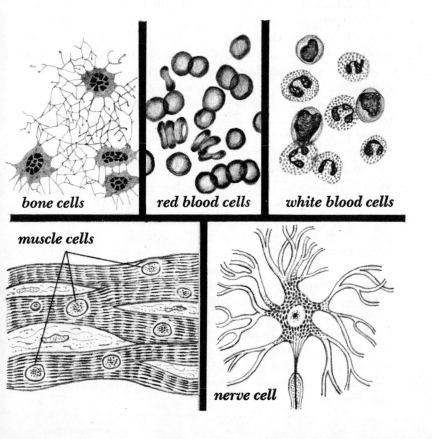

bone cells   red blood cells   white blood cells

muscle cells

nerve cell

membrane and the glands are equipped to secrete their particular fluids; muscle cells contract; nerve cells are differentiated among themselves to receive and respond to stimuli in particular ways. The cells of each body organ and system perform functions special to that part of the organism. Almost all cells, however, have in common certain functions essential to life: they maintain themselves, defend themselves, reproduce themselves.

The amoeba, simple creature, does all this for itself within the one tiny cell that is its all. It responds to the stimulus of a particle of food floating by, oozes after it, embraces it, absorbs it. It consumes its food and excretes its waste. It reacts to unfriendly changes in its environment, such as a change of temperature, and squirms away toward a kinder climate a few inches distant. And it reproduces itself by what we call simple division, although the division of a cell is not nearly so simple as it sounds.

In our bodies the cells have sacrificed this total self-reliance for specialization. They must wait for the blood to bring them their food and carry away their wastes. They need help from other specialists in the body to defend them from attack. The nerve and muscle cells have lost the ability to reproduce themselves, and they grow only in childhood and youth. The mature red blood cells have entirely lost the nucleus within the cell body.

It is odd that, with so much exhaustive investigation into the functioning of living cells, we cannot agree on a satisfactory definition of what constitutes life. Yet it is perhaps not so odd, since the more minutely we observe the cell, analyze it, even dissect it as we are able to do today, the more the puzzles multiply. As the microscope revealed more and more bacteria to be identified and classified, the question arose about some: were they animal or vegetable? Now that we have tools powerful enough to investigate viruses, there is an even more provocative question: is the virus animate or inanimate?

Between plant and animal life, we are ready to believe, there is not necessarily a sharp dividing line, at least among the microscopic organisms. Is it possible that the same is true also of life itself? That nonlife may flow into life across a blurred, indecisive borderline in the molecular world? We believe the viruses may be borderline organisms, aggressive like living cells in the struggle for survival, yet unable to perform the essential functions until, like pirates, they invade a living cell and turn its mechanisms to their own use.

LIFE AND NONLIFE

An entire branch of scientific investigation, virology, has grown up around the viruses, not only because they are among the most insidious enemies of plant and animal life, including our own, but also because, as inhabitants of that borderline limbo between the nonliving and the living, they may yield significant clues to what constitutes life.

A few years ago investigators succeeded in tearing a virus apart and then putting it together again. The resulting stuff, whether a substance or an organism, behaved exactly as it had before they operated on it. It reacted in the same ways to tests; it was just as infectious, and in the same specific ways, as it had been before. Had they killed a living organism and brought it back to life? Or had they merely split a complex molecule, a particle of nonlife, and reconstituted it?

What they split apart and put together again was a combination of nucleic acids and proteins. This combination is at the very basis of life. More complex living cells contain in addition some sugars, fats, and minerals, plus water. Three-fourths of a cell is water. But nearly all of the remaining one-fourth is this stuff of life, the substance whose name, protein, means "of first importance."

In the textbooks four properties of living matter have long been classic. Matter is said to be alive if it grows, metabolizes, responds to stimuli, and reproduces itself. This is no more than a description, expedient but far from adequate. Yet a better one still eludes us. Perhaps the viruses will help us to formulate it.

Another group of investigators has been approaching the same question from the opposite direction. They have been trying to synthesize the proteins of a living cell in the laboratory, under the conditions that we believe must have existed on earth when life began.

What these experiments have so far achieved is to synthesize, from various gases such as we know exist on other planets and must have existed on earth, certain substances called amino acids. These substances are part of the protein molecule which in turn is basic to protoplasm, or living matter. There are twenty-four or twenty-five amino acids in the molecule plus, perhaps, a few more that have not been identified. The experimenters managed to synthesize a molecule of as many as sixteen.

We have mentioned earlier that the difference between one protein and another may be no more than the arrangement of one or several atoms in the molecule. Until this mysterious molecule, in its many infinitesimal variations, yields up its structural secrets, we are not likely to solve the innermost mystery of the material basis of life.

THE UNIT OF LIFE

While these ultimate enigmas still elude us, we have meanwhile observed a good deal about the cell and how it functions. The cell has been likened to a power plant, a furnace, a chemical laboratory. In its reproductive functions it has been described as a factory complete with manager's office, files of blueprints and plans, intercommunication system, assembly line with foremen and workers.

None of these fanciful analogies does justice to the living cell. All these man-made systems put together, however ingenious and efficient, could not reproduce the functioning of this single unit of life, too small to be seen with the unaided eye.

Under the ordinary microscope, what is visible of the cell appears to be a simple structure, mostly space filled with water and surrounded by a membrane. A tiny dot, the nucleus, is quite dense; the balance, called the cytoplasm, is thin and watery. Within the cell we can also see other minute parts: chromosomes in the nucleus, threadlike mitochondria in the cytoplasm. The temperature within the cell is gentle and even, the climate equable. The surrounding wall or membrane is thinner in some cells, thicker in others, but by any standard it is thin and fragile.

Yet within this tenuous shelter, at this gentle, even temperature, the most remarkable activities are going on. Complex molecules are being broken down, other equally complex ones built up; each is synthesized according to a specific formula and for a specific function. Exactness is all important, even to the final placement of the final atom in each molecule; one atom out of place, one reaction misfiring, may mean death to the cell. In the course of these activities, meanwhile, powerful chemicals that might destroy life are neatly avoided or bypassed, and temperatures that might destroy life are precisely controlled. What man needs fabulous machinery and extreme temperatures to accomplish, the cell performs every living second, smoothly, quietly, efficiently within its own delicate walls, with its own watery physicochemical magic.

THE PARADE OF MOLECULES

What the cell's activities are we can discern reasonably well, although we are far from knowing how it accomplishes some of the most interesting of them. We know and can even diagram how the cell converts its basic nutrient, the glucose molecule, into energy, as we shall see in the following chapter. But we still can only speculate on how that energy is transmuted into the power of muscle cells to contract, or into the electrical impulses that are sent along the cables of nerve cells. Little by little we are beginning to penetrate even these secrets.

The blood courses through the body, dropping off through its capillary walls a great variety of substances into the watery bath that surrounds each cell. From this intercellular fluid the cell takes some substances and rejects others. The cell envelope is what we call a semipermeable membrane, meaning that it can be penetrated by some substances, but not by all; furthermore, it is highly selective about what it will pass and what it will bar. It is as though the membrane had a porous surface like that of a sieve or colander, with holes of just the diameter to allow molecules up to a certain size to pass through, and no larger. The same principle is applied in the automatic industrial sorting of oranges or eggs according to size. Yet the mechanical principle alone does not explain all instances of selectivity among the cell membranes, for some membranes permit the passage of large molecules and bar the way to smaller ones. Workers in one of the newly developing branches of biological science, called biophysics, are seeking the answer to the puzzle of the semipermeable membrane in the principles of physics.

Another control that regulates the flow of substances through the cell wall is based on the behavior of molecules. We noted earlier how molecules of one substance tend to diffuse throughout another substance: the lump of sugar in the coffee, the few drops of perfume spilled in a room.

We can look into this behavior a little more closely now, because the cell depends upon the molecules to parade in and out through its walls, frequently under their own power. Molecules are constantly in motion. In solids they are restricted to small movements, perhaps no more than oscillations. In liquids they move rapidly, in gases most rapidly of all, and they spread as far as they can until some obstacle halts them. Also, like water, they seek their own level. They press on until they have distributed themselves evenly throughout the medium that contains them.

Within the body there is a constant migration of molecules through membranous walls by this normal molecular behavior, which we call diffusion. Fluids and substances in solution are steadily passing into and out of the blood through the thin walls of the capillaries, in the same way as they pass into and out of the cells through the cell membranes. This process of passing back and forth through the membranes we call osmosis, and the pressure of the molecules to equalize their numbers on both sides of the membrane is osmotic pressure.

Water molecules may go where other molecules are barred, and thus it is often the water that passes through to equalize the solution. If there is a strong solution of salt, for example, on one side of a membrane and a weaker solution on the other, the salt may not pass through but the water may, and enough water will tend to pass through into the strong solution to equalize it with the weaker one. It is as though the salt in the stronger solution were drawing or attracting the water molecules.

This powerful equalizing or regulating pressure is vital to the activities of the cell and to the body as a whole. It is one of the mechanisms that control the flow of substances to where they are needed and in the necessary amounts.

Some solutions are kept from equalizing on both sides of a membrane. For instance, the plasma around a red blood cell is quite rich in sodium chloride. Within the cell, however, there may be little or no sodium, but there is always a good deal of potassium. The cell membrane keeps the sodium out. Furthermore, it keeps the potassium in, where it is needed, but bars it from going out into the blood stream where its diffusion would affect the heartbeat. At the same time the osmotic pressure on both sides of the red cell wall remains in equilibrium despite the seeming imbalance of molecules, at least the molecules of these two inorganic substances. Even though the sodium chloride level of the fluid outside the cell is higher than within, as long as it remains at its normal level in the plasma, the water content within the cell is not disturbed.

THE PATTERNMAKERS

Among the powers of the living cell at which we marvel is its power to reproduce itself, and to reproduce itself exactly, down to the precise placement of each atom in the fabulous structure of proteins and nucleic acids that constitute this particular cell.

Not just any combination will do, or even an approximation. It has to be exact. The cell has to have the right proteins, for example, that make it a human cell rather than a cell belonging to another species. The vegetable and animal proteins that we eat cannot be taken over bodily as human cell material. They must first be "humanized," broken down in the course of digestion into the raw materials of protoplasm. The cells then reassemble the molecules according to their own particular patterns.

The cell must also have the right molecular patterns for the chemical operations that go on within its walls, for turning fuel into energy and for the production of the enzymes, hormones, or secretions of various kinds that it may export to other parts of the body by way of the blood.

Each time a new life is born we stand in awe; even though we can recapitulate the physiology of reproduction like a textbook, the first cry of the newborn is still a source of wonder, and with reason. This is one of the miracles that explanations do not explain away; the more we know, the more we marvel. It is much the same with reproduction in the cell.

The cells are reproducing themselves quietly all the time in a constant series of microscopic miracles. They reproduce at a phenomenal rate in the first months and years of life until the individual grows to maturity, and they continue to reproduce throughout life in a steady process of molecular rejuvenation. The bony skeleton is totally replaced within a year, the lining of the small intestine every few hours. Cell by cell, at differing rates, the body renews itself; yet it remains the same, with the same hair and eyes, the same shape of fingernails, the same look, walk, memories, and behavior patterns. All this is so because each tiny cell is certain of repeating its own exact pattern. How is it done?

As with other baffling scientific puzzles, it has taken scientists of several different disciplines to piece together parts of the very complex answer to this one; genetics here owes something to bacteriology and virology. From the curious behavior of animal and plant viruses and their effect on the cells they invade, we have some new concepts of how a living cell may duplicate itself.

A cell reproduces by mitosis; this means merely that it divides into two daughter cells, each one an exact replica of the parent. But it is not at all a simple process. Each daughter not only has the same hereditary characteristics as the parent but will also pass them on again to the next generation. Somehow these characteristics have been not merely divided between the daughters but duplicated in each. The exception to this is in the cells that are specialized for reproduction, the ova and spermatozoa, in which each has only half the requisite number of genes from each parent.

Within the nucleus of a cell a material that we call chromatin is spread like a fine network. When the cell is preparing to divide, the chromatin gathers into a set of rodlike bodies, the chromosomes. Carried on the chromosomes are the genes, the effective hereditary units.

For a long time we have known that the cell's single set of chromosomes somehow reproduces itself to become a double set, and that each set goes with one of the daughter cells. Quite recently we have begun to see how this self-replicating act is performed. To follow the unraveling of this mystery we begin with another long-standing mystery, that of the genes.

THE MYSTERY OF THE GENES

What are these genes, which carry to the new cell all the inherited traits of the old? We have met the word many times in discussing the color of hair and eyes and how heredity is passed on from parents to children, from generation to generation. It is the same word, with the same meaning; it comes from a Greek word for breed, or kind. We meet it now, not in the specialized sperm and egg cells of human reproduction, but in the constant process of cell reproduction that goes on everywhere and all the time within our bodies, everywhere in the plant and animal world down to the tiniest organism. Wherever there are living cells that reproduce themselves, there are genes. In every case it is the genes that carry the precise pattern of hereditary characteristics belonging to that particular cell.

The genes have to do not only with reproduction of the cell itself but also with production within the cell. It is the genes that direct the formation of enzymes, the crucial catalyzing agents of the cell's metabolic processes. These enzymes, specific protein compounds each performing a specific function in the body's chemistry, have to be exact. The variation of a single atom in an enzyme can change its chemical functioning and change the direction of a vital body process. Here, as in the reproducing process, the genes have to do with synthesizing substances, and with exactness in synthesizing them, as though the genes held the pattern or die of all these molecules down to the last detail.

The genes, those singularly powerful directors, consist of nucleoprotein, a common substance in living matter. It is present in all living cells, and it is present in viruses. In each instance it is a combination of a specific protein with nucleic acid, a complex, critically important biologic acid, containing special types of organic bases, sugars, and phosphates.

The virologists have discovered that when a virus invades a cell, its nucleoprotein behaves in much the same way as a gene. It directs the invaded cell's mechanisms to make virus protein instead of the protein that is characteristic of the cell. It is as though invading Caesar decreed that the conquered must no longer raise crops and manufacture goods for their own use but only for the conqueror's, and in fact that is what conquerors have done throughout history, down to our own time. The pattern of conquest seems to have been laid down first in nature, and we might say that the Caesars and the Hitlers are no better than viruses. On the microscopic level, the invading virus with its alien nucleoprotein dethrones the cell's native gene government and installs its own self-serving puppet ruler.

Elsewhere in the microscopic world alien nucleoprotein even affects hereditary characteristics. Transferred from bacteria of one kind to bacteria of another, it brings about changes that are passed on to the descendants of the host bacteria.

PORTRAIT OF A MOLECULAR GIANT

Biochemists have found ways to analyze this remarkable substance, nucleoprotein, that constitutes genes. By X-ray diffraction they make a portrait of its molecule just as, by the lines and bars of a spectrum, the astronomers make a portrait of the elements on a distant star. We have already mentioned that nucleoprotein is a combination of protein and nucleic acid. The nucleic acid, we find, is a giant molecule, wound in a double helical chain through a rod of protein like lead through a pencil.

There are two kinds of these molecular giants in a cell, both with long difficult names which scientists have conveniently shortened to symbols. The primary one is DNA, which stands for desoxyribonucleic acid. The secondary one is RNA, ribonucleic acid.

DNA is the nucleoprotein of the genes, and it is found where we would expect to find the genes, within the cell's nucleus. DNA is the molecule with the double chain twisted around itself within its protein rod. RNA, apparently with one chain instead of two, is mostly found in the watery body of the cell, the cytoplasm. But about 10 per cent of it is in the nucleus, along with the DNA. This curious fact leads scientists to conjecture that RNA may be the intermediary that carries the pattern of the enzymes from the genes.

DNA is the self-replicating giant molecule, the wonder of living matter, indeed the wonder of the universe. Nothing like it exists on the sun or the stars. If there is an ultimate secret of life accessible to biological science, this is probably where it will be found, in the molecular giant that directs the reproductive function of the cell and holds the power of kinds and species, forms and functions, and the immortality of living things.

It is the DNA that directs the synthesis of essential proteins in the cell, and apparently it also synthesizes itself in the course of the cell's division into two cells. One corroboration of this theory is that the DNA content of the cell doubles as the cell prepares to divide. Another is that when mutations are experimentally produced in cells by X ray and ultra-violet rays, the wave lengths that bring about the mutations are the very ones that are absorbed by DNA.

The chain of which this giant molecule is composed is a series of minor groupings called nucleotides; actually there are only four different ones. But four units can be linked together in a chain in an enormous number of combinations, provided the chain is long enough.

Consider how many combinations you could make with the four suits in a deck of playing cards: 4 to the 52nd power. One mathematically minded student of the subject calculated that if the chain of DNA were only one hundred units long, the number of possible combinations would be 4^{100}, a thousand times more than the estimated number of atoms in the solar system.

We would need this number of possible combinations, or something close to it, to allow for all the details of heredity that must be passed on from one generation to another of a species, if not for a single cell. Man characteristically has forty-six chromosomes in each cell (in some individuals, 47 or 48); a single-celled marine creature. the radiolarian, has 1600. Most species have between ten and fifty chromosomes. It is not the number of chromosomes, however, but the number and kind of genes that determine hereditary characteristics, and the number of genes in the human cell has been estimated at from 10,000 to 40,000. Each gene, it is thought, may be a single nucleoprotein molecule, and each may control one or several characteristics.

How does the giant molecule actually duplicate itself in order to pass on the exact hereditary information in every detail? On this we can still only speculate. One ingenious suggestion is that the double chain unwinds itself, and each half synthesizes an exact duplicate of the other as its new molecular sister. The four units in the chain, the nucleotides, appear to have a pairing tendency; like the animals in the ark they march along two by two. Each member of a pair in the original chain might pull a replica of its former partner into the opposite spot in the chain, and thus the sequence of the links might be reproduced exactly.

When it comes to the mechanism by which the DNA controls the synthesis of enzymes and other chemical substances in the cell, the possibility is that its auxiliary, the RNA, may serve as the messenger that carries the patterns. But that is another story, one which the biochemists have not yet entirely deciphered.

The chemists like to remind us that one of their great men, Antoine Lavoisier, observed as long ago as the eighteenth century that life is a chemical function. It may have seemed a disparagement, at the time, to those who saw no miracles in chemistry to match the miracle of living matter. But, as we explore a step farther and watch the routine daily activity of the cell, we may share Lavoisier's wonder at the chemical magic of life's ordinary processes.

13

A BILLION QUIET FIRES

WE ARE ACCUSTOMED to saying that the living cell "burns" fuel
—that is, food—to produce its energy. Or we may call the
process combustion, or oxidation. All these terms are correct, yet
none of them suggests the true wonder of how the cell converts
food-fuel into the body's warmth and its power to move and function.

For the image they all evoke is the familiar one of fire. To be
sure, some oxidation goes on at low temperatures, for example,
the rusting of iron, which occurs by simple exposure to air. But
we are far more likely to think of hot fires and bright flames, of
the wood burning in the fireplace, the coal in the furnace, the
candlewick, the match end, or perhaps the electric spark igniting
the gasoline in an automobile motor. Some substances oxidize
with a hotter flame, some less hot, according to their chemical
nature and the rate at which they burn. For the most part the
process goes on at temperatures that living matter could not with-
stand. The wonder of the cell is that it performs this transformation of matter into energy at the gentle temperature of the body.
For a long time scientists were puzzled to explain how this could
be done.

Oxidation, like other chemical reactions, gives off heat; like
most chemical reactions it also needs some heat to start it. Man
and the higher animals, all the warm-blooded species, keep up a
level of heat in the body; in man it is the familiar normal temperature of 98.6° Fahrenheit.

Plants and the lower animal forms depend upon their environment to provide enough heat to keep their cellular chemistry going. In the polar winter there is little vegetable life and no animal life except warm-blooded species on the land. Contrast this with the tropics where animal and plant life is lush. The mighty dinosaurs throve in the subtropical temperatures of their epoch, but they could not survive the Ice Age. The freezing temperature deprived them not only of their food but also of the energy to pursue the search for food. It chilled their huge bodies, cooling little by little the low-burning fires of cellular activity.

Man and the warm-blooded animals burn some fuel to keep up their body temperatures, and this body temperature in turn keeps the cell's tiny metabolic furnaces going. Theoretically the burning of 100 grams, about 3½ ounces, of glucose which is the body's fuel sugar could produce enough mechanical energy to lift a 3,000-pound automobile 383 feet into the air. Or it could produce enough heat to bring all the water in the body's blood stream to a boil. To be sure, we do not have the muscle power to lift an auto. But neither does our blood boil.

Yet we burn up several times the theoretical 3½ ounces of sugar a day. The metaphor of fires and furnaces is poetic but illusory. It really tells us nothing about what actually goes on in the cell, how the cell converts its fuel into the various forms of energy —caloric, mechanical, electrical—that the body needs, without burning itself up in the process.

THE METABOLIC WHEEL

In 1953 the Nobel Prize was awarded to Dr. Hans Adolf Krebs, who first described what lies behind the familiar figure of speech. He pictured not a fire but a wheel, a series of minute chemical alterations in which, step by step, the molecule of carbon-hydrogen-oxygen that is fed to the cells is converted into energy and harmless wastes.

What man in all his cleverness cannot do except at flaming temperatures the cell accomplishes gently, quietly, in this way. It takes its fuel in, not in mass supplies, but virtually molecule by molecule. Each molecule is partially broken, and one of the pieces is handed in succession to a series of at least nine chemical substances. Each of these substances changes the bit of fuel minutely before passing it on to the next. The first change, for instance, is to citric acid, the mild acid familiar to us in the juice of lemons and other fruits.

At each step around the wheel a little carbon, a little hydrogen, is liberated from the fuel fragment to meet a little oxygen supplied by the blood. With each minute oxidation a small packet of energy is produced, and a little bit of waste—mostly water, H_2O, and carbon dioxide, CO_2—is given off and carried away through the cell wall, to be disposed of by the body's various disposal systems. Around and around goes the metabolic wheel, carrying its tiny quantities of fuel to be broken down, molecule by molecule, into energy and innocuous waste products, also in tiny quantities. And the entire operation goes on at a mild temperature that does no harm to the fragile tissues of life.

The nine chemicals presiding over the delicate process are nine enzymes, catalytic agents that the cell itself synthesizes, each for its own special place in the metabolic wheel. The body carries on many other metabolic processes, but this one, the Krebs citric-acid cycle, is the principal one by which it converts its food into energy.

The steady turning of the wheel goes on in the cytoplasm, the watery body of the cell that surrounds the nucleus. Here are the mitochondria, submicroscopic particles that are separate entities within the surrounding protoplasm. In each of these particles are assembled the enzymes of this particular metabolic cycle, each in its place around the imaginary wheel. Each of these chemical substances in its turn takes the fragment, acts on it, and hands it to the next like a man in a bucket brigade. Each of the billions and trillions of cells in our bodies contains not one but many such little wheels, or bucket brigades, or furnaces, whichever image one prefers. The warmth of our bodies and the nourishment of our tissues is the sum of all these tiny chemical wheels turning in the less than microscopic particles within each cell.

THE KINDS OF ENERGY

In each cell, all the time, a number of these processes are actively going on, serving various functions. There is a constant flow of the energy the cell itself requires, to keep itself warm, to reproduce itself when growth, replacement, or repair is needed and to carry on its special services for the rest of the body. The muscle cells need mechanical energy; the brain and nerve cells need electrical energy. Other specialist cells must have energy to make their unique products: tears, sweat, saliva, gastric juices, hemoglobin, seminal fluid, mother's milk, hormones.

All these and many more the cells produce, each according to its specialty, for the functioning of the body's various systems. Using the foods that we eat as their raw materials, the cells produce these many complex substances by the steady breaking down and putting together of molecules, the catabolism and anabolism, that are the two opposite but co-ordinated processes of metabolism.

All this they accomplish at the gentle temperaturé of the body, which remains virtually constant at 98.6° Fahrenheit. It does not remain absolutely constant throughout the twenty-four hours of the day, as investigators have discovered comparatively recently. Our metabolic activity slows, and our temperature declines as well, during sleep. Both metabolism and temperature rise again during our waking hours on a highly individual curve; each of us reaches a peak of cellular activity and body warmth—and efficiency—at a particular time of day. But these falls and rises are contained within a narrow span, so narrow that if the temperature varies more than a degree in either direction we are aware of it—as fever when it rises, as lassitude and debility when it is low. To realize the wonder of this steady combustion at low and even temperatures within the living cell, we need only recall the intense heat of man-made fires and the even fiercer temperatures at which nature carries on the transformations of matter and energy in a volcano's crater or the heart of the sun.

THE INDISPENSABLE ENZYMES

A key to these astonishing processes going on in the cell is in the enzymes. Enzymes are proteins. They are made up of the familiar four elements—carbon, hydrogen, oxygen, nitrogen—plus, usually, sulphur and, sometimes, phosphorus. In some there is a minute proportion of one of the trace minerals. Vitamins, essential for us to take in with our food because the body cannot produce them, are also involved in some enzymes.

There are apparently thousands of different enzymes in nature; they are produced by every sort of living matter. Molds, bacteria, plants all yield their specific enzymes. We extract many enzymes from vegetable and animal sources for use in industry. Even before men knew what the effective agent was, they used enzymes in brewing, baking, and a variety of manufacturing processes.

Enzymes accelerate the splitting of starch molecules in paper-making and cotton-goods manufacture and they remove spots in dry cleaning. They are added to cake mixes and they are invaluable in candy manufacture; the melting cream and syrupy liquid fillings of candies are possible because of an enzyme, called invertase, that breaks down the sugar crystals in the filling after the chocolate coating is put on. We take the enzyme pepsin as an aid to digestion, and we use enzymes to reduce bruises and swellings and, in some new and valuable pharmaceuticals, to break up blood clots. Molds, bacteria, and even the dangerous Streptococcus germs are grown in huge vats to produce some of these enzymes, in the same way that Penicillium and Streptomyces are grown to produce antibiotics.

The word "enzyme" was coined by a German chemist, Eduard Buchner, in 1897 when he extracted a substance from yeast that would turn sugar to alcohol; he won a Nobel prize for the achievement. The name means simply, "in leaven"; we also call enzymes by the simpler name, ferments.

Like all other living cells, human cells make enzymes. Some of our body enzymes are old familiar friends. Salivary glands make ptyalin, an enzyme that begins the conversion of starches into sugar while we are still chewing them. Stomach cells make the enzyme pepsin which acts on protein. Another protein-splitting enzyme is trypsin, from the pancreas. Other enzymes break up fats; still others convert carbohydrates into fats for storage or into glycogen for short-term storage. There are enzymes that convert complex carbohydrates and even parts of proteins into the sugar, glucose, that is immediately usable by the cells as fuel.

Now the biochemists tell us that the mitochondria, those tiny particles in the cell's body where the metabolic wheels go round, are nothing more nor less than assemblies of enzymes working together, catalyzing the successive stages of the energy-producing cycle. At the University of Wisconsin's Institute for Enzyme Research, where they study these chemical foremen of the cell's metabolism, investigators succeeded in creating an assembly of enzymes like a mitochondrion in the living cell. They put together nine enzymes, which converted fatty acids into heat and energy in a cycle like that which goes on in the cell's own turning of the metabolic wheel.

THE ROLE OF THE CATALYST

The enzyme's role is that of a catalyst, promoting a chemical re-action without being permanently changed itself. We often use the word as a figure of speech; we speak of an individual—or per-haps a nation or an event—acting as a catalyst, bringing about an alteration in the relationship of others without himself, or itself, being substantially affected. In the enzyme we meet a catalyst in literal, not metaphorical, action.

Enzymes are by no means the only catalysts; water is an ubiqui-tous one. Sodium and chlorine in dry form, for instance, are inert; mix them together and nothing happens. But put them together in a beaker of water and they combine to form sodium chloride —table salt. The water itself is unchanged, except that now it contains salt in solution and of course it tastes salty. But each water molecule is intact; each is H_2O. The water has simply pre-sided over the marriage of sodium and chlorine.

Water is also a necessary catalyst for the cell's elaborate chemi-cal magic, but it is not the star performer. Here the enzymes carry on the sleight of hand which, with all our precise scientific tools, we still understand only incompletely. Moreover each enzyme, of the many hundreds in the body, has its particular task and is constructed for that task. A protease, or protein-splitting enzyme, acts only on protein; a lipase, or fat-splitting enzyme, acts only on fats. These are some of the broad categories. Within the categories the enzymes are still further specialized.

The enzymes are everywhere. As endlessly varied substances in the body are transmuted back and forth—from their original foodstuff compounds into fuels or storage forms of fuel, into the raw materials for making enzymes or hormones or secretions or the protoplasm of the cells themselves, and again when those molecules essential to life are synthesized—at every point, it ap-pears, an enzyme or a group of enzymes performs the task.

The enzymes need water for their work. And they need the right temperature: too cold, their chemical activity slows down; too hot, they are likely to be destroyed. They need trace elements, vitamins, and on occasion they need stimulation or braking by appropriate hormones. Each one, at its moment, under its proper conditions, performs its task and that task alone. Each enzyme is a key to only one lock.

TOLERANCE FOR ERROR

Now we can see why the genes—or the self-replicating molecule, the DNA, which constitutes the genes—present such a fascinating puzzle. Somehow the DNA contains and passes on the precise pattern of each enzyme for which a particular cell is responsible, and that enzyme is synthesized by the cell, down to the last atom in its proper position in the molecule.

The geneticists believe that in this link from gene to enzyme, and the possible error, the garbled message or faulty pattern that may be transmitted on occasion, lies the significant clue to many ills, including ills of the central nervous system and perhaps of the mind. In one rare form of mental retardation they have traced the cause to a misfiring of enzymes, resulting in an inability to metabolize a particular portion of a protein. The practical proof is that infants born with this metabolic difficulty (it is called phenylketonuria and it is inborn) have developed normally on a special diet with a low content of this substance.

When such exquisite precision is required, at so many points, for the body to develop and function normally, it is the more remarkable that errors are comparatively rare. We can hardly believe that there are never any mistakes except those serious ones that reveal themselves in disease. Our body systems must, we think, have the added protection of a tolerance for error. Now and then we are aware of what may be an enzymatic error, with no very grave consequences. The enzymes of digestion, for example, seem to miss now and then for a variety of causes, without more than a case of indigestion as the result. The old-fashioned word "dyspepsia" puts us in mind that chronic indigestion may conceivably begin with a faulty production of the gastric enzyme pepsin.

Yet the failures are marvelously few when we think that at every moment of every hour, waking and sleeping, the enzymes are being precisely and routinely synthesized in the cells, according to the patterns transmitted from the genes. And precisely and routinely each enzyme performs its minuscule task in the fabulous processes of metabolism.

THE RIGHT TICKET TO THE FERRIS WHEEL

All the food we eat goes into the metabolic mill and is translated into energy or the storage of future energy, the growth or replacement of cells, and waste. Starches and sugars, fats, proteins—the enzyme system can convert virtually all of it, no matter what its original composition, into the right ticket to the Ferris wheel, the two-carbon compound that enters into the Krebs citric-acid cycle. Only the nitrogen and sulfur of protein are not consumed in the turning of the wheel. If they are not needed to form some of the cell's essential proteins they can be harmlessly drawn off and excreted in the form of urea and other wastes.

There are enzyme systems which can, if necessary, transform all kinds of foodstuffs into energy. This explains why the rice eaters and the fish eaters, the meat eaters and the vegetarians all have energy to work with their muscles and think with their minds. Enzymes help make man an omnivorous species. We can scarcely guess how large a part they have played in our adaptability, our diversity, indeed in our survival.

Simplest of all for the enzyme systems to turn into energy are the sugars and starches, the carbohydrates. These it transmutes back and forth at need—into glucose, the sugar which is ready fuel; into glycogen, the animal starch which is stored fuel; into fat, the most compact form of fuel storage.

A somewhat more elaborate process breaks down the fat molecules, which then can be converted into either immediate or stored fuel. A still more complex series of enzymatic steps leads to the formation of glucose from proteins. Other processes take the amino acids of proteins for cell-building material, for hormones and the many body secretions, for the DNA and for the enzymes themselves. The splitting of the various foodstuffs is done by specialist enzymes synthesized in the special organs.

Even more remarkable is the fact that the body can store energy that it has already produced. In case the cells turn their metabolic wheels rather more than necessary at the moment, the extra energy does not have to go to waste. It goes into the making of a dynamic phosphorus compound, a kind of molecular storage battery, called adenosine triphosphate. This compound, ATP, is a key in many of the body's most important processes. In the muscles, for example, one of its three molecules of phosphoric acid bursts from the compound, and this explosive chemical change seems to set off the contraction of the muscle fibers in a way that is roughly like the succession of small explosions in an automotive engine. The cells also keep a constant supply of another high-energy substance, the acetyl coenzyme A which starts the citric-acid cycle on its course.

THE CELL'S SERVICE SYSTEMS

The oxygen that we breathe is essential to the cell's work; it is the cell, finally, that breathes. The entire respiratory system that takes oxygen in and carries carbon dioxide out of the body is a supply and waste-removal service for the cell. Every cell must have a constant supply of the breath of life. And it must also have a way to get rid of the waste gas resulting from its oxidation process. The twin bellows of the lungs, the special circulation through their tissues that aerates the blood, the whole elaborate structure from nostrils to tiny aereoles that make the exchange of gases with the blood—all this is a service system for the cells.

The digestive system is another such service. The foodstuffs we eat are never acted on directly by the oxygen we breathe. Broken down, sorted out, and converted into molecules usable by the cell, they and the oxygen are carried by the blood and dropped off as needed through the capillary walls into the fluid that bathes the cells and thence through the cell walls into the cell. Not until they are within the cell, and on their way around the metabolic wheel, do the carbon and hydrogen fuels meet the oxygen.

This, the final transaction, is the "burning" process, the oxidation of our food that provides us with our energy. Biologists, mindful that this is the vital result of our breathing, refer to the cell's oxidation activity as respiration, and they call the enzymes involved in it the respiratory enzymes.

Besides the familiar waste products, the water and carbon dioxide, that result from its respiration, the cell produces other wastes. Some of them are potentially powerful acids. Sulphuric acid and phosphoric acid are destructive to living tissue, and they too are products of oxidation. Yet they are disposed of continuously without harm. The cell itself counters and buffers them and then passes them on through the body's system of neutralizers for disposal. Harmless sulphates and phosphates are metered through the kidneys, which efficiently return to the body the right quantity to supply its needs and excrete any excess.

Nitrogen is essential to life; we take it into the body in all the proteins we eat, and the cells use it to make their own living material and the other life substances they produce. Nitrogen plus oxygen and hydrogen makes nitric acid. But in the cells nitric acid is never produced. Instead the nitrogen is converted by stages into the innocuous neutral compound, urea, which is the chief nitrogenous component of urine. One of the great triumphs of nineteenth-century chemistry was the synthetic production of urea. Until then it was believed that only the living cell could break down protein for its use and throw off, as an end product, this harmless waste.

Another by-product of all this chemical activity is heat. We have seen that the cell keeps its fires low. Yet even this slow stepwise combustion may produce more heat than the cell requires. Furthermore, as the temperature rises, chemical activity accelerates, and so there would be a mounting cycle of rising temperature and accelerating tempo—unless there were also a cooling system.

The body has its own excellent system of temperature control, complete with thermostatic devices. But there is also a local cooling system immediately surrounding the cell. It is simple, efficient, and familiar to us in countless types of machinery, including the automobile. It is, simply, water.

14

THE INLAND SEA

E VERYWHERE WITHIN THE BODY lies its inland sea, the watery environment that the first groping organism carried with it when it crept out of the warm Cambrian waters onto the land, half a billion years ago according to the record of the rocks. The salt sea flows through the blood vessels and all the body's ducts however tiny. It moistens linings within and evaporates from the skin without. It laps every cell wall and fills every cell.

There is no part of the body from which water is barred, not the bones and not even the teeth. No part of the body could survive without it. We think and speak of the blood as life's fluid, but water is the true fluid of life just as oxygen is its breath. The astronomers, musing on where in the universe there might be life, muse also on what other gases besides oxygen life might be adapted to breathe, supposing that oxygen were not available elsewhere as it is on earth. But they do not muse on what substitute there might be for water because, so far as we know, there can be none.

Dr. Harlow Shapley, as we mentioned in an earlier chapter, is one of the astronomers who speculate on this question of life on other planets. He rules out, as a possible home for living creatures, any planet that is too close to or too far distant from its sun to have water in liquid form.

Water as gas, in vapor, or water as solid, in ice, will not do. Water as liquid, flowing and lubricating, warming and cooling, dissolving vital substances and yielding up its solutes, carrying in colloidal suspension the molecules that nourish life and that constitute life—for this, it appears, there is no imaginable substitute.

THE GENTLE FLUID

For cooling, water is ideal. Theoretically, as we have been told, a 3½-ounce packet of sugar could bring the blood stream to a boil if the cells did not have their bucket-brigade system for producing energy or heat in minute quantities. Even so, the chemical activity going on everywhere in the body all the time, waking and sleeping, plus the heat of muscular activity when we are doing physical work or exercise, produces enough heat to burn us up. The water in the body saves us, quite literally, from being consumed in our own fires.

The water that bathes the cells and seeps through the tissues absorbs the excess heat as fast as it is produced. It vaporizes in the exhalations from our lungs and continuously from the skin in perspiration that we do not even feel, the perspiration the physiologists call "insensible." Water takes off heat with an efficiency that few other liquids can match.

To be sure, alcohol on the skin cools more quickly than water, ether still more quickly. But these volatile liquids cannot perform water's many other functions. If any other liquid than water were our cooling agent we would have to take in unmanageable quantities to keep both the temperature and the fluid balance in order. Water is by far the most efficient cooling medium per unit of fluid.

One of water's advantages is its stability: it can carry many chemicals in solution and many more in suspension without being itself chemically changed. It is the nearest thing to a universal solvent. It can assist in many chemical reactions as catalyst without any change in its own simple chemistry. Its molecule is easily constituted by the meeting of hydrogen and oxygen, but it is not so easily split apart. It is one of the principal wastes given off by the body's chemical processes, and it is neutral and harmless.

Water vaporizes readily enough to cool our skins, yet it will absorb up to 212° Fahrenheit of heat at sea level before it boils. And it has another convenient property at the low temperature extreme of its liquid state. It reaches its maximum density and weight a few degrees before it freezes, and then actually becomes lighter at the freezing point. Thus the ice that covers the pond on a wintry morning is lighter than the water beneath it, or it would not lie in a sheet across the top. It would sink like a stone to the bottom.

We hardly realize how much our lives depend upon this commonplace fact about water. If ice were heavier and sank to the bottom, then a vast amount of the world's water would freeze solid from the bottom up and there would never be heat enough to melt it.

As it is, even under the perpetual ice that caps the Arctic, the tides flow, the fish swim, and the brief summer sun brings running streams out of glaciers and green growing life to the land. The land mass of the Antarctic lies frozen the year round, but the ocean laps at its edges and will not remain frozen. Warm and cold currents keep the seas in motion to their abyssal depths; from their surfaces rise the vapors that condense and fall on the land, and with the ceaseless flow of the waters goes the streaming life. We can scarcely imagine what our world would be like if water froze solid and locked half the green earth that we know in a perpetual bleak and frigid ice age.

THE BODY'S WATER

Within the body it is the properties of water at the gentle temperatures of living matter that make it essential to life. Its chemical versatility as solvent, catalyst, and neutral carrier we have already noted; its ability to hold sodium and potassium in solution is indispensable to the electrical impulses that activate muscles and nerves. Its physical properties are hardly less vital.

It is not only a heat absorber but a shock absorber. The ocean can carry a coconut shell thousands of miles around the world, toss and whirl it in stormy seas, and lay it unbroken on a chilly beach in Maine behind the receding tide. It bounces a thin-walled electric light bulb in its surf and gives it back intact to the shore.

Living tissue is not so brittle as glass but it is scarcely less fragile. The resilient sea within us cushions bones and joints, organs and nerves against the thousand jars the body must take from the solid world in which we move. Without it the pounding of heels on the pavement, of a hammer in the hand, the jolting of a bumpy ride would probably be nearly unbearable if not actually damaging to tissues. Even a slight accident might result not in a bruise but in grave injury. The organs and especially the brain are sheltered from shock in a fluid bath; so is the fetus in the womb.

The body's water helps to maintain the body's shape, and the body copes efficiently with an excess of water, even a violent excess like a beer binge. A champion beer drinker of a few generations ago downed twenty quarts in a day, some forty pounds of fluid, adding nearly half again to the total normal weight of water in the body. Yet the man's eyes did not bulge, his tissues did not inflate, his skin did not burst; the cells and their delicate mechanisms remained intact. All that happened was that his kidneys received notice of the overloading of blood and tissues and worked overtime to dispose of the monstrous excess of fluid.

Judging by weight alone, we are mostly made of water. It accounts for between 50 and 60 per cent of the body's weight, 100 pounds in the average adult male. Fifty per cent of the body's water is within the cells; another 20 per cent lies around the cells and within the lymph and blood vessels; the blood itself totals an average of five quarts of water. The balance, some 30 per cent, is divided chiefly between the fluid that bathes the brain and the fluid that carries food and waste through the digestive tract.

The apparently solid bones are some 20 per cent water, the even harder enamel of the teeth is 2 per cent water, the blood plasma is 95 per cent water. A combative feminist might gloat over the fact that the male is more watery than the female, 62 per cent in the average man compared with 52 per cent in the average woman. But the reason for the difference is not much to boast about: the female characteristically has more fat than the male, and fatty tissue holds very little water.

THE WATER SUPPLY

The body's water supply, like its food supply, needs to be constantly replenished. Under normal circumstances we take in fluids with even less thought than we give to our food; they are incidental. We drink about one and one-half quarts, in water and other beverages, in the course of a day. We get another quart of fluid in our foods for, dry though they seem, most foods, even solid meats, are as watery as we are ourselves. About a half pint is contributed to the common pool of liquid by the cells in their turning of the metabolic wheels; water, as we have seen, is one of the principal products of combustion. Thus the total daily intake adds up to about two and one-half quarts.

On an average day the output is about one and one half quarts of urine, three fluid ounces in the stool, and about a quart of invisible water lost in cooling vaporization by way of the lungs and skin. In the high temperatures of a summer day, or in strenuous muscular exertion, we lose more water than this through the sweat mechanism. But then we also take more water into the body; the sensation of thirst is the signal.

Under extreme conditions the water loss is dramatic. A man walking in the tropical sun with a minimum of clothing may lose twenty-eight quarts in a day. And he had better make up the loss of both water and salt or he will finish his walk on a stretcher.

The modest balance of two and one-half quarts of intake and output gives no adequate picture of the active movement of fluids going on constantly in the body; our water economy is far bigger business than this. In the course of a day some 180 quarts of fluid are filtered off from the blood and restored to it by the kidneys. They require only about one and one-half quarts to dissolve and carry away the waste materials in the urine; the remaining 99 per cent is returned to the body.

The water in the body is steadily being exchanged like fluid currency among the organs and systems. The cells contribute only a half pint of water to the outgoing stream, and a few ounces depart in the stool, but some ten quarts—including the urine—are being produced within the body every day.

The salivary glands deliver one and one-half quarts to moisten the mouth and lubricate food, also to begin the first step in enzymatic splitting of the food molecules in the course of digestion. The stomach produces one and one-half quarts of digestive juices and the pancreas pours in another quart. About a pint of bile comes from the liver and two quarts more of juices from the intestines. What part of all this fluid is not reabsorbed on the way through the small intestine is ultimately used in the large bowel as it makes stool material, or else returned to the body through its walls.

Until recently we could not determine whether any water remained permanently fixed in the body. We might imagine that some, at least, of all this fluid would perhaps stay trapped in or around the cells or the organs. The answer was discovered recently by the use of "heavy water"—an isotope, molecularly heavier than ordinary water but with the same properties—as a tracer. In ten days 50 per cent of the tracer disappears, and in a few weeks it is all gone.

So it appears that there is no fixed supply of water in the body. Like all the other streams and tides in nature, ours also flows in, through, and away.

THE WATER ECONOMY

All living matter must have its supply of water replenished in some fashion, but some species make a more efficient use of the water available to them than others. The desert rat, darting about the sandy wastes, giving suck to its young, is no mere mirage of a thirst-crazed wanderer, nor does it have a hidden water supply. What it does have is a perfect adaptation to a nearly waterless environment.

It never drinks water at all, but derives enough fluid from what it eats. It excretes little fluid. Its urine is four times as concentrated as human urine, seventeen times as concentrated as blood plasma. Indeed it is so nearly dry that it may solidify as soon as it passes out of the animal's body and is exposed to the air. In the laboratory these remarkably adapted little creatures can live on dry oatmeal. They have to be taught to drink water.

Man has no such adaptation; his water reserves are far less than his food reserves. A man lying quietly in a cool room could live eight or ten or at most twelve days without water, but with water he could fast for more than two months.

Wartime survival manuals for troops lost in the desert or flyers downed at sea laid great stress on how a man might conserve the water in his body, for whatever hazards these men might face, dehydration was one of the gravest. Navy physicians studied the possible water gain from eating raw fish, drinking sea water, or even a man's drinking small quantities of his own urine. But the salts and proteins from such sources required so much water to excrete them that the gain was either negligible or cancelled altogether; with sea water and urine there was also the danger of water loss from vomiting. The best water source, in the opinion of these investigators, would be the blood of birds, provided the castaway could catch them.

If they found themselves in such circumstances, the men were taught, they must conserve their body fluid by avoiding exertion and protecting themselves as best they could from the sun; they were told to sprinkle sea water on the skin, thus supplying moisture for cooling instead of losing it from the body. Desert troops who might be lost were advised to lie quietly by day and walk at night.

The monumental construction of Boulder Dam was possible only because the construction workers were educated in living and working in the desert. They learned to take water and salt at frequent intervals and to make maximum use of shade. The air conditioning of offices and sleeping quarters was a substantial help. Even with all these protective procedures, the men often had to replenish their internal water supply by as much as thirty quarts a day.

DR. LATTA'S MIRACLE

It is only comparatively recently that physicians have known how significant water is to the body's functioning, indeed to its survival. We are quite sure today that in the great cholera epidemics of the past the cause of death for many of the victims was dehydration from high fever, diarrhea, and the bleeding which was the accepted therapy of the time. George Washington might well have survived his fatal chill if his doctors had not drawn off so much of his blood.

An astute London physician, struggling with an outbreak of cholera in 1832, decided that all the standard treatments were "either useless or hurtful" and determined on one of his own: "to throw the fluid immediately into the circulation." He reported his experiment in a letter to the London Board of Health in this wise:

In this, having no precedent to direct me, I proceeded with much caution. The first subject of experiment was an aged female, on whom all the usual remedies had been fully tried, without producing one good symptom; the disease, uninterrupted, holding steadily on its course. She had apparently reached the last moments of her earthly existence, and now nothing could injure her—indeed so entirely was she reduced, that I feared I should be unable to get my apparatus ready ere she expired. Having inserted a tube into the basilic vein, cautiously —anxiously, I watched the effects; ounce after ounce was injected, but no visible change was produced. Still persevering, I thought she began to breathe less laboriously, soon the sharpened features, and sunken eye, and fallen jaw, pale and cold, bearing the manifest impression of death's signet, began to glow with returning animation; the pulse, which had long ceased, returned to the wrist; at first small and quick, by degrees it became more and more distinct, fuller, slower, and firmer, and in the short space of half an hour, when six pints had been injected, she expressed in a firm voice that she was free from all uneasiness, actually became jocular, and fancied all she needed was a little sleep; her extremities were warm, and every feature bore the aspect of comfort and health.

Dr. Latta's small miracle, brought about by his "Aqueous and Saline Injections," caused no stir in medical circles and was forgotten for the rest of the century. In the early 1900s, however, a wave of choleralike illness, largely the consequence of poor refrigeration and lack of pasteurization, swept through the child population; the popular name for it was summer diarrhea. It was, in fact, nothing new. Summer diarrhea carried off 2,000 babies in eight weeks in seventeenth-century London.

This time physicians tried Dr. Latta's treatment, by then nearly a century old. Drinking the needed fluid was no help since the stomach and bowels would not retain it. But the intravenous injection of fluid brought the child patients around in a matter of minutes. Today this is routine treatment in any situation in which the body's water supply is depleted.

THE SIGNAL OF THIRST

With the continuous dynamic movement of water in and out and through the body it is astonishing that the water balance remains so steady, with almost no change from day to day in our basic 100 pounds, more or less, of fluid. How do we know when we need water? And how do we know how much water we need?

We think of thirst as a sensation of dryness in the throat; we feel the throat itself is parched. Actually the signal comes originally not from the throat but from the blood. When we have played a game of tennis or golf in the hot sun, for example, and sweated off a couple of pounds, what we have lost is mostly water. The loss is mainly through the skin, but very soon it is manifested in the blood, which thickens.

There are other times when the blood thickens, as a normal response, for instance, to cold. The lowered water content of the blood is part of the heat-conserving mechanism of the body. But then there are other changes as well, and all of them together constitute the body's total response to a lowered environmental temperature. In such situations the thickening of the blood is not a sign of disturbance to the water balance.

But when the blood is thicker than its proper consistency for the temperature and condition of the body at the time, this state of affairs constitutes a chemical signal. And when it flows past a notifying point in the brain (probably, as we mentioned earlier, in the hypothalamus) a message is sent to the mouth and throat, where there are mechanisms of the nervous system that make us aware of the sensation of thirst.

We drink, the thirst is satisfied, the water balance is restored. The greater the need, the greater the thirst. The brain registers not only that something is wrong but also by how much it is wrong.

But there is another oddity about thirst and the satisfaction of it. When we drink to satisfy thirst, we know almost at once when we have taken enough fluid. The sensation of thirst disappears and we stop drinking. Yet the water balance cannot possibly have been restored so quickly. It takes time for the water to seep through the walls of the digestive system into the blood stream and out through all the capillaries to replenish the thirsty tissues throughout the body.

How do we know when it is time to stop drinking? The physiologists have not yet found the explanation; but they believe there is a kind of water meter at the back of the throat, a set of nerve endings or perhaps special cells, which sends the message back to the brain when the right amount of fluid has gone down the gullet.

We also become thirsty when we eat salty foods, not because we have lost water from the body but because we have taken in extra salt. This thirst, we may speculate, is perhaps an inheritance from those ancestral living cells that first enclosed within a protective membrane a microscopic droplet of the sea in which they drifted, back in the Cambrian age of the earth's history. For the body maintains not only its water balance but also its salt and water balance, just that nine-tenths of 1 per cent which, we believe, may have been the salt content of the ancient sea that formed the first nurturing environment of life.

Whatever the reason, whether it stems from life's beginnings or purely from the intricate relationships of chemistry, the salt holds the water in the body, and in just the correct proportion. If there is more salt, we must have more water. And when we lose water, for example, through sweating, it is salty water that we lose and we must restore the salt as well as the water.

Curiously, the body thirsts for water but does not know when it lacks salt. In the usual course we take in enough salt in our food to make up the loss on a hot day or after strenuous exercise and sweating. Some animals, for instance, cattle and deer, have a salt-craving mechanism, but it was somehow omitted from the human equipment. Its absence has made physicians alert for symptoms, and people today are generally aware that when they are feeling the heat and perspiring excessively they can do with some extra salt as well as plenty of fluids.

Good water to drink has played its part in history; men have fought over water sources and poisoned each other's wells in times of strife. A thoughtful official reporting on American aid in the Middle East observed that until those lands were assured of a safe and abundant water supply, poverty, disease, conflict, and a focus of danger to the world would continue to suppurate there. There are many places in the world where good water to drink cannot be taken for granted.

We give hardly more thought to the water we drink than to the air we breathe. Yet both are essential to life. Without air we cannot live at all, and without water we can live only a little longer. We are, after all, a watery species.

PART IV

THE TIDES
OF LIFE

15

ISLANDS IN THE

LIVING SEA

THE BODY GROWS and matures; tissues repair and cells reproduce themselves, and the processes of life go on in an orderly,
harmonious way. The inland sea that bathes each cell and tissue,
each muscle and organ, maintains the equable climate necessary
for their functioning, supplying the raw materials of their chemistry and carrying away their wastes. Their activities, as we know,
are steady and constant but not uniform in pace; from hour to
hour, even from moment to moment, the functioning of an organ
or a system may be accelerated or retarded. The rhythms change,
the chemistry alters in sensitive response to the external environment and to the body's inner dynamics of maintenance and
growth, activity and rest.

The more we contemplate the interlocking systems and organs,
so specialized and yet so tuned to each other, the more we wonder. How are the stimuli of the outer environment converted into
such a variety of messages? What cryptic code trips the many
different mechanisms and organizes their taut mobilization in the
face of challenge or danger?

Even more provocative are the questions about the body's own
inner rhythms, the timing of its cycles as though by a biological
clock. Where is the motive source of our apparently self-starting
drives and self-generating bursts of energy? What inner signal
propels the explosive growth of infancy, slows it to childhood's
more moderate pace, and then rings again at a given moment
for the second thrust of development at puberty?

With the comparatively young science of endocrinology we are apparently on the threshold of answering these tantalizing questions. We find that there is just such a set of coded signals within the body; we call them the hormones, from a Greek word that means "to excite." Hormones are chemical substances, and the code, which the scientists are slowly, painstakingly deciphering, is written in chemical formulas.

Hormones are produced in various organs and tissues of the body, but there are certain organs that are specialized to produce them, the endocrine glands. They are extraordinarily powerful— and extraordinarily small. The largest, the thyroid gland, weighs about an ounce. The parathyroids are barely large enough to be visible, and each of them weighs about a fourth of a gram, one one-hundred-fourteenth of an ounce. The pituitary, which has vitally important functions of its own and also regulates the others, measures a little more than half an inch at its longest.

Nine glands are usually named in a list of the endocrines, and you may see where in the body they are located from the illustration. One, the pineal, tucked away in the back of the brain, is still a mystery; we are not certain whether it is a gland at all. Another, the thymus, situated behind the breastbone and extending a short way into the neck, is also rather mysterious. When its hormone, called the Peter Pan hormone, is extracted from mammals and injected into the pupa of a moth it delays the pupa's development into a mature insect. We are tempted to speculate that it may have some youth-prolonging value to human beings, which could perhaps be exploited to postpone the aging processes; but the investigators are cautious, and there are some who believe it is merely a leftover curiosity of evolution. The gland is large and active in childhood and especially at puberty, but it shrivels and may disappear entirely later in life.

About the other glands we know more: the pituitary in the skull, the thyroid in the neck and the four tiny parathyroids imbedded in it, the adrenals sitting one atop each kidney, the pancreas nestled among the digestive organs in the abdomen; finally the sex glands, in females the ovaries sheltered in the pelvis, in males the testes suspended outside the body cavity in the groin.

We call them the endocrine glands (endo, a Greek word element, means "within," and crine, also from the Greek, means "separate") or the ductless glands or glands of internal secretion. The most obvious difference between them and other kinds of

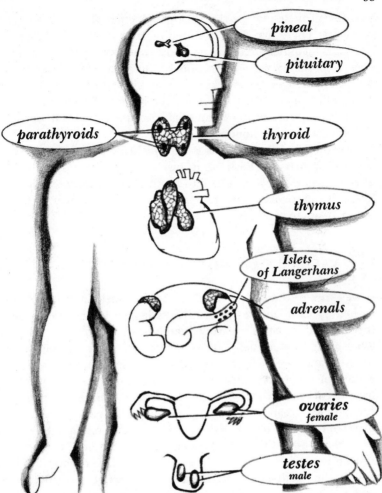

pineal

pituitary

parathyroids

thyroid

thymus

Islets of Langerhans

adrenals

ovaries
female

testes
male

glands is in the way their secretions are distributed. The sweat and tear glands, and the mammary glands, when they are active in a nursing mother, discharge their secretions through ducts to the outside of the body. The salivary glands and the glands of the stomach and intestines send their digestive juices into the alimentary tract. But the endocrine glands deliver their product directly into the blood, and the blood carries it throughout the body.

Astonishingly, by this roundabout manner of distribution, each hormone finds its particular target organ or organs, no matter how distant these may be from the gland where the hormone was produced. There may be a hundred or several hundred kinds of hormones manufactured in the body; we have so far identified what is probably only a fraction of the total. Each gland apparently produces several kinds. The pituitary makes at least seven different ones that we know; the adrenal cortex alone produces twenty-five or more, and its medulla or central portion yields additional hormones.

How they find their targets is dependent on the chemical composition of each one. Each has its own formula which, like the address on the letter you drop into the mailbox, guarantees its delivery to a particular organ no matter what route it takes with the blood stream to get there.

VALUABLE CARGO

If we think of the body as a self-contained world, and the organs bathed by its inland sea as continents lapped by the ocean, then the endocrine glands are tiny islands scattered over the ocean, some close to continents and some farther away. Despite their insignificant size, each of these islands has something of value to export, of which sometimes one and sometimes several continents have need. And so each island launches its minute but precious cargo on the ocean, and the cargo arrives at the port to which it is directed though it may go half around the world on the way.

How are these little packages addressed so accurately? We have broken the code for a few, and we find that their chemical differences—the "addresses" that make them effective at certain sites and not at others—are clearly marked. The sex hormones and the many hormones of the adrenal cortex all belong to a large group of fatty or waxlike substances, the steroids; estrogen, testosterone, and the famous cortisone are of this family. Pituitary and parathyroid hormones and the pancreatic hormone, insulin, are proteins or portions of proteins. The thyroid hormone, thyroxin, is an amino acid, one of the constituents of protein.

Within these groups the differences may be infinitesimal. For example, no more than the presence of a few atoms distinguishes the male hormone, testosterone, from the female, estrogen, yet their difference determines some considerable differences between the sexes. Male hormones are produced not only in males but also in the adrenal glands in females, and in males they are secreted not only in the testes but in the adrenals as well. From our medical experience with them we have learned that some of the functions of these hormones are interchangeable between the sexes.

Perhaps the oddest aspect of the endocrines is that they are also interchangeable among species. Extracts from the pancreas of cattle enabled diabetes sufferers to live normal lives long before the chemistry of insulin was understood. All that was known was that diabetes was the consequence of a failure in the ability to metabolize sugar, and that this was due to some malfunction of the pancreas.

Other gland extracts have had some surprising effects when tried on different species. We have already mentioned the Peter Pan hormone and its effect on moth pupae. There is a kind of salamander, called the axolotl, which looks as though it were an overgrown tadpole, a case of arrested amphibian development: it has gills, a finned tail, and four little legs, and it normally lives out its life wholly in the water. When it is fed thyroid hormones, an astonishing transformation occurs. It loses its gills and fin, develops air-breathing organs, and hops out of the water to become a land-dwelling animal.

We who can scarcely exchange a bit of skin with each other can apparently exchange endocrine chemicals with a salamander! And—we may speculate—perhaps some such mutation as the development of a thyroid gland could first have spurred some ocean-dweller to creep up out of the warm seas onto the land, long ago in the youth of the world.

THE YOUNG SCIENCE

The endocrine system kept its secrets from prying scientists for many centuries; only in the past seventy years have some of them been unlocked, one by one, and their study has become the science and the medical specialty of endocrinology. The name is new, and most of what we have learned is new, but the idea that a natural balance is somehow maintained in the body goes back to antiquity.

The ancients surmised that some organs exuded life-giving substances and that these must be carried by the blood. The earliest known medical text, the Ebers Papyrus, was written down about the year 1550 B.C., but it contained the wisdom of Egyptian priest-physicians for many centuries before. In its discussion of perhaps seven hundred drugs it includes the benefits of certain extracts from organs. More than a thousand years later Aristotle recommended such extracts, and Pliny the Elder in his *Natural History,* written in the first century A.D., used the term materia medica—medical materials—for the medicines derived from the bodies of both men and animals. Centuries again passed before these Graeco-Roman ideas were given the form of a scientific hypothesis by the sixteenth-century Swiss physician, Paracelsus, who is considered the father of pharmaceutical chemistry. In the medical style of the time he stated his theory in a Latin axiom: *Similia similibus curantur,* "Like cures like"; that is to say, a diseased organ can be cured by a medicine made of the same organ.

Out of this theory flowed a steady stream of medicinal preparations made from animal and human organs. Pharmacists concocted them; physicians prescribed them; patients put their faith in substances with such names as *cranium humanum,* and the gruesome fact that the human extracts came from the bodies of executed criminals dampened their popularity not at all. A well-stocked European pharmacy of the eighteenth century would have more than a hundred such organ preparations on its shelves.

Because it lacked an experimental basis, an odor of magic continued to cling to the ancient like-cures-like theory until the mid-nineteenth century. Then a physician from Göttingen, A. A. Berthold, came forward in 1849 with the first experimental evidence that endocrine substances were carried in the blood. He transplanted the testes of a barnyard rooster to another part of its body with no loss of the cock's male characteristics. The effects of castration, or removal of the testes, had long been known. If the testes could be reimplanted elsewhere with all their normal connections severed, such as nerves and ducts, and still maintain the animal's sexual character, then they could be acting upon the organism only by way of the blood. So Dr. Berthold argued.

Like so many scientific pioneers, he attracted little attention. A few years later the French scientist Claude Bernard advanced his theory of the inner environment, the *milieu intérieur*, that kept the body's organs functioning in harmony. But it was the search for eternal youth, or for the restoration of youth's vigor and potency, that gave a scientific direction to the like-cures-like theory and at the same time narrowed it to the endocrine glands.

The true beginning of the young science, its historic birthday, was on June 1, 1889, the day when another French physician, Charles Edouard Brown-Séquard, stood before the Biological Society of Paris, a lively old man of seventy-two, and described for his astonished fellow scientists the miraculous rejuvenation he had experienced as a result of injecting himself just beneath the skin with a preparation made from the testes of a dog.

His catalogue of evidence was uninhibited—the increased strength and forcefulness of his stream of urine, for example. Even more impressive were his obvious vigor and his infectious enthusiasm. We know today that his recapture of youth must have been more psychological than physical, for his canine extract could scarcely have brought about such wonders. But his reasoning was brilliant, however mistaken his proof. He outlined for future endocrinologists the scope of the glands of inner secretion and described them as a system that integrated the body's functions, separate from the nervous system and to a large extent independent of it.

Even his error—if error it was, as we now believe—had its value. It spurred the medical world to pursue this apparent clue to the long-sought fountain of youth. The vision of such a goal gave early investigators the courage to persist in the long, arduous experimentation that has already yielded treasures, not of eternal youth, but of physiological knowledge, life-saving therapies, and understanding of many mysterious conditions that we now know to be due to endocrine imbalance.

By the turn of the century the existence of endocrine substances had been verified and the word "hormone" had been coined for them. Since then, more and more separate hormones have been isolated and identified, the chemical composition of some crucial ones has been analyzed, and a few are being produced synthetically for medical use.

Much of the endocrine system remains mysterious. We still need to learn much more of the interrelationships among the glands, and we cannot yet describe precisely how they integrate the functioning of the body's organs. But we know enough to be certain that hormone function is a crucial pivot on which the body's well-being turns.

GOVERNOR OF THE ISLAND SYSTEM

The geography of the endocrines is simple enough to remember: every adult has six different, clearly defined glands distributed from the top of the body downward. One is in the head, two are in the neck, two in the abdomen, and one more is in the groin. Two, the adrenals and the sex glands, or gonads, come in pairs, while the parathyroids are a quartet of tiny bodies buried in the tissue of the thyroid. Whether the location of the glands has any physiological importance we do not know, except in one instance. The pituitary, the master gland, is appropriately lodged within the skull and close by the hypothalamus.

The hypothalamus, as we shall see when we come to explore the nervous system, is a center of the autonomic nervous system and it is also a center of the emotions in their most primitive form, undirected by the higher brain centers. Part of the pituitary is physically connected with this area of the brain, the hypothalamus. And so the pituitary, which interacts so potently with the other glands, here connects the endocrine system with that part of the nervous system that operates below the level of consciousness and itself controls the automatic functions of the body. In its connection with the hypothalamus, the pituitary also binds the endocrine system to the primitive emotions, especially those of rage and fear. We shall see how significant this connection is when we come to look more closely at the combined responses of the endocrine glands to stimuli from the outer world.

The pituitary is about the size of a cherry, and it hangs like a cherry on a short stem below the brain, nestling in a small recess inside the skull. It is in two parts, or lobes, which grow together before birth with a thin band of tissue joining them. Each of the two lobes produces several different hormones. Some have vital stimulating functions to perform for the entire body, and some are specifically directed at other glands in the endocrine system. All the glands interact to some extent, one with another. But only the pituitary, the master gland, has this special function of arousing other members of the system to produce their particular hormones.

Six separate hormones have been extracted from the anterior or front lobe of the pituitary; several more, whose action is known, have not been isolated. First among the pituitary's products is the growth hormone, which insures the proper growth and development of the body's skeleton and general stature. Then there is a whole series of hormones whose effect is to stimulate the other glands. Each was originally named for the gland at which it was found to be aimed, plus the suffix *tropic,* from the Greek word for *turning.* Thus the thyrotropic hormone would be the hormone that turned in the direction of the thyroid. Recently the endocrinologists have been changing the suffix to *trophic,* from a word meaning *nourish,* on the grounds that this more accurately describes what the pituitary hormones do.

And so we have the thyrotrophic hormone, which stimulates the thyroid; the adrenocorticotrophic hormone, famous as ACTH, which stimulates the cortex of the adrenal glands (whose equally famous hormone, cortisone, is one of the results of this stimulation); two gonadotrophic hormones, or hormones directed to the sex glands, and a hormone that stimulates production of milk in the breasts. All these hormones are produced in the anterior lobe of the gland.

From the posterior lobe come hormones that constrict the blood vessels and thus raise the blood pressure in the arteries. They also stimulate contraction of various smooth muscles in the body, and by this function they play a role in childbirth and the remarkable series of physiological events accompanying the arrival of a new life in the world. It is this group of hormones that stimulate the contractions of the uterus and later the "letting down" of milk in the breasts so that the newborn can be nourished. When men first took to milking cows and goats, ewes and mares—in 6,000 B.C. or thereabouts—they may even then have noticed that there were times when the animal seemed to withhold her milk. Just how old this bit of lore may be we shall never know, but we can be sure it is very old indeed, much older than this nursery rhyme in which it has come down to us:

> Cushy cow, bonny, let down thy milk,
> And I will give thee a gown of silk;

A gown of silk and a silver tee
If thou wilt let down thy milk for me.

Today the hormone responsible for the letting-down reaction has been isolated and named—it is called oxytocin—and it may be found helpful to mothers who have difficulty in nursing their babies.

If we were asked to choose the most important of the pituitary's many powers, we would be hard put to answer. Thanks to its control of skeletal growth, most of us are neither dwarfs nor giants but a comfortable human size. Thanks to its stimulation of sexual growth at puberty, most of us mature into men and women capable of reproducing the human race. But probably the most impressive work of the pituitary is in its role as governor of the endocrine system, keeping all the other glands performing their tasks according to the body's needs, hour by hour, year by year.

Just what train of events sets in motion this reciprocal interchange between the master gland and its subordinates, we can still only speculate. Through the hypothalamus the pituitary may go into action in response to stimuli from the outer world. The spur may be a sensory one, or perhaps an emotional one, that sets the master gland to secreting the specific hormones for the specific glands so that they in turn will secrete what the body requires in a certain situation. And besides the outer stimuli, there are the inner changes that call upon the pituitary to summon now this gland, now that one, or more likely a combination of them, to keep the *milieu intérieur* correct for the body's functioning. One day the endocrinologists will be able to explain the mechanism in all its marvelous complexity. The wonder will not be less for the knowledge of how it works.

THE DRIVING THYROID

One of the great differences we observe between one individual and another is in the amount of drive or energy that each seems to possess; often we say dismissively that it is all a matter of glands. If someone were to pin us down when we say this, we would be obliged to admit that drive is not a matter of any single aspect of the individual, not even of glands alone. There are powerful and complex psychological factors involved in the dynamism of one person and the placid, perhaps stolid calm of another. But the generalization has its grain of truth: there is frequently a measurable difference in the rate of metabolism of the energetic individual compared with the slow-moving one, and the gland that seems most directly involved in metabolism is the thyroid.

The thyroid is roughly shield-shaped; its two lobes, connected by a bar or isthmus, flank the larynx and that prominent upper part of the trachea that we call the Adam's apple. We speak of the growth hormone in the pituitary, but the thyroid, too, plays a part in skeletal growth, sexual growth, and the normal development of the brain. Its connection with growth, as nearly as we know, is by way of its metabolic function. The thyroid hormone apparently acts as a catalyst in the oxidation, the fuel-burning action, within the tissue cells, by which the food we eat is converted into new cells and into energy. The texture of the skin and the vigorous growth and luster of the hair are also affected by the smooth working of the thyroid gland.

We mentioned a few pages back the curious case of the axolotl, the oversize tadpolelike salamander that changes from a water-dweller to a land-dweller when it is given thyroid extract. The thyroid reminds us in another way that we are creatures born of the sea: it needs iodine. Only a very little, to be sure—two ten-thousandths of a gram a day—but it is an indispensable little, an essential part of the molecule of thyroxin, the thyroid hormone.

The sea is rich in iodine, and peoples who live on the coastal plains and have fish and shellfish as a regular part of their diet never lack for it. Those who live far from the sea, in areas like the Alps that have long been leached of the iodine content in their soils by the erosion of down-rushing streams, may not be taking in even the tiny amount that they need. Not only human inhabitants suffer from this lack. The tiny brook trout in mountain streams may also be afflicted with goiter, the enlargement of the thyroid, and they also can be cured by the addition of iodine to the water in which they swim and from which they take their food.

The thyroid manufactures its hormone and releases it into the blood when it is stimulated to do so by the pituitary's thyro-trophic hormone. When the thyroxin in the blood reaches a certain level, the stimulation is cut off, and the thyroid is inhibited from secreting actively until the blood level of thyroxin drops again. This circuit of control by way of the level of a particular hormone in the blood is characteristic of the pituitary's interaction with the other endocrines.

So involved is the thyroid function with the personality that it is puzzling to decide whether a quick, active, impatient (and perhaps easily irritated) individual is so because he has an active thyroid or the other way round. It is a question like the classic one of the chicken and the egg. Does the gland drive the person, or does the person drive the gland? And like the egg-versus-chicken argument it is probably insoluble. When the thyroid behaves abnormally in either direction, when it is seriously over-active (hyperthyroid) or inert (hypothyroid), the symptoms of malfunction are usually quite clear; but the normal range is wide enough to allow for many degrees of variation and many kinds of people, and we would not, and could not, all run at a uniform pace even if our thyroid glands could be doctored to function at the same rate.

THE TINY PARATHYROIDS

The four little glands embedded like peas in the thyroid apparently just happen to be there; there seems to be no special connection between the parathyroids and the thyroid except that of location. These tiny bodies have a major function: they stimulate the release of calcium into the blood from the skeletal bones, especially the ends of the long bones where stores of this element are laid up.

The bones require calcium; it is the substance that gives them and the teeth their hardness. But a level of calcium apparently has to be maintained in the blood serum, and it is the task of the parathyroids, as far as we know, to regulate that level as part of the stability of the internal environment.

ISLETS IN THE PANCREAS

Comet-shaped, with a thick head and elongated tail, the pancreas nestles among the organs of digestion with the stomach and the duodenum curving around it. Most of the gland is concerned with producing pancreatic juice for the digestion of proteins in the stomach and for splitting starches and fats, in response to a hormone from the small intestine and the duodenum. It used to be called the abdominal salivary gland because, when we smell or taste food, the pancreas pours out its juice much as the salivary glands do in the mouth. In these functions the pancreas is part of the digestive system, producing enzymes in its juice for the digestion of the three principal components in our food, proteins, carbohydrates, and fats.

The pancreas also has a set of quite different cells, in little island clusters dotted through the general cell texture of the gland; these are the islets discovered by the German pathologist Paul Langerhans in the last century and named for him. In response to the insulinotrophic hormone from the pituitary, these clusters of cells, smaller than the regular pancreatic cells, produce insulin.

This is the crucial hormone that regulates the sugar economy of the blood. It promotes storage of the body's sugar compounds in muscles and liver, shuts down the liver's production of sugar when it is not needed, and stimulates the body tissues to oxidize carbohydrate, in other words, to use up fuel. By virtue of its insulin-producing islets, responsive to the pituitary and performing a necessary function in the regulation of the internal environment, the pancreas is a member in good standing of the endocrine system.

In addition to insulin, the pancreas also produces a hormone lately isolated and named glucagon, secreted in cell clusters side by side with those that produce insulin. The function of this hormone seems to be mainly to regulate the sugar-burning effects of insulin. It also has an effect, so far unexplained, on the kidney's excretion of sodium and potassium and perhaps of several other inorganic substances such as calcium and phosphorus. This suggests a second line of defense such as we find in other areas of the body where vital metabolic functions are involved. The glucagon system may in some way back up the sodium-regulating function of the adrenal glands, which we come to next in our tour of the endocrine system.

THE GLANDS OF STORM AND CALM

The adrenal glands lie like a pair of pyramid-shaped caps, one atop each kidney, and even among the endocrines, each of which has its own curious architecture, their structure is unique. The adrenals are not twin-lobed like the pituitary, nor are they dotted with islands like the thyroid and the pancreas. Each of them is a gland within a gland. Its inside, or medulla, is distinguished from its outside or cortex in embryonic origin, in cell structure, in the stimuli to which it responds, and most particularly in function.

The medulla is the emergency gland, the mobilizer of the body to action in the face of storm and stress. The cortex is a gland of maintenance and conservation, regulating subtle chemical functions that go on steadily, quietly, waking and sleeping; we might call them vegetative functions. It also provides a second line of defense against stress, but in terms of putting out fires and restoring tissues to normal.

When we come to the nervous system we shall see a similar division in the autonomic branch which controls the unconscious or involuntary body functions. We shall see there a division called the sympathetic system and one called the parasympathetic system. The sympathetic system is, like the adrenal medulla, an emergency mechanism, and the parasympathetic system is a vegetative or conserving one.

The sympathetic system, we discover, is closely connected with the adrenal medulla. Both of them evolve from the same group of cells in the embryo of the newly developing human being. In the fully formed infant they are differentiated into nerve and gland structures, but they remain intimately related in what the physiologists call the sympathoadrenal system. This is the body's set of alarm and mobilization signals.

From the adrenal medulla come powerful stimulants, the adrenal hormones, which accelerate the heart, raise the blood pressure, contract the smooth muscle in the skin—the familiar sensation of the skin prickling or the hair standing on end. The adrenalines give us all those sensations that we associate with anger, fright, or challenge, even if only the challenge of an after-dinner speech or a game of tennis. What is happening, when we have these sensations, is that the body is being galvanized to its maximum efficiency to meet stress.

The potent adrenal hormones stimulate the liver to release its stores of sugar and speed up its manufacture of more of this fuel for muscular action. They contract blood vessels, diverting blood from the skin and raising the pressure at which it is pumped through the brain, lungs, and muscles. The heart and pulses quicken; the breathing quickens; we can feel our body heat rising. Muscular fatigue is postponed. For the emergency the muscles work overtime, incurring an oxygen debt which the body will pay off later when the emergency is over and there is time to rest. At the same time the ability of the blood to coagulate is increased; this is also a part of the body's defense reaction, for if there is to be a fight there may also be wounds. This readiness of the blood to clot was a marked advantage, surely, through the long evolutionary struggle of tooth and claw. Any creature that possessed it had, within his own body, the magic to staunch bleeding and heal injuries.

This entire series of defense reactions, though it takes many words to enumerate, goes into effect within moments. It is a very nearly instantaneous mobilization brought about by the sympathetic system together with the adrenal medulla, in response to an alarm. The adrenalines are delivered by the gland, and they are further reinforced by adrenalines produced at the sympathetic nerve ends. There is a hormone produced in the brain, called serotonin, which has a similar stimulating action, possibly in the transmission of nerve impulses. The chemical composition of these several substances is very similar, although not identical. We have a good deal yet to learn about the operation of this emergency system of nervous, glandular, and muscular mobilization, with its rapid succession of chemical changes; but even these fragmentary glimpses reveal one of the body's wonders in the way it responds to a threat of danger and prepares to defend itself from harm.

We do not find the cortex of the adrenal gland similarly connected with the other half of the autonomic nervous system, the parasympathetic branch; the body's arrangements are rarely so mechanically symmetrical. The cortex has no nervous connections whatever, so far as we know. Only the correct hormone from the pituitary can stimulate it to action, the adrenocorticotrophic hormone, ACTH.

Nor do we know why the cortex, apparently so unrelated to the medulla, should be situated not only close to it but fitted around it like the cover of a baseball. In its cellular origin the triple layer of cortical cells is cousin to the sex glands, and we have already noted that its hormones, unlike those of the medulla around which it is wrapped, are steroids, chemically of the same family as the sex hormones.

In the multiplicity of its functions the adrenal cortex gives us a demonstration of the endocrine system as the delicate, subtle regulator of the internal environment. The adrenal cortex is involved in the metabolism of proteins, carbohydrates, and fats, and it acts as a check on the sugar metabolism of insulin. It regulates the body's levels of sodium and potassium and thereby influences its water content. It produces two female sex hormones and one with male activity, and it appears to have an influence on the development of the sexual functions.

Besides all this, it joins in the body's defense system, accelerating its secretion of hormones in times of stress. Almost incidentally, as it were, the cortical hormones have the beneficent effect of reducing inflammation in the skin, the connective tissues, and other areas of the body. This became clear when Doctors E. C. Kendall and Philip S. Hench, of the Mayo Foundation, demonstrated that the cortical hormone, cortisone, could help sufferers from arthritis and rheumatic disease. This is why cortical steroids are prescribed in some cases for eye inflammations, dermatitis, even in ointment form for poison ivy.

Since the discovery of cortisone some two dozen cortical hormones, the corticoids, have been isolated. The corticoids are concerned with sodium and potassium regulation, nitrogen balance, and the production of certain of the white cells, with pregnancy, with kidney, liver, and heart function, and possibly with blood pressure. These powerful hormones, with their complex metabolic effects, have already taught us a great deal about endocrine functioning, and they will undoubtedly teach us much more as investigators continue to plumb the mysteries of this one tiny but potent organ of the system, the adrenal cortex.

THE GLANDS OF NEW LIFE

The gonads or sex glands, the ovaries in women and the testes in men, are significant members of the endocrine family, not only in relation to the sexual function, but also in ways that seem only distantly connected with the production of new life. The pituitary stimulates them by sending out its gonadotrophic hormones, and the glands produce the ova and spermatozoa that continue the species, plus hormones that affect the growth and well-being of the entire body. They are so much a part of the life cycle of the individual that we shall discuss their functions in detail in separate chapters.

STRESS AND THE BODY'S WISDOM

Stress has become a parlor word. It has lost its precise meaning in much the same way as "complex," "fixation," "id," and "superego" became conversational small change in the 1920s and 1930s, and "psychosomatic" became a synonym for "imaginary" in the more recent past. In the current national vocabulary stress is used as though it were an abbreviated form of *distress*.

To restore shape and meaning to the word, we might define it as the engineers do. To them, stress is a combination of forces causing strain or distortion. In this sense all living is stressful. The only existence without stress is life in the womb. There, floating in the amniotic fluid, cushioned from bumps and bruises and changes of temperature, with food carried in and wastes carried away on a gentle steady stream and the placental barrier holding off nearly all hostile invaders, the unborn lives in effortless, mindless bliss. Indeed the serenity of this state and the subsequent, jarring transition from uterine limbo to the stress of life so impressed one group of psychiatrists, followers of the late Dr. Otto Rank, that they ascribed virtually all neuroses to the trauma of birth. Physiologists have since pointed out that, thanks to the undeveloped state of the newborn's brain and nervous system, little of this strenuous experience is likely to leave a permanent mark.

From the moment of birth on, everything that happens to an individual may properly be considered stressful. Growth and bodily change, exertion, new physical environments are stresses; so are accident, infection, and illness. All of these cause strain and distortion—that is, adaptation. Learning, accepting the disciplines of family and society, experiencing frustration and fear, disappointment and sorrow, effort and challenge, achievement and failure all produce strain and distortion, or adaptation.

The engineer builds his bridge or his skyscraper to meet and cope with stress. He takes stress into account, so that his structure can absorb it and still stand. The bridge vibrates with the trains roaring across it, the skyscraper sways with the pressure of wind against it, and neither of them falls if it is properly built. The body is also built to absorb stress. It makes its adaptations and continues to function.

Life offers us many kinds of stress, but we can divide them into two principal kinds, to which the body reacts in quite different ways. There is emergency stress, the situation that confronts us with an immediate threat—a near accident in an automobile, a rattlesnake encountered in the path, a wound or an injury. And there is continuing stress, less a situation than a state of affairs or a condition: the burst of growth at puberty, the new demands on the metabolism in pregnancy. All disease states are stressful, especially those that involve infection; so is chronic exposure to excessive noise, vibration, fumes, chemicals. Today the new stress of man-created radioactivity is added to the normal radioactivity in our natural environment.

Psychological stresses may be of the emergency kind, but more often they are continuing: the changes involved in a new home or a new job, pressures of work and tensions in relationships, anxieties both real and fancied about oneself and about those one loves—or fears, as the case may be. Emergency stress situations outweigh the continuing ones in some lives—lives of action and adventure—and at some periods of life for most of us.

And there are emergency stresses even in our comparatively safe urban and suburban lives. Flood and blizzard may be rare, ravening wolf and coiling snake may never challenge us on Elm or Market Street, and it is a long time since any family in the United States has had to defend itself against an Indian raid. But the mid-twentieth century has its challenging emergencies too. Most of us have had the experience of driving peacefully along a familiar route, automatically obeying traffic lights and stop signs, when another automobile has come plunging through a signal and threatened imminent disaster.

What happens? You jam your foot on the brake, your hand on the horn. You raise your voice in furious and unflattering protest at the other driver the instant both cars jolt to a stop, perhaps an inch apart, perhaps with dented or scratched fenders. Then you become aware that your heart is pounding, your vision is blurred, your hands are shaking, your palms and armpits are wet with sweat. You are no longer a quick-acting, brilliantly co-ordinated, automatic mechanism but a scared, quivering human being, suffering the uncomfortable aftereffects of a large dose of adrenaline. In a few minutes this, too, passes, and you drive on, the familiar sights and sounds a little keener to your perceptions because you have just had a close brush with danger.

The same outpouring of adrenaline, quickening the heart and raising the blood pressure, emptying sugar supplies swiftly into the blood stream and dilating the blood vessels in the muscles to give them immediate use of the fuel—all this happened to the paleolithic cave dweller and forest hunter as it does to us. His pulse also pounded at the sight or sound of a mammoth or tusked wild boar, and the pupils of his eyes also dilated so that he might see better the danger he was in. The superb mechanism that served for his survival also serves for ours. And we still need it. Civilization has not abolished emergency stresses. It has only changed their character.

The adrenal medulla as the seat of this emergency reaction to stress was intensely explored by the late Professor Walter B. Cannon of Harvard, one of our great American investigators of the endocrine system. Since he published his classic work, which he called *Bodily Changes in Pain, Hunger, Fear and Rage,* other observers found that the body has not one but at least two lines of emergency defense. As we have seen, supporting the adrenal medulla is the sympathetic arm of the autonomic nervous system. Its production of adrenaline-like substances at the nerve junctions reinforces the adrenal secretions and calls forth the same body responses.

And, as we have seen, only the adrenal medulla, the emergency gland, has this direct nervous connection. The other glands respond only to hormone stimulation (excepting always the pituitary, the master gland, with its apparent connection to the hypothalamus in the brain). Through the eons of evolution the swift messages from senses to muscles, and along involuntary nerve pathways to heart and viscera and blood vessels, have proved their survival value. So has the direct connection to the adrenal medulla. The roundabout stimulation of the gland, by way of hormones traveling through the blood stream, would never be quick enough to save the deer sniffing the scent of lurking tiger or the man finding the fresh tracks of the ferocious cave bear.

For animals, and perhaps for man in the youth of the species, the signal for this danger response would come almost exclusively by way of the senses. The sight or sound or smell of danger—or the touch, as of something hot—is the signal for instant muscle reflexes and sympathoadrenal responses. Even as we become aware of the danger sign in the higher centers of the brain, the muscles, nerves, and adrenal glands are already in action, the body is galvanized for defense.

So deeply and permanently implanted is this danger response that for man, who, with his complex associative mind, can imagine, foresee, and even fancy danger, it comes into play when the danger is not physical and even when there is no danger at all. The mere thought of danger, or the vicarious danger of a suspenseful story, play, or film, may be enough to tense the muscles and set the adrenaline pouring. A psychological situation can have the same heart-thumping, sweat-beading effect. We know that when we stand up to make a speech, no physical harm is likely to come to us. Nor are we in literal danger when we take an examination, or face a stranger for an interview that may have an important outcome for us. Yet we experience the primitive danger reaction.

Actors and concert artists call this danger reaction stage fright, and the experienced performer welcomes it as the taut nervous forerunner of a mettlesome performance. Without it he would labor against a dead-weight slackness of body and mind. But the same reaction that brings vibrant tension and power to the veteran can be the undoing of a novice, who may find himself trembling, drenched with sweat and, incidentally, tongue-tied under the onslaught of his own defensive hormones.

The body's ancient and indispensable mobilization to meet danger is rather more efficient than the situation of psychological danger requires. It is like calling out three hook-and-ladder companies to put out a blaze in a wastebasket, and snarling up normal traffic in the process. The time-honored way to counter this overenergetic defense is obviously to be so thoroughly prepared or rehearsed that confidence may keep the psychic alarm signals to a tinkle, or at least so that we may be able to begin the performance in spite of the jolting rush of adrenaline.

So much for emergency stress. When it comes to long-term or

continued stress, our knowledge of the body's response is quite recent, and it stems mainly from the work of Professor Hans Selye of Canada. In his animal experiments Dr. Selye observed that in addition to the specific defense that the body musters for a specific stress—the manufacture of antibodies, for example, to cope with an infection—there is also a generalized response of the body to all kinds of stress. He named this the General Adaptation Syndrome.

The principal organ involved, according to his theory, is the adrenal cortex, and its first response, the alarm reaction, is to pour its hormones into the blood stream at a greatly increased rate. One of the effects of these hormones, as we have seen, is to reduce inflammation. Apparently there are other functions the steroids perform that mitigate the acute period of stress.

The second phase is that of resistance. The gland has apparently settled down to its task of increased hormone production. It appears well-nourished and may even become enlarged as it manufactures a steady supply of the defensive hormones that presumably increase the body's general resistance.

If the stress is overwhelming, as in the case of an extensive third-degree burn or an uncontrollable infectious disease, then the third phase of the syndrome sets in: exhaustion—the adrenal steroids are used up—followed by death. Some chronic diseases, such as arthritis, may possibly represent the nonfatal effects of this third stage, an unsuccessful adaptation to stress.

Medical scientists are cautious about applying laboratory findings, arrived at under controlled experimental conditions, to human beings living the varied and unpredictable life of the real world. But the stress theory gives us new insight into the body's second and perhaps third lines of defense against harm, and it may lead us toward a new understanding of the effects of wear and tear. We may even learn to discover the early signs of exhaustion in the endocrine system and deal with avoidable stresses before the body has drained all its remarkable resources.

Clearly, in the endocrine system we have only begun to explore what Professor Cannon eloquently called "the wisdom of the body."

16

CYCLES OF GROWTH

The universe, the earth we live on, and the bodies we inhabit alike beat to the eternal rhythm of some cosmic pulse. Philosophers and poets have known intuitively what science has observed, measured, and recorded: almost everything, in the world we know, moves in tides and cycles. Planets and suns, stars and the galaxies in which they ride, all have a life cycle. And so also have all living things on our earth, from the millenniums of the giant redwoods to the bright brief day of the butterflies.

How the eternal cycle began, men have wondered since the dawn of civilization and, for all we know, perhaps before. A story of creation, the battle of benign divinities against the titans of chaos, was already ancient when Abraham abandoned idol worship for a nomadic life in the service of Jehovah. Modern cosmologists are still not agreed on an answer to the riddle posed by the mystics and prophets through the centuries. Some adhere to the theory that the universe is being continuously created, that new hydrogen atoms are constantly being born, and from them the many kinds of matter are formed by the vast forces of fusion and fission. Others prefer a "big bang." They talk of a Universal Atom which, exploding, gave birth to the swirling galaxies and set the universe's time clock ticking.

Time has vastly different rhythms, running out its billions of years for stars and planets, its geologic ages for seas and mountains, its years and decades in the lives of men. Shakespeare described the cycle of human life when he set the melancholy Jacques to reflecting, under a tree in the Forest of Arden, on the seven ages of man. "All the world's a stage," he began, in the speech that many of us learned by heart in our school days.

The endocrinologist more or less bears out the poet. The life cycle does indeed proceed by ages, and at each age it is governed by significant hormones. Thus from birth to puberty the growth hormone of the pituitary dominates the body's activity. From puberty to full maturity the sex or gonadal hormones are in the ascendant, testosterone and other androgens in the male and estrogen in the female; throughout the childbearing years the gonadal hormones and the pituitary's gonadotrophic hormones play reciprocal roles. And in the years after the reproductive cycle has ended, hormones play an important role, one that is still not completely understood.

In the biological cycles, growth and reproduction are the major themes. The motif is not that life ends but that it does not end, that it is self-perpetuating. Following the mysterious promptings of the biological time clock, the endocrine system brings each individual to his reproductive peak. Bud opens to flower, flower yields to fruit, fruit harbors seed, and so the species is renewed; the cycle begins again.

Meanwhile, in fulfilling the reproductive cycle, the vitalizing hormones confer on each individual the capacity for the living of his own life. Many plants, like the garden annuals, live only to bloom and produce their seed, and then their cycle ends. The gardener knows that he can prolong their bloom by plucking their fading flowers and preventing their going to seed, for they will put out flowers again and again until they can fulfill their cycle by producing the next generation of their kind. Many insects lay their eggs and then die. Among the animal species the salmon is one that exists only to reproduce its kind. Magnificent in its maturity, it swims upstream, leaping rapids and waterfalls, climbing over man-made dams with astonishing strength and persistence. Having spawned, it shrivels to old age and within days it is dead.

In most of the animal species the cycles of life and of reproduction are not so dramatically synchronized. Most enjoy a mellow afterglow when the reproductive period is ended. In man the life cycle has been lengthening through the thousands of years since prehistoric times, when the cave-dwelling hunter lived little beyond the age of thirty; the most heartening gains in life expectancy have been made in this century.

We have indications that the reproductive cycle is lengthening. Puberty seems to be coming earlier to girls and menopause later to women than it has in the past. Whether this is also true for boys and men is more difficult to observe, since the beginning and end of the reproductive cycle are not so clearly marked. The addition of years to life is a matter of statistical record: an American boy born in 1900 might expect to live 46.3 years, a girl 48.3. Boys of the 1956 crop had an average of 66.7 years before them, girls 73 years.

Man alone, moreover, has the life of the mind to make his later years rich and significant. The brain does not necessarily age at the same rate as other parts of the body, and those who cultivate the powers and pleasures of the mind extend still further the human cycle of useful, enjoyable life. To this end the endocrinologists are working hard to make their particular contribution, directing their researches toward discovering what part hormones may play in maintaining healthy, vigorous old age.

NEUTRAL GROWTH

The first fact that strikes us about a young living thing—whether it is a healthy plant, puppy, or child—is its powerful, passionate urge to grow. This begins with dizzying speed long before the new individual has a pituitary gland of its own to provide growth hormones. From the moment that egg cell and sperm cell unite, even while the embryo of a new human life is still on its way along the Fallopian tube to its uterine nest, the cells are already dividing and dividing again. Nor is the growth in any way haphazard. For all its speed, it proceeds according to a pattern already laid down in the genes of the original ovum and sperm.

What kind of creature it is to be, whether baby elephant, whale, or human child; the rate of its growth, the precise order of its development, the time when it will stir, the moment when it will be ready to move out of its mother's body and take up life on its own—all are predetermined. If it is the child of human parents, in 280 days—give or take a few—it will have grown from a single cell to a human infant. Its weight will be seven pounds or a bit more or less, its length from top to toe some twenty inches. It

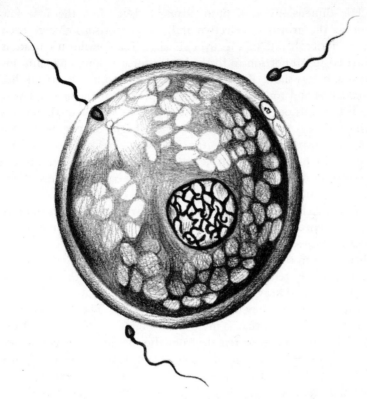

will be complete with all its bones, muscles, nerves, organs, its fingernails and toenails, down to the tiniest hair follicle. Its sensory end organs will all be there, although not all fully developed. Its teeth will be in its gums, and a female baby will have immature ova already stored in her ovaries.

For the first weeks of independent life the intense rate of growth continues, and then gradually it decelerates. The classic weight gain of a half pound a week, which generations of mothers have been taught to expect, actually goes on only for the first three months or less. Then it diminishes to about four ounces a week at six months, to two or three ounces weekly at one year; in the second year the gain is half a pound a month or less. The average baby spurts from seven to fourteen pounds in his first five months, a growth in body weight of 100 per cent. But at the end of the year he has grown only 50 per cent more, to about twenty-two pounds.

His dimensions, too, push strongly, but after the first few months the growth is selective and the proportions change even more noticeably than the over-all size. The newborn's head is outsized in proportion to his body; his torso is long and thin, his arms and legs short. Between three and six months his trunk has broadened and rounded into baby shape, but at the age of a year he still stands only ten inches taller than he was at birth and his arms and legs are still short. Now these begin to lengthen; from his first birthday through the childhood years, most of his growth in height is in his lengthening legs. As he approaches puberty he is mostly arms and legs, with a comparatively short, possibly chubby and high-hipped torso.

This eager, leggy first stage of growth from infancy to puberty we call neutral growth because there is no marked differentiation between the sexes. Boys and girls are much alike—if we made no distinction in the way we dressed them and combed their hair we could scarcely tell which was which. Boys are on the average a shade taller and heavier than girls.

Psychologically they are not at all asexual. The human child belongs to a species that is divided into male and female, and the child is either male or female from the moment it is conceived. The child's external sex organs exist from its fourth month of life in the womb. At birth it possesses all of its primary sexual equipment, as well as the potential secondary sexual characters that will appear at puberty.

It also possesses, as observers from Freud to Kinsey have pointed out, the primary sources of erotic pleasure. The child, like the adult it is destined to be, is a sexual being. The difference in these neutral years is that childhood is autoerotic; its sexuality is mainly self-stimulating and self-satisfying. Only in the second stage of growth does the sexual urge become specifically directed toward another individual.

There is a foreshadowing of this in that rather baffling age, somewhere between the ages of two and five years, that marks the change from babyhood to childhood, what we might call the little adolescence. Here begins the long process of self-identification and awareness that goes on well into maturity, regardless of chronological age. Here begin anxieties and fears, and that astonishing first demand for individual and sexual recognition in which Freud saw an infantile acting out of the Oedipus story, the classic Greek tragedy of the hero who unknowingly killed his father and married his mother.

According to Freud, the little boy at this stage sees himself as his father's rival for his mother's love. The little girl also engages in competition with the mother for her father's love, although her emotions are likely to be more masked than her brother's, and for good reason. A young child cannot afford to wish her mother out of the way; the ties are still too close. The boy is not in the position of reversing his attitude toward his mother, but his new ambivalence toward his father is uncomfortable. He is not so dependent on his father as on his mother, but he nevertheless needs his strong father's protection and he fears his strong father's anger. This stormy time, when powerful emotions are in conflict, we have come to call the Oedipal stage. In a loving family, and with an ordinary absence of undue stresses in the environment, boy and girl gradually relinquish the unequal rivalry and accept their status as children, rather than fantasied lovers, of their parents.

We may imagine that the young psyche accepts defeat at this point with relief, for we see the child launching into years of exuberant, almost carefree growth and learning in all aspects— physical, intellectual, social. This is called the latency period, because there is little outward evidence of sexuality through the years until puberty. The name is misleading, however. There is a lively sexual curiosity and often a certain amount of sex play and experimentation on a childish level. But not until the pre-pubertal years is there any very strong specific interest shown in the opposite sex, and then it is more often shown in reverse, by demonstrations of scorn, ridicule, and rejection.

Throughout this first stage the dominating endocrinological factor is the growth hormone of the pituitary gland's anterior lobe. This does not have the target properties of other anterior pituitary hormones, which act on individual glands. It stimulates all the tissues and organs with impartial energy. The boy continues perhaps two years longer than the girl in this neutral phase; the first signs of changing growth patterns may begin in the girl as early as the age of eight or nine, in the boy at ten or eleven. Then the time clock of the pituitary signals the moment for a new stage of growth. It sends out its gonadotrophic hormones, and the sex glands begin to secrete their own hormones.

THE SEXUAL GROWTH PHASE

The first indication that puberty is near is usually a slowing down, a pause in growth that suggests a regrouping of forces or perhaps a change of gears. Then the new push begins, almost as explosively as in the first few months of life, and this time it is truly linked to sexual maturing.

For the girl the growth spurt takes place between eleven and thirteen on the average. Her hips become rounded, her breasts develop, her body loses the lean or chunky tomboy look; she may become chubby all over at first. Then her body begins to curve with the soft sculpturing of a subcutaneous layer of fatty tissue which is one of the secondary sexual characters. She may grow as much as four or five inches in a year; at this age, for the only time in the growth tables, half the girls are taller than the average boys of their age. Her underarm and pubic hairs appear, and she has her first menstrual period. At the onset of menstruation her growth slows again. If she begins to menstruate at thirteen, she will ordinarily reach her adult height and physique before her seventeenth birthday.

The boy follows the same pattern roughly two years later. First comes the pause, for some boys the general chubbiness. Then we see the sudden weedlike shooting up in height, with lengthening arms and legs, big hands and feet, the uncertain and then the deeper voice, the downy shadow of a beard. Shoulders broaden, muscles grow in size and power, the bony frame becomes larger and heavier. A boy whose pubertal growth spurt comes at about fourteen generally reaches most of his adult height by the time he is nineteen.

When pubertal growth is completed, the sexual differences extend even to such a minor detail as the way in which the pubic hair grows: in the male there is a line of hair extending upward to the navel, while in the female the growth of hair forms a clear triangle over the pubis, pointing downward.

Behind the scenes of this dramatic growth to sexual maturity are the sex glands, or gonads, and behind them in turn are the gonadotrophic hormones of the anterior pituitary. The pituitary's hormones directed to the sex glands are two: one stimulates the ovaries in the female and the testes in the male to produce their reproductive cells, ova and sperm, and the other stimulates them to secrete their sex hormones, estrogen and testosterone. The gonads in turn provide the body not only with the cells necessary for reproduction of the species but with the powerful sex hormones that orchestrate the pubertal push to adulthood, and thereafter supply the stimulus for the reproductive aspect of adult life.

The secondary sexual characteristics develop at the stimulation of estrogen and testosterone. Sexual desire and sexual potency also take their cues from these hormones but, interestingly, the psychic aspect of sexual experience is so powerful that even the loss of the testes does not necessarily end the sexual potency of the male. In the animal behavior laboratory of the American Museum of Natural History, the scientists cherished for years a grizzled, beat-up tomcat which, though castrated, continued to perform in vigorous tomcat fashion.

With the end of pubertal growth, the stage is set for the reproductive phase of the life cycle, which in nature is the principal, even the entire objective, the continuation of the species.

THE REPRODUCTIVE PHASE

In boys the first traces of the male hormone appear in the urine at about the age of ten. From then on the hormone is normally excreted as androsterone, a form which differs slightly in its chemistry from the testosterone in the body and is also less powerful in its effect. Testosterone is produced by cells in the testes separate from those that produce sperm. Thus even in the sex glands themselves the sexual function and the reproductive function are independent of each other. A man with a normal supply of testosterone is a sexually potent male, barring psychological impediments to potency; his potency exists without regard to his fertility.

Fertility depends upon the sperm count, the number of lively sperm cells in the ejaculate. On the average, this is about 250 million. So prodigal is nature with the production of sperm that one normal man in his active sexual lifetime could theoretically replenish the earth's entire population several thousand times. But only one sperm cell is needed to merge with an ovum, or egg, and beget a new human life. The millions more that his testes produce for each act of copulation are merely insurance, and expendable.

The curiously unprotected site of the testes, suspended outside the body cavity in the scrotum, which is nothing more than a sac of skin, may be one of those accidents of evolution that never required correction. In order to produce sperm, the testes need a temperature three or four degrees lower than that of the body. Some physiologists recently questioned whether male fertility may perhaps be endangered in our time, and they were not discussing the hazard of radioactivity in a nuclear age. They meant simply that trousers may be too warm! They suggested, seriously or not, a return to the codpiece of Renaissance days, or perhaps a widespread adoption of Scottish kilts.

The testes in the male child develop within the groin and drop down, in most instances before birth, in some boys not until puberty. The failure to descend does not affect normal sexual development or behavior, because testosterone does continue to be produced. What it does affect is fertility, the production of sperm cells.

One descended testicle is enough to insure fertility, if other factors are normal. The scrotum has its own temperature-controlling mechanism: in warm weather it is soft, relaxed, offering its largest surface for evaporation and cooling, while in cold weather muscle tissue tightens the sac, making it smaller, and at the same time brings it closer to the warm torso. Any man can observe this for himself when he takes a cold shower or goes swimming in cold water.

The production of reproductive cells in the male is not cyclic; it goes on continuously, stimulated by the spermatogenic hormone of the pituitary as we mentioned earlier. Neither is sexual desire cyclic in the male. Such variations as there are in male desire are not periodic, as they are in many women, but are rather a matter of individual vitality and circumstance. Sexual desire is a complex phenomenon, dependent upon many factors both psychic and physical besides the supply of testosterone. Some of these factors are constitutional, varying considerably from one individual to another, and some are temporary, having to do with the momentary state of health and emotions.

Generally speaking, a normal healthy male can be sexually aroused by an appropriate stimulus at any time. The frequency of sexual activity that he establishes at the beginning of his mature life is likely to be the pattern he follows throughout his active years, circumstances permitting. He may be aware of a periodic intensification of desire, but what proportion of this is physical and what psychological is not determined. It is not, as was once believed, so simple a matter as the pressure of accumulated seminal fluid in the genital tract. The fact that men of normal physical endowment can abstain from sexual activity for long periods, or even for life, if the motivation is adequate, is testimony to the power of the psychological factors. On the other hand, the wise old rabbis of medieval times used to advise their disciples to marry young and enjoy their wives every night so that they might concentrate on their Talmudic studies by day untroubled by lustful thoughts.

By contrast with the male, the female reproductive mechanisms function entirely by cycles. Fertility, pregnancy, lactation all are cycles, interwoven with the basic cycle of the woman's reproductive life, the menstrual cycle. The same anterior pituitary hormone that stimulates sperm production in the male, in the female sets off the maturing and release of an ovum from one of the ovaries each lunar month, and thus initiates that astonishing series of physiological events that we take so for granted, the preparation within her body for the shelter and nurturing of a new life. In every normal female past puberty, everywhere in the human family, the menstrual cycle takes place more or less regularly, except at those times when it is interrupted by a cycle of pregnancy.

Just how profoundly this lunar rhythm of her body influences a woman's life and personality seems to depend on the culture in which she lives. For here, too, as with the male, psychological factors are powerful, but they stem less from individual than from social attitudes. Among primitive peoples, to whom blood is a most potent symbol of life and death, dangerous and terrifying in a world peopled by good and evil demons, the menstruating woman is often taboo and often must spend her period in a special hut, isolated from the community. Even among highly civilized peoples of the past, whose medical lore was magical rather than scientific, she was unclean and untouchable.

Many superstitions still hover around her in the twentieth

century—for example, that if she touches fresh flowers they will wilt and die. In the romantic era when women were looked upon rather as fragile china, when they were held to be made of more refined and delicate stuff than men and were expected to submit to their husbands' carnal desires out of wifely duty, the menstrual period was not infrequently a time of semi-invalidism, at least among those women who could afford servants or persuade their husbands to wait on them.

Most women today would scorn such a retreat from activity. They have too many things they would rather do than take to their beds once a month. Unpleasant symptoms have a way of disappearing when a woman is busy and interested, or, if they persist, she is likely to go to her doctor and demand relief so that she can get on with her busy life. Today menstruation is hardly more than an annoyance to most women, and to many it is not even that, but merely a fact of female physiology.

Yet the physiological basis for a certain periodicity in a woman's life is there. The moodiness, depressed spirits or irritability of premenstrual tension are factual enough to justify one physician's description of woman as "a part-time witch." Many women also experience a burst of energy and optimism with the onset of menstruation or when the period ends. Many women experience a noticeable rise and fall of sexual desire in rhythm with the menstrual cycle.

The menstrual cycle begins with a surge of estrogenic activity when the ovary, stimulated by the particular hormone of the anterior pituitary, produces a mature ovum. At the same time the ovary secretes its own hormone corresponding to testosterone in the male; today this is called by a new term, estradiol. Estrin, the term formerly used for this hormone, and estrogen are now applied to any substance that produces the same effects in the body; estrone and estriole are names for chemical variants of the ovarian hormone that are excreted in the urine. So much for terminology, which has undergone all these changes in recent years in a race to keep up with the rapid progress of endocrine chemical research.

The estradiol, poured into the blood stream as an ovum matures, stimulates the preparation of the uterus for a pregnancy. The lining thickens and becomes plentifully supplied with blood vessels, and the whole organ mobilizes for the demands that presumably will soon be made upon it. Meanwhile, as the ovum breaks from its site (called a Graafian follicle) in the ovary and proceeds down the Fallopian tube toward the uterus, another hormone is being produced. The now empty follicle fills with a new grouping of cells, the corpus luteum (or yellow body). This, in turn, produces the hormone progestin, which will stimulate the growth of the placenta around the growing embryo in the uterus, if a pregnancy takes place. If a pregnancy does not take place, all this prepared tissue for the prospective embryo's nourishment is sloughed off and discharged from the body and the "disappointed uterus," as it has been called, returns to its resting size. This is menstruation as we are ordinarily aware of it. The lowered level of estrogenic hormones in the blood is a signal to the pituitary, which again secretes its gonadotrophic hormones, setting the ovaries to work on the next preparatory round with the maturing of another ovum. Another menstrual cycle has begun.

Armed as we are today with knowledge of the hormones, the anatomical changes and all the other aspects of the menstrual cycle, we still do not know whether menstruation serves a useful function. Dr. George Corner, whose studies in the subject are medical classics, has this to say about it:

Menstruation, then, is still a paradox and a puzzle—a normal function that displays itself by destruction of tissues; a phenomenon seemingly useless and even retrogressive, that exists only in the higher animals; an unexplained turmoil in the otherwise serenely co-ordinated process of uterine function.

If menstruation is useful, the most logical explanation of its use is that the menstrual blood itself may be required to nourish the fertilized ovum during the first days of its life in the uterus. Yet of the many species of warm-blooded animals, only monkeys and apes menstruate. The others manage to conceive and bear their young without it.

We shall have a closer look at ovulation—the production of the ripe ovum—when we come to consider the reproductive process and its endocrine background in the next chapter. In this chapter, concerned with growth cycles and the ages of man, we come now to the end of the reproductive phase.

THE MELLOW YEARS

Childbearing in women is a cycle with a clear beginning and a clear ending: the onset of menstruation signals its beginning, and the cessation of menstruation marks its end. Women have become pregnant during the year or two after menstrual periods seem to have ceased. In earlier generations a woman would be considerably embarrassed by the arrival of a "menopause baby," and in the Bible, of course, Abraham's wife Sarah laughed when the angel announced that she would bear a son when "it ceased to be with Sarah after the manner of women."

Physicians still cannot say exactly when ovulation ends; they can only say that it ends within a year or two of the end of menstruation. The ova no longer mature in the ovaries, and the secretion of estrogenic hormones dwindles accordingly. Earlier generations of women approached menopause as though it were the end of all active, enjoyable living, the end of sexual desire and the ability to attract or to respond erotically. Menopause was also expected to usher in a series of miseries and complaints covered by the unlovely umbrella of "women's troubles," the implication being that suffering and illness were the inescapable fate of females once they had outlived their role as mothers. Not all of this was myth. Frequent childbearing without adequate rest or medical care did reduce many women to a state of semi-invalidism in their middle years. But the myth was powerful, and it took a woman of unusual spirit and vigor, or one for whom the passing of youth was cushioned by a happy marriage, to resist it.

Modern medicine and new attitudes have deflated the myth, and many women sail through the menopausal changes with little or no discomfort. They continue actively all the kinds of living they have enjoyed before, including sexual enjoyment. All that ends with menopause is childbearing.

The withdrawal of the estrogenic hormones necessarily causes some changes and some possibly unpleasant symptoms. There may be the familiar "hot flashes," the sudden sweats as though a high fever were running. There may be moodiness and irritability, a tendency to cry easily, a variety of physical and emotional indications of the nervous system's instability during the glandular readjustment. Occasionally the menopause will trigger a depression that goes beyond moodiness, but in these instances menopause is not the cause but only the added stress that tips the scale of an already precarious adjustment.

For many women menopause is not an end but a new beginning, a second sexual bloom. When the lifelong preoccupation of body and mind with pregnancy comes to an end, a woman's sex life often flowers anew with an unreserved enjoyment enriched by experience and the long intimacy of marriage. There is no physiological reason why a woman should not continue indefinitely to experience sexual desire and its satisfaction, as long as there is a man to stimulate and gratify it.

In men the psychological effect of the passing years is the only measurable one. There is no physical evidence of a male equivalent of the menopause, a "climacteric," that would mark the end of fertility. The male reproductive cycle does not end; our hardy forebears not infrequently fathered a second and a third family, well into their seventies and sometimes beyond, wearing out a series of wives along the way. That was in the days when the majority of Americans lived on the farm, and a large progeny was economically not a burden but an asset.

Today, to be sure, families are growing larger again. The arrival of a third and even a fourth child is no longer a rarity; the number of families with more than two children has doubled since 1946. Even so, the time for having children usually ends well before the physiological end of childbearing in the wife, and most men have no occasion to discover that they are still capable of becoming fathers in their later years. If they had, the psychological effect of creating new life, or at least of possessing the power to do so, might well disperse, as with a fresh wind, the miasma of fears, regrets, and psychosomatic symptoms that haunts many men in their middle years.

A NEW LOOK AT THE AGE CYCLE

Despite the many new discoveries medical science has made, it is undeniably true that no one really knows what happens in the process of aging; we cannot even be sure that death itself is inevitable. When we consider that modern biological research is only a century old and reflect on the miraculous advances it has made in that eyeblink of historical time, it seems presumptuous to regard anything as inevitable. The young science of endocrinology has shown us that we can modify the menstrual cycle, the growth cycle, and the birth cycle, ease the passage through menopause, and restore the energies and spirits of the very elderly. Extending the life cycle is not necessarily beyond the reach of science.

That aging has a strong endocrine basis we have surmised for some time. The subtle working of the endocrine system is not easy to follow, but one medical scientist who happened also to be a fishing enthusiast, Dr. O. H. Robertson of the University of Chicago Medical School, believed he could learn something about this by observing what happens when nature speeds up this ordinarily long-drawn-out process. After a lifetime spent in the study of infectious diseases, he turned in retirement to the study of aging salmon and trout.

Salmon, as we have mentioned, lead an uneventful life until the moment when the powerful urge to spawn turns them from the sea and sends them fighting their way up the rivers. Then in a few days they pass from vigorous adulthood to old age. Dr. Robertson, working in California, and Dr. Bernard Wexler, of the May Institute for Medical Research in Cincinnati, studied this phenomenon together. They found that at this climax in the salmon's life the pituitary function became so active as to produce symptoms of acromegaly, a sudden burst of growth. The indication was that growth hormones and other pituitary hormones were being released explosively at this mature stage.

In biological science we are most careful not to assume that what is true of one species is true of any other, especially man. Yet it often does happen that with further research we find an analogy: the kidneys in dogs, for example, function very like human kidneys. And, as we noted, the endocrines seem to be virtually interchangeable among the species, a fact that physicians have made the most of in those instances in which the necessary hormones have not yet been produced synthetically, or perhaps have not been isolated.

And so it is tempting to theorize, from the studies of salmon and trout, that all aging may prove to be due to a time clock in

CYCLES OF GROWTH   229

the pituitary gland, or perhaps in the brain. If this turns out to be true, we may well learn how to slow the clock, stop it, or—who knows?—perhaps turn it back. The secret of eternal youth that cost Faust his soul sent Ponce de León adventuring at the cost of his life, and kept medieval magicians and alchemists brooding over cabalistic formulas, may yet be unraveled by the endocrinologists.

17 | BIOLOGICAL LOVE STORY

IN NATURE, life exists to reproduce life, and to this end, as we read in Genesis, "male and female created He them." Among most animal species and even in the plant kingdom, sex is an essential for reproduction, and among many of the birds and beasts, including man, love also has its biological value.

In the long span of evolution, sex is comparatively young and love is even younger. Yet we cannot say how either began; we do not know the beginning of the biological love story. The origin of sex is as darkly shrouded in mystery as the origin of life itself. No one yet knows how life emerged from the nonliving, or sex from the nonsexual.

For countless millenniums, as we now believe, life persisted on earth without benefit of either sex or love. Each individual speck of living matter floated in biochemical solitude, independent of every other. We surmise that the first living or half-living forms were probably like filterable viruses, and that they had some ability to duplicate themselves, probably by synthesizing their own chemical organization out of the medium in which they drifted.

Then, on the evolutionary ladder, cells began to reproduce by dividing themselves in half. This comes about as a mathematical economy, a balance between mass and surface that is necessary for the cell's survival. When a cell grows to twice its size, the mass that has to be nourished increases eightfold, but its surface—through which all food enters and all wastes exit—increases only fourfold. Something, obviously, has to give, and it does. The cell pinches itself in two, and each half goes on its way, a self-sufficient individual with half the original stock of protoplasm, to grow in its turn until imbalance threatens again and again the cell divides. One-celled organisms like the amoeba and some multicellular ones reproduce by this mathematical mode.

Monotonous as it is, this method has one advantage: there is no death. The first amoeba that ever lived is theoretically still alive and swimming about somewhere. The amoeba under any microscope today may be made of the same protoplasm as the original one, which presumably has been dividing contentedly through all the millenniums since its birth and is still dividing. In these immortal organisms, aging and death are not inherent. Life ends only in the absence of food or an encounter with a more powerful enemy.

Life for these forms is at its simplest. The blue-green algae, for example, apparently have virtually no differentiation in their protoplasmic pulp. All parts are capable of performing all the necessary vital processes, and when its insides become too crowded the individual simply squeezes itself together through the middle until it splits, and floats away from its twin reduced to a comfortable size.

But division of labor is apparently as advantageous in nature as in human society, for, in a family of algae cousins, the green algae, the protoplasm is already separated into specialized parts. There is a nucleus within the cell body; chromosomes have appeared, and cell division is no longer accomplished by a simple splitting down the middle, but by the more complicated method of mitosis. This is the name for the process we talked of earlier, in which the chromosomes in the cell's nucleus separate into two duplicate sets, so that when the cell divides, each of the new cells receives a complete set of hereditary characteristics.

Mitosis is the method by which cells in all the higher organisms reproduce. It is, as we have seen, the way in which the cells in our own bodies reproduce when the body is growing and also when cells need to be replaced. With mitosis, we believe, begins the long development toward sexuality.

Now we come to organisms that lead a double sex life. Some of the protozoa, the single-celled organisms, go through cycles of nonsexual division, but from time to time they also conjugate and exchange bits of specialized protoplasm with each other. The "mate" that such a protozoon chooses to conjugate with has one essential qualification: it must be other than a relative, that is, not a product of the individual's own line of cell divisions, or family. Exogamy, or conjugation with an outsider, is necessary to the eternal youth and the immortality of these microscopic animals.

So strong is this biological incest taboo that when one family of paramecia (a fresh-water protozoon species) was isolated from nonrelatives in a laboratory study, it continued to reproduce by cell division for some 180 generations, its members meanwhile steadily dwindling in size and vitality, before some of them attempted to mate with their relatives. The matings were unsuccessful and the individuals that tried it were left more wretched than they had been before. Finally, about the 215th generation, the exhausted family was reduced to formless abortions without the capacity either to live or to reproduce, and so the ordinarily immortal animalcule tribe came to its end. Even at this low level of animal life, as one biologist rhapsodically commented, "Only through the fire of love can the phoenix of the species renew its youth."

Some animal forms are equipped with both ovary and testis. Among the leeches and snails, for instance, each individual can lay eggs and also fertilize its mate's eggs with spermatozoa, a two-way mating. The higher we rise in the animal scale—and even in the vegetable world—the more clearly the sexes divide. Each individual is equipped with the specialized sexual structure that makes it unmistakably male or female. And we find the species increasingly developing secondary characteristics that serve for sexual identification and the allurement of members of the opposite sex.

The variety of these reproductive arrangements is beyond counting; their fantastic elaborateness has provided some of the most diverting pages in scientific literature. The hermaphroditic snails that we mentioned earlier, having double work to do, remain locked in sexual embrace for as long as fifteen hours. The slipper limpets copulate in series: the first limpet that attaches itself to a rock becomes a female if the second to arrive is a male, this one changes its sex when a third male joins the pair, and so on until a chain of sexual activity is in progress; the bottom limpet is always female, the top one male, regardless of the sex each had when the chain began to form.

With these biological patterns courting rituals appear that put the most gallant human lovers to shame. Preening males strut, execute stately dances, and engage in battles with competing males that are for the most part formalized and end in no damage to either contestant. The Australian bowerbird decorates a cleared patch of jungle floor with leaves, shells, orchids and other flowers, and insures its privacy with a palisade, which he paints with berry juices; only when his bower is ready does he issue forth to capture his mate. The male scorpion ogles and caresses his bride and takes her for long strolls; his unfortunate end is as the entrée for his cannibalistic mate's solitary wedding breakfast. The even deadlier female, the praying mantis, sometimes enjoys her mate simultaneously as lover and as dinner, devouring him while in the very act of love. Ladies of several spider varieties also practice the sexual cannibalism for which the black widow is most widely famed, but some spider wooers take the precaution of first tying the female down with the threads they are so skillful at weaving, and others prudently come courting with dinner already prepared, in the shape of an insect appropriately gift-wrapped in spider silk.

Some of the sexual patterns we find in nature strike us as grossly inefficient and some as positively destructive, but we assume they are serviceable to some degree or the species would not survive. As for sex itself, its advantage is clear even in the tiny paramecium. The offspring of two unrelated individuals has a mixed heredity, hence greater variety and greater adaptability in a constantly changing environment. Variety is not merely the spice of life but its preserver, a necessity for survival in a precarious world.

When and how love entered upon the scene, no one can say for certain. There is clearly an advantage when the mates remain together to rear the young. Cold-blooded species such as the reptiles can lay their eggs and depart, leaving the young to hatch and find their first food unaided. But once the warm-blooded species developed, such casual parenthood was no longer possible.

Birds must sit on their eggs and stay around to feed, guard, and teach the fledglings how to fly (young fish, we might note, need no swimming instructions). Mammals bear their young alive but with a short or long period of infant helplessness during which protection and teaching are almost as necessary for their survival as mother's milk. Among many kinds of birds and mammals the parents remain together, sharing these child-rearing tasks at least for a season. With man and some of the higher primates, reproduction remains cyclic; the menstrual cycle, as we have seen, revolves around the periodic production of a ripe ovum in the female. But sexual activity knows no season. Unlike the other animals, man and his closest biological relatives can mate at any time.

And here may, perhaps, be a second biological basis for love, in this ability of the highest organisms to mate independent of estrus, the period of being "in heat," as we say of female dogs and cats, or "in season," as farmers say of their cattle. Given a powerful biological drive which can be satisfied at any time, provided only that a member of the opposite sex is available and willing, how much simpler life becomes if the two who first came together by sexual selection—or even by accident, necessity, or convenience—manage to remain together. Among the higher primates, couples mated to each other have strong emotional attachments and are believed to be monogamous not alone in zoos but also in nature. Add to this the social advantages of monogamy, with its orderly arrangements for mating and child-rearing, and the economic advantages of this system in a primitive community, and you have society's stamp of approval, as well, on love.

Thus, out of the biological advantage that first appeared when one animalcule exchanged bits of protoplasm with another, came the ever more elaborate differentiation of male and female and the devices for bringing them together to fulfill their reproductive function. And on this foundation of sexual and reproductive interdependence there arose, by way of many adaptations, the complex psychic and emotional, also nervous and glandular, phenomenon that we know as sexual love.

LOVE AND THE ENDOCRINES

Estrus, the season of mating that humankind and the higher apes have left behind in their evolutionary climb, is in many ways a curious phenomenon, and it interests us in our study of man because there are still traces of it in our physiological ways. Except at estrus the females of the lower animal species will not receive the males. Guinea pigs go a step further and are actually prevented from mating by a membrane of skin that closes the vagina except at estrus. In cats and ferrets the ovarian follicles do not release their ova unless mating takes place, and in rabbits the ova will not even ripen.

Daylight and temperature influence the estrus cycle; some species that live in regions where there are no seasonal variations do not have the equivalent variations in sexual activity. Migrant birds, that winter in the south, flock to fly north for their breeding season at the same time each year, and some arrive at their breeding grounds on the same day and even at the same hour, after a flight of hundreds, in some cases thousands, of miles.

What moves the birds to take flight at a certain time and not a week earlier or a week later? It is not the weather, since a spell of cold weather does not delay them or a heat wave hurry them. Ornithologists have found that the gonads of birds setting out for their breeding grounds are enlarged and active, and that is to be expected as the breeding season approaches, but what stimulates the gonads?

A team of investigators decided that the one invariable factor for any given day of the year is the position of the earth in relation to the sun, in other words, the length of the day. They tested this by delaying a group of crows setting out on their fall migration southward and subjecting the crows to an artificially lengthening day. Sure enough, as though it were spring, the crows when released did not fly south but headed back instead to their accustomed breeding grounds, despite the fact that the fields were under a blanket of snow. Fortunately crows are a hardy lot that can scratch food even in winter, and they do not need to fly south at all in order to survive. That some do migrate is one of the oddities of adaptation. Incidentally, it has the advantage of distributing the bird population over a wide feeding area.

So it would seem to be the lengthening daylight to which the gonads respond. We may surmise that this adaptation of the endocrines was a lucky development related to the season of abundant food, when there would be enough to fill the yawning mouths of nestlings and the hungry litters weaned from their dams in the lairs and burrows of the mammals. Creatures that mated at such a time as to bring forth their young in a barren winter land would **have** little chance to survive; quite probably there were such maladapted ones along the evolutionary road, and quite probably they perished. The species we see are the ones whose adaptations were successful.

In the human species we see only the trace of an estrus related to the season of abundance; the poet accurately observed the direction of a young man's fancy in the spring. Perhaps man and the higher apes emerged in climates where the seasonal variations were slight, and so the estrus was not timed to the food supply. What remains of a reproductive cycle we see only in the periodic ovulation of women, and that is timed, as are the tides of the sea, rather to the moon than to the earth's seasons.

THE FERTILITY CYCLE

The human female is both able and willing to receive the male at all times; if she is not willing she usually has other than physiological reasons. So detached, in fact, is the sexual act from its natural function of reproduction that some women experience their liveliest sexual desire during or immediately following menstruation, when there is the least possibility of conception.

The "safe period" is a familiar term. It means, strictly, all that part of the menstrual month when there is not a mature ovum in the genital tract waiting to be fertilized. Once in the menstrual month a single ovum bursts from one of the ovaries and makes its way along the Fallopian tube toward the uterus, maturing as it goes.

This event, which is called ovulation, occurs almost exactly fourteen days before the onset of the next menstrual period. To put it another way, it takes fourteen days, from the time the ovum is produced, for the uterus to relinquish its prepared nest. Long before that, however, the ovum itself has lost its vitality and deteriorated; it remains vital for only about forty-eight hours. Only during these forty-eight hours is the female capable of becoming pregnant.

Sperm cells also remain vital for about the same length of time, and thus an ovum may be fertilized by a sperm cell remaining in the genital tract from intercourse during the previous forty-eight hours, or it may be fertilized by intercourse during its own period of vitality. The time when intercourse may result in pregnancy is thus only about four days out of the—roughly—twenty-eight that constitute the average menstrual cycle. All the rest of the time, *theoretically*, is "safe" in terms of contraception, or valueless for conception.

The practical difficulty in establishing this fertile period for individual women is that many women have menstrual cycles varying by a few days from one period to the next. Few are absolutely regular whether at twenty-eight days, the average figure, or more or less than twenty-eight. Even in women whose cycle is ordinarily regular, unusual conditions of stress or sometimes merely a change of environment may cause an irregularity.

Some women experience signs of ovulation—a transitory backache, or soreness of the breasts. But with most women the occasion passes unnoticed. The one fairly reliable method of determining the fertile period is by body temperature. In the first part of the menstrual cycle this is slightly below normal, about $97.8°$ F. on waking in the morning; at the time of ovulation it rises to $98.6°$ F. and remains at that level until the menstrual period. A woman who is interested in determining her fertile period, whether for conception or contraception, is advised by her physician to keep a temperature chart for several months, and from it he may be able to fix the time of ovulation with some accuracy.

REPRODUCTION: THE MALE ROLE

Fertility in the male is not cyclic, as we have noted, but constant. For the first demand that the reproductive function makes of him, that of producing sperm cells, he is always ready. Encouraged by the spermatogenic hormone of the anterior pituitary gland, the sperm-producing cells in the testes continue to manufacture their steady millions of tiny sperm cells from puberty virtually throughout life.

The second part of his task is to place the sperm cells where they will meet and fertilize the female ova. This, the active role, is characteristically assigned to the male from the very beginning of sexual differentiation. Even the modest paramecium, which has the beginnings of differentiation in its two different cells, indicates the tendency: the micronucleus, as it is called, is small, hungry, mobile, while the macronucleus is well-nourished and quiescent. Among the sexed species of animal life it is characteristically the male that seeks, pursues, captures or captivates the female. In man the reproductive cells themselves repeat the pattern: the large (almost visible) waiting ovum, and the microscopic sperm cell, one six-hundredth of an inch long, vigorously lashing its tail, swimming in the stream of seminal fluid up through the vagina and uterus and into the Fallopian tube in search of its mate.

The first step in the journey of the sperm cells from the testes, where they are produced, is to the organ whose function it is to place them within the body of the female, that is, the penis. The direct distance is very short; the testes in their sac are suspended directly behind the penis. But the tiny cells follow a long, round-about path, first through tubules coiled around each testis, then into the larger convoluted tube called the epididymis, and then upward through the spermatic duct, the *vas deferens,* into the pelvis, through which they continue along the genital tract into the urethra and so out of the penis at the proper moment. On this lengthy journey they mature, as they pass along the epididymis they become active, and the secretion in which they are carried acquires additional seminal fluid from the prostate gland and the seminal vesicles along the way.

The urethra's other function is, as we know, to serve as a passage from the bladder for the excretion of urine. Urine, being acid, would be harmful to the sperm cells, and so we find two mechanisms protecting them. In the course of precoital arousal, tiny glands adjacent to the duct pour an alkaline fluid into it, clearing and neutralizing any acid there. And with the reflex muscular contractions of ejaculation, the prostate gland shuts off the upper part of the urethra as the genital tract empties its seminal fluid into the lower part of the duct.

Endocrine stimuli have instigated the preparation for the act. But the act itself comes about through such a variety of possible erotic fillips that no list could cover them all; every male would have to list his own. Dr. Kinsey recorded no fewer than thirty-three psychological stimuli to which American males respond, from female nudity in the flesh to a random thought of sexual pleasure accidentally brought to mind. All the senses contribute their bit: sight, sound, smell, touch, and taste, plus any associations of ideas that are part of an individual's own experience. Every culture provides a few characteristic stimuli of its own, and

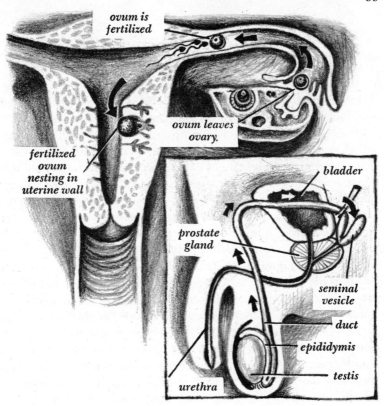

ovum is fertilized

ovum leaves ovary.

fertilized ovum nesting in uterine wall

bladder

prostate gland

seminal vesicle

duct

epididymis

testis

urethra

every culture also provides its controls. Besides the stimulus there must also be a suitable time, place and, above all, the appropriate female partner.

If all these requirements are met, then by reflex action of nerve centers in the lower part of the spine the blood vessels of the penis become engorged, producing an erection, and this is followed in due course by reflexive contractions of the genital tract and the prostate gland, forcing the seminal fluid through the urethra under pressure and ejaculating it into the vagina of the chosen female. Thus the male fulfills the second part of his reproductive function, which is to place the sperm cells in the body of the female where one of them may fertilize the waiting ovum.

THE CYCLE OF PREGNANCY

Considering how carefully the millions of male sperm cells are conducted along closed, protected passageways from their origin in the testes to their ultimate destination, it is astonishing to discover the haphazard way in which the ovum begins its journey. Pregnancy is the only state of value in nature, since it reproduces the species, and the most elaborate devices have evolved to prepare for it and protect it. Yet at the very start the arrangements for bringing the ripe ovum to its proper place for fertilization appear at least risky, if not downright careless.

The one precious female reproductive cell, produced only once in the menstrual month, is not guided along a closed set of ducts from ovary to uterus, as we might expect. It is tossed out of the ovary into open space in the abdominal cavity, to be caught in midair, so to speak, by the open end of the Fallopian tube. The tube has a trumpet-shaped mouth, to be sure, and it is equipped, moreover, with a tentaclelike fringe to trap the errant ovum. And considering the facts of human reproduction, the arrangement is probably more dependable than it seems. Apparently the ovum is caught reasonably often, and from then on it is safely carried, maturing as it goes, toward the uterus.

If, when it is on its way, a vital sperm cell is present, or if one makes its way there during the ovum's journey, then conception may take place. Only one sperm cell is required to fertilize the ovum, but ordinarily many cluster around it. Of the millions that are deposited in the vagina in the act of intercourse, the most active ones swim rapidly into the uterus and on into the Fallopian tubes. Since they are so small, they are swimming rapidly when they cover one-eighth of an inch a minute, but they have some help from the momentum with which they are ejaculated, possibly from uterine contractions, and possibly also through some attracting power that the ovum appears to exert.

We have already noted that as soon as one sperm cell succeeds in penetrating the ovum with its head or nucleus, its tail disappears, its nucleus merges with the nucleus of the ovum, and a thickened coat forms around the ovum that prevents any further sperm cells from entering. The fertilized ovum begins immediately to grow. Its cells divide while it is still proceeding toward the uterus, and it is already multicelled, rather like a mulberry, by the time it arrives in its prepared nest and imbeds itself in the uterine wall.

Now the endocrine system goes into high gear; a pregnancy is precisely the opportunity for its fullest functioning. In 280 days, sometimes less and sometimes a bit more, the barely visible egg and the far smaller sperm will grow into an infant capable of independent life outside the womb. Wonderful as this is, it is in a way more remarkable that the mother's body can harbor such explosive growth without itself being affected by the growth hormones pouring from her own pituitary under this stimulation. She gains weight, but she does not grow larger in bone and body structure, and the changes in her weight and shape are only temporary. When the pregnancy is ended, she returns to virtually her previous size.

The outpouring of hormones, from the mother's endocrine system and from the placenta that quickly begins to build around the embryo, accelerates so rapidly that a diagnosis of pregnancy can be made within a few days of the first missed menstrual period. All the pregnancy tests depend upon this hormonal increase, and mainly upon the hormones from the placenta.

The placenta is an extraordinary phenomenon. It is a special structure, created only in pregnancy, and it is the creation, one might say, of the endocrine glands. Part of it develops from the outer covering of the ovum, and part from the inner wall of the uterus. In its tissues, built from both the mother's body and the new life growing within her, the blood of the fetus and the blood of the mother circulate past each other with only the thinnest of capillary walls between them. They never mix, but through the delicate walls, nutrients needed by the growing fetus pass into the fetal blood, and its metabolic wastes pass into the mother's blood to be carried away. The placenta's capillary walls are so constructed that they permit only the passage of nutrients and bar almost all noxious substances from entering the fetal blood. This remarkable structure grows under the stimulation of the hormone progestin, which begins to be secreted in the ovary the moment the ripened ovum has gone forth on its journey, and continues to be secreted at an accelerated rate the moment the ovum has been fertilized.

Besides functioning as an exchange point for the baby's food and wastes and, incidentally, as the baby's anchor within the womb, the busy placenta also performs as a potent endocrine gland. It secretes estradiol like that of the ovaries, and a second hormone like that of the anterior lobe of the pituitary which stimulates the ovaries to produce progestin. The presence of this anterior-pituitary-like hormone (APL) in the urine of a pregnant woman is the basis of the standard pregnancy test, the Aschheim-Zondek test. If the urine sample, injected into a sexually immature mouse, contains this hormone the mouse develops the hormonal responses of estrus within four days.

Throughout a pregnancy the placenta has the liveliest assistance not only from the ovaries but from the entire endocrine system in the mother's body. Her thyroid gland speeds up her metabolism to take care of the rapidly growing, hungry cells of the fetus. Her parathyroid glands act to liberate calcium and phosphorus from storage in her skeletal system to supply the baby's growing bones. Her adrenal cortex liberates its protective hormones against stress for, natural though it is, pregnancy is a stress situation in the physical and nutritional demands it makes on the mother.

One hormone in particular, from the pituitary's anterior lobe, is an important actor; this one is called prolactin. In the course of the pregnancy it seems to help in maintaining the supply of progestin from the ovaries. But its principal function, as its name indicates (from the Latin: *pro* plus *lact,* the word element for milk), is to stimulate the production of milk in the mother's breasts.

This phenomenon is remarkably timed to coincide with the end of the pregnancy. The liberation of prolactin is apparently one of those physiological events which—as we now find—are at the basis of what we have long considered instinctual behavior, in this case the behavior prompted by the maternal instinct. Virgin laboratory rats injected with prolactin begin to build nests as though they were about to give birth to a litter.

This is not to say that mother love is due to nothing more than hormonal chemistry. The highly patterned instinctual behavior of the lower animals is not characteristic of the human species. As we shall see when we come to discuss the central nervous system, the human brain in the course of evolution has shed a great many fixed, inborn responses in favor of freer choices and associations.

But we cannot say categorically that prolactin does not play some part in the complicated emotions of a mother toward her new baby.

Other hormones are also involved in the preparation for nourishing the newborn: estradiol, progestin, a hormone of the adrenal cortex, and finally a new hormone from a new source, the posterior lobe of the pituitary. This is oxytocin, which we mentioned in an earlier chapter as the milk "let-down" hormone. This newcomer comes into action when the pregnancy reaches its end. A contractor of smooth muscle, it stimulates the uterus to contract and propel the baby through the birth canal.

And so we come again to the baffling question of timing. What signal rings for the end of a pregnancy? And, we may ask, why does the human infant live 280 days, or thereabout, in the womb, instead of 640 days like the elephant's child, or eleven like the opossum's?

One of the theories about the timing of pregnancy's end is that the infant has reached the maximum size the uterus can accommodate. Another is that the placenta, which is, after all, an emergency structure, is worn out and no longer adequate to supply the baby's needs. A third explanation is that the uterine oxygen supply is no longer sufficient for the fully developed infant. A signal apparently reaches the pituitary, by way of some still mysterious hormonal messenger, that the work is done. And so labor begins, and the baby is launched on the road to independent life.

THE LACTATION CYCLE

When both the baby and the placenta, or afterbirth, have been delivered and the uterus is empty, the hormone oxytocin continues to act, stimulating it to contract to its normal resting size. And now another mechanism becomes involved, this one from the nervous system. If the baby is placed at the mother's breast and begins to suck, the let-down action of oxytocin—or, in physiologists' terms, the galactagogue principle—becomes active in response. The milk flows, and with the continued stimulation the pituitary's posterior lobe continues to secrete oxytocin. This is the basis of the traditional, and apparently correct, belief that nursing accelerates the return of the uterus to normal size.

If suckling continues and no pregnancy intervenes, mother's milk may continue in supply for as long as four years. Indeed, according to some anthropologists, in certain primitive tribes, when an infant is adopted, its foster mother is able to produce milk from her breasts by suckling even if she is childless—and even if she is past menopause. But there is no evidence, in spite of a very widespread folk belief, that continued nursing can prevent a new pregnancy. Nor does mother's milk continue to be adequate nourishment for a child beyond nine months or so. Some of the saddest cases of deficiency disease occur among primitive or poverty-stricken populations where children are nursed too long.

We have been talking about lactation as a physical mechanism. As if that were not complex enough by itself, it is further complicated by psychic factors, and these are not only individual and personal but social, economic, esthetic, and even philosophical. Fewer and fewer mothers nurse their children today. This is so not only in the United States but in the Western world generally; for other lands, in other stages of historical development, we have no statistics.

Statistics alone do not tell us whether women cannot nurse their babies these days or whether they will not. All the statistics show is that more and more of them do not. Physicians are in danger of becoming sociologists when they contemplate this situation. Is our way of life so geared that mothers are too tense to produce milk? For the let-down principle, as even dairymen know, requires some relaxation and serenity to function; a leading dairy company used to advertise that its milk came from "contented cows."

Fashion does not frown on the well-developed bosom today as it did in the flapper twenties and as it did in the first Queen Elizabeth's time, when court ladies aped a Spanish queen who flattened her bosom with an iron corselet rather like armor (some historians ungallantly attribute the fashion to Elizabeth's own lack of impressive womanly development). On the contrary, we have become a nation of mammary worshipers. The object of worship is not, however, the functioning breast of motherhood but the oversize bulges of the Hollywood variety measured by caliper rather than by productivity. How did this particular secondary sex characteristic become primary for sex and secondary or even nonexistent for motherhood?

Looking backward a few thousand years, we find that our society is neither very original nor very blameworthy. The custom of nursing their babies has declined among mothers in every period of prosperity and cultural sophistication. Wet nurses—hired nursing mothers—were an institution in ancient Egypt, Greece, and Rome, as in eighteenth- and nineteenth-century Europe. Being able to hire someone else to suckle one's children has long been a sign of wealth and upper-class status.

Among primitive peoples the illness or death of a mother or her inability to nurse was virtually a death sentence for the infant; there simply were no adequate or safe substitutes for mother's milk. Among the poor of all cultures, mothers nursed because it was the safest and least expensive way to feed their babies. Upper-class women were considered eccentric if they insisted on breast-feeding their own children. A queen of France has come down in history for no other reason than that she was furious with one of her ladies in waiting who dared to offer the infant prince her breast, and the queen even made the baby vomit up the offending milk. History does not say whether the queen was angry because her maternal instinct was so intense or because she felt that only the royal breast was suitable for a prince of the blood. In those days, not only the nutritive value and cleanliness of breast milk were considered important, but also the character and morality of the nurse. Flighty manners, loose morals, fondness for more than an occasional mug of ale or porter were all severe disqualifications in a wet nurse, on the firm conviction that the innocent infant would surely imbibe the woman's vices with her milk.

In the twentieth century the technique of sterilization and the chemistry of nutrition made formula feeding safe, and a whole industry has grown up to supply scientific substitutes for mother's milk. Yet many physicians today are convinced that there are valuable physical benefits to both mother and baby in breast-feeding. As for the emotional benefits to both, the family counselors and child development specialists have long been urging them. The child-care pamphlets from the Department of Health, Education and Welfare, classics in the field, urge breast-feeding, when it is possible, as the cheapest, safest, and most convenient way to feed a baby. And the *Journal of the American Medical Association* has editorially chided physicians and hospital staffs for not encouraging, urging, and teaching mothers to nurse, particularly for not helping them to overcome the discouragement of unsuccessful first attempts.

From all these combined signs it is possible to hope that the decline of breast-feeding may be arrested, perhaps even reversed. Status symbols change rapidly nowadays. Women are again counting their children competitively, and a mother of three or four feels superior to a mother of one or two. They are interested in childbirth without anesthesia and in rooming-in arrangements by which they care for their babies even before they take them home from the hospital. Some even insist on breast-feeding, whether or not the hospitals encourage it or the nurses have time or patience to help them with it.

Probably these bold mothers are a small minority and generally of an independent turn of mind. Nevertheless they may be the forerunners of a trend back to natural feeding, along with natural childbirth and other nostalgic returns to nature, such as trees in city streets and gardens flowering in the windows of city banking institutions and the entrances of office buildings.

PART V

THE GREAT

INTEGRATOR

18

THE COMMUNICATING NET

MOST MOVING TO US, of the properties of life, is its responsiveness, its ability—even more, its necessity—to take note of the surrounding world. We rejoice in the power of living things to grow, we are awed by their ability to perpetuate their kind, and we marvel at their life-sustaining chemistry. But it is the capacity to respond that we most readily recognize as the quality of being alive.

Always and everywhere men have tried to draw a living response from the world around them. They have poked, pricked, and prodded every form of matter, and when they could get no response they invented one, hearing answers from streams and mountains, forests and clouds. In folk legend and fairy tale the tree moans under the woodman's ax, the rock cries out when it is struck. Today only little children invest every object with life. But that all life is capable of response is no childish fantasy but biological fact.

Every living organism makes responses to stimuli; its *irritability,* as the biologists call this responsiveness, is one of the basic properties of life. Even the amoeba moves away, however slowly, from unfavorable stimuli—too hot, too cold. A plant, though rooted, nevertheless does a good deal of moving: its leaves turn toward the sun, its stem bends and leans toward the light. If it is growing in a crowded bed, it grows tall and spindly, reaching toward the light. If it is growing in a pot and the pot is placed on its side, the plant will turn and grow upward at a right angle —this is its response to the pull of gravity or the need for light, or both. Underground its roots reach and probe toward moisture, and if it is watered too lightly the rootlets will turn upward to catch whatever moisture they can in the top layers of the soil. A few plants have swifter, almost animal-like responses, for example, the Venus's-flytrap, whose leaves close at a touch.

Not only every organism but every cell of an organism has this property of responsiveness. Matter without life only stands and waits for its environment to act upon it; it does nothing to promote its own continuance. But living matter must feed and grow and reproduce. In some measure, however imperceptible, it must respond to stimuli that relate to these functions, or it dies. As the cells become more highly organized and specialized with each step up the evolutionary ladder, both the stimuli to which the organism responds and the nature of its responses are increasingly complex. And so it is not surprising that, in the course of specializing, some cells become specialized to receive stimuli and integrate responses, and these in turn become organized in a system: the nervous system.

A plant has no nervous system. While some of its activities are as complex as those in animals—for example, photosynthesis— it does not have cells specialized to transmit stimuli directly from one part of the organism to another. In the animal world the specialized nerve cells appear very near the bottom rung of the developmental ladder. The fresh-water species of polyps, the hydras, are simple organisms composed of layers of cells, yet there is already a network of nerve cells connecting parts of the organism. In flatworms the nerve cells have clustered together into groups or masses, and in more complex creatures—for example, in earthworms—the nerve clusters, or ganglia, are organized into chains and are beginning to concentrate at the front or head of the organism.

The nerve cells themselves begin to specialize. Although they still conduct impulses in much the same way, the sensory nerves have the single task of receiving information and conveying it to the center, while the motor nerves only carry instructions out from the center. Thus at each stage, animal organisms are able to receive more varied stimuli, and to make more elaborate responses by means of an increasingly organized central system for receiving the information and sending out impulses to bring about appropriate action, a system interrelated and interconnected within itself as well as with every part of the body. In man and the higher animals it is that mechanism of conscious and unconscious responses, consisting of the brain and spinal cord, which we call the central nervous system. Marvelous and still largely mysterious, it is possibly the most complex structure in all the vast universe.

THE BRANCHING CELL

A diagram of the nervous system looks like a plant with a slender flexible stalk, the spinal cord, some three feet long in an average man, bearing at its top a rounded, domelike flower, the brain. The plant extends its branches not upward but downward, spreading to the sides and front and back, dividing into ever finer twigs and tendrils, reaching to the remotest parts of the body.

The unit of the system is that highly specialized cell, the nerve cell or neuron. Its body may be roundish, oval, or pyramid-shaped; the largest of the cells are about one two-thousandth of an inch across. What distinguishes the nerve cell from other cells is principally its extensions. The dendrite, a crown of branching fibers like the crown of a tree, spreads to receive stimuli that set off the cell's own impulse. A trunklike extension, the axon, carries the impulse along to the next nerve cell or group of them, or to the organ to be stimulated. The fibers of the connecting nerve cells do not meet or even touch each other at their points of connection, but communicate their impulses chemically across gaps, or synapses.

The tiny cell body is the heart of the nerve cell, yet in proportion to its spreading fibers it is the least conspicuous part of this remarkable structure. The fibers of some cells are only a fraction of an inch in length, but others—those of the sciatic nerve, for example—extend for two or three feet! They reach into the muscles and organs throughout the body, to the ends of fingers and toes. There are nerve ends at the root of every tooth and hair; they cluster by the thousands in areas no larger than a pinhead in the skin. There are so many of them that if all the nerve fibers in the body were stretched end to end they would go several times around the earth at the equator.

As these fibers, lines of a vast communicating network, draw to-

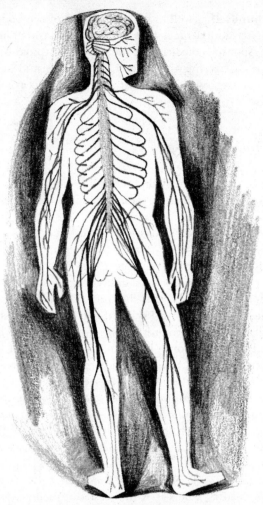

gether from the extremities toward the center of the body, they
gather into cables running into the spinal cord. A considerable
part of the spinal cord is a two-way thoroughfare of nerve fibers,
carrying information upward toward the brain and instructions
downward from the brain. All along the cord's length are clover-
leaf junctions like those on a superhighway, where nerve fibers
go in and out of the main cables and where impulses of some
kinds are sorted and integrated as well as relayed to the higher
centers.

Information comes into these centers from everywhere in the

body, and instructions go out equally widely. The messages, both incoming and outgoing, are almost unbelievably complicated even for what seem to be the simplest acts. Suppose you are eating. You have speared a morsel of food with your fork. Messages from your eyes and the muscles in your hand tell you that it is ready to be lifted to your mouth. How does your brain instruct your arm to flex and lift the fork precisely to where you want it to go?

In each of the separate muscle fibers that together constitute the biceps muscle in your upper arm, there are endings of motor fibers. One motor nerve with its branching fibers may control thousands of muscle fibers. Similar motor nerve endings are in the opposite muscle at the back of the upper arm, the triceps. When you want to flex your arm, the instruction to the biceps is to contract, but an opposite inhibitory message goes to the triceps—yet only just inhibiting enough, or the powerful biceps, unrestrained by its antagonist, would snap your forearm up like a steel spring.

All through the body there are pairs and groups of muscles like these, constantly in a state of *tonus* or partial contraction, in readiness for messages from the nervous system. Merely to hold a man erect, more than two hundred pairs of muscles are constantly responding to instructions to give a little and take a little in this wonderfully sensitive elastic system, in response to messages from the sensory nerves indicating the position of the body and its limbs.

The individual nerve cell works on an all-or-nothing principle: it is either on or off, like an electric light or a vacuum tube; there is no in-between. We tend to speak of the nerves as though they were wires carrying electric current, and it is true that a nerve in action gives off electrical waves. It is also true that a bundle of nerve fibers is rather like a bundle of electric wires, each of them sheathed within its own insulation, although a nerve fiber is infinitely finer than any electric wire.

But a nerve does not transmit its impulses as a wire transmits current. A nerve's action is basically chemical. Physiologists compare a nerve's way of transmitting an impulse to that of a spark running along a firecracker fuse: once lighted, the fuse burns along its whole length, unless there is an obstruction. A nerve, activated to discharge, discharges along its whole length in much the same way. But, while a fuse is used up after one discharge, leaving nothing but ash, a nerve needs only a fraction of a second to recover and then it is ready to discharge again. A nerve can discharge several hundred times a second. The thinnest nerve fibers, about one twenty-five-thousandth of an inch in diameter, transmit an impulse comparatively slowly, at the rate of about one foot per second, but these operate only over short distances. The thicker high-speed fibers that serve the most distant parts of the body can send their impulses at a speed of 450 feet per second— more than 300 miles an hour.

In the body, where no distance is greater than the length of arm or leg, this means that communication even to widely separated limbs and organs is virtually instantaneous. And in the interval, perhaps a thousandth of a second, between one discharge and the next, there is time for an inhibiting message to arrive and prevent the nerve from transmitting.

We do not know how the inhibiting mechanism works. Nor do we know just where nerve fatigue is located. In one experiment, the subject lifted a weight with a single finger a number of times, and eventually he could not lift, no matter how strongly he willed his finger to do it. Yet with electrical stimulation directly to the muscle, the finger lifted as briskly as it had done when it was fresh. Muscle fatigue sets in eventually, with an accumulation of lactic acid, the waste product of muscular effort. But in this experiment nerve fatigue clearly came before the muscle was too tired to continue. The present belief is that nerve fatigue may come at the synapse, the gap across which the activating impulse must be transmitted from the axon of one nerve to the dendrite of the next. Or it may be in the central nervous system, the brain or spinal cord. In that most curious mystery of all, the mystery of sleep, which we shall come to in another chapter, other experiments have shown that it is the central nervous system that needs sleep. The body only needs rest.

THE MANY LEVELS

We can scarcely imagine the number and variety of messages that travel up and down the nervous pathways. Sensory impulses come from the special sense organs and from receptor nerves virtually everywhere in the body. They enter the lower centers and go on to the brain's own separate sensory areas to be sorted out, analyzed, acted upon, associated with other information, and stored as memory. Activating impulses go out to move or inhibit muscles, dilate or contract blood vessels, start and stop glands secreting, hasten or slow the work of organs, regulate the heartbeat, blood pressure, breathing rate, the balance of water and sugar and other chemical constituents vital to the body's functioning.

Above all this, there are the surging needs and drives of the emotional brain and the thinking, planning, deciding of the cortical brain—all coded, cross-referenced, molded and refined, the inborn and the learned, so intertwined that there is almost no thought, feeling, or act that does not somehow draw upon all parts of the system.

All of it is timed, correlated, co-ordinated so that most of the time we can think, feel, act, and do all these on different levels, perhaps even at cross-purposes, all simultaneously. Caesar was said to be able to do seven different things at one time. Any average one of us is constantly doing a great many more than seven things at a time, mostly without being aware that we do.

A man driving to work in the morning is carrying out, virtually automatically, a vast number of complicated voluntary movements directed by his motor nerves, all the learned reflexes of driving. He guides the wheel with his hands, presses his foot on the accelerator, shifts it to the brake, changes gear when necessary; his eyes move constantly, looking ahead, to the sides, and into his rear-view mirror. At the same time he is taking in and responding to messages from his sensory nerves, also nearly automatically: a turn in the route, a wet or icy road, traffic signs, the behavior of other drivers, pedestrians crossing, children or pets appearing within his range of vision that may run into his path. Other messages transmitted by his sensory nerves he may ignore as irrelevant—the temperature, a promise of rain or snow in the air, passing sounds and odors—but he is half listening to the news on his car radio, brought him by his acoustic nerve.

He may be smoking his after-breakfast cigarette or pipe and savoring the tobacco more or less consciously by way of his taste and olfactory nerves. Or perhaps he is chewing gum, with his mouth pleasantly lubricated through the stimulation of secretory nerve impulses coming to his salivary glands. Meanwhile his digestive system is taking care of his breakfast, with the help of nerves that signal the outpouring of gastric and intestinal secretions and stimulate peristaltic contractions and relaxations of the stomach and intestines.

While he is doing all this, he is experiencing an underlying mood or personal climate of comfort or discomfort, an amalgam of body sensations external and internal and of the state of his mind, whether cheerful or gloomy, confident or anxious, depending upon his temperament, the sum of his experiences and prospects at the moment, and whether or not he has had a good night's sleep. And with the very top of his mind, his most conscious, active cortical cells, he may be pondering a problem in the day's work to which he is going.

For this capacity to do so many things at the same time—carry on body functions, physical activities, sensory perceptions, states of feeling, intellectual processes all at once and without serious confusion—we must thank the organization of the nervous system. It is no johnny-come-lately, this fabulous structure. It is a slow accretion, over evolutionary eons, of functions and mechanisms to perform the functions. Part of it is as ancient as the ancestor of the jellyfish; part is younger than the tree-dwelling ape that fathered the chimpanzee and man. It is a combined aquarium and zoo, dating back almost to the beginning of living things, preserving in layers like geological strata—but not fossilized, indeed very much alive—the traces of the many nervous systems that have gone before.

It is interwoven, the old with the new, in such intricate ways that everything that happens to one part sends its echoes through all the other parts. It is also provided with controls and inhibiting mechanisms so that ordinarily these reverberations are not too loud, not too disturbing to permit the various parts to perform their own necessary functions.

SYSTEMS WITHIN THE SYSTEM

Inevitably this complex system, controlling so many varied activities, developed in the form of several specialized systems. The dinosaurs, indeed, were so specialized that they even had two brains, the second one at the lower end of the spine. Like the steersman at the rear end of the hook-and-ladder fire truck, this lower center guided the great rear end of the creature, in particular its monumental legs. The forward brain might be the size of a hen's egg; the rearward brain was as much as ten times larger. The human nervous system has a series of nerve centers in the spine, too, but they are comparatively modest, no more than local substations.

Of our several nervous systems, the one of which we are ordinarily aware is the voluntary motor system by which we raise an arm or leg, sit down, stand up. We perform these acts consciously and at will—for the most part; there is a considerable group of muscular acts, some inborn and some learned, that we perform involuntarily or else so automatically that we are unaware of them. Then there is the network of sensory nerves; this supplies us with information, also conscious for the most part, but we are extremely selective about what part we will give our attention to, or we would be drowned in the flood of stimuli that pours in continuously through our sensory nerve endings.

And then there is the autonomic nervous system. Its name is misleading because it does not work autonomously, that is, independently of the rest of the nervous system, but only without conscious control (again, for the most part—there are exceptions even to this, as we shall see). While the voluntary motor system manages the striped or skeletal muscles, the autonomic system governs the smooth muscles, like those of the digestive system, the bronchial system, the skin. It slows or accelerates the heart, dilates or constricts the smaller blood vessels, stimulates or inhibits the sweat glands and digestive glands, and works intimately with certain endocrine glands.

The autonomic system is rather like the underground network that keeps a metropolis functioning, while above ground the citizens go about their business and scarcely give the utilities a thought. If we had to remember, for example, to turn on the gastric juices and throw the many switches of the digestive system, one after another, each time we ate a meal, we would be in a sorry state of indigestion most of the time—or we would have little time to think of anything else. As it is, we manage to disrupt the smooth working of the autonomic system now and then by interference from our emotional and thinking brains, but that is part of the price of being human and not lower organisms, nor yet machines.

MOBILIZATION AND MAINTENANCE

The autonomic system is itself further specialized into two subsidiary systems, the sympathetic and the parasympathetic; they
are opposed and at the same time complementary to each other.
We might call the sympathetic system the mobilizing branch and
the parasympathetic the maintenance division.

If you are called upon to run a race or make a speech, dodge a
car or put out a fire, if you are angry or frightened or exhilarated
with joy, it is your sympathetic system that makes your heart beat
faster, your skin prickle, and sweat bead your brow and dampen
your palms and armpits. The sympathetic system also provides the
wherewithal for you to meet the emergency. It sets the adrenal
glands to pouring adrenaline, a powerful stimulant, into your
blood and it hurries glucose out of storage in the liver to supply
your muscles with energy. The sympathetic system goes into high
gear with every situation of challenge or stress, or even with the
threat of such a situation.

The parasympathetic system is not idle meanwhile. It stands
by to keep matters from getting out of hand and to calm things
down when the excitement is over. It will not let the heart beat
too fast or the blood vessels, stomach, and intestines contract too
much. Just as the sympathetic system leads in the active functions, the parasympathetic system takes precedence in the conserving functions: it stimulates secretion of the gastric juices,
dilates the blood vessels of the digestive organs, stimulates the
movement of their muscle walls.

At times one arm of the autonomic system dominates, at times
the other, but every function of the unconsciously operating organs is the result of both divisions working together, checking and
balancing each other. Between them they keep the body in repair and keep its internal environment in a state of balance. We
mentioned in connection with the endocrine system the *milieu
intérieur,* as the French physiologist Claude Bernard called it,
the gentle sea of blood and lymph bathing the cells and creating an internal environment in which they could function. This
internal environment is somehow kept in balance. As the Ameri-

can physiologist Dr. Walter B. Cannon pointed out, that it does this in spite of extensive changes in the outer environment is one of the wonders of the body's functioning. In the autonomic system with its two arms, one pushing and stimulating, the other quieting and restraining, we see how the nervous system makes its contribution to the state of balance—the homeostasis—that Cannon told us was so important for the organism's steady, efficient operation.

TEMPERATURE CONTROL

The sympathetic system, with its aggressive take-charge functions in the face of challenge, seems somehow more youthful than its partner, and in terms of evolution it did actually begin to meet its major challenges rather late. Some ancestor organism, perhaps, first gained an advantage by going forth and aggressively hunting its food rather than waiting for food to float by. And much, much later came the major adaptation of maintaining a constant body temperature against the changes in the external environment.

In the warm-blooded animals the entire organism is geared to function at the given temperature for the species, in man the familiar 98.6° Fahrenheit. Curiously, this body temperature, so vital in the internal environment, is also a weapon for survival against the external environment. The dinosaurs with their two brains were not too stupid to survive the Ice Age, as is sometimes said; they were too cold! The insignificant little warm-blooded mammal, about as big as a mouse, that hid under the great fern-like trees and bushes of the carboniferous jungle while the giant lizards thundered by, had no pated armor like Stegosaurus or twelve-inch fangs like Tyrannosaurus, no cruel triple horns like Triceratops or a weight of seventy-five tons like Brontosaurus. But it had an answer to the creeping glacier that blighted the lush forests with its icy breath and reduced the cold-blooded dragons, after eighty million years of proud empire, to sluggish helplessness. The little mammal had a system for keeping warm.

We still have it, a free gift from that humble but talented ancestor. And it is the sympathetic branch of the autonomic system, in collaboration with the adrenal glands, that mainly keeps us warm. The sympathoadrenal system constricts the blood vessels in the skin so that the blood is not exposed to too much cooling, contracts the skin's smooth muscle tissue and gives us "goose flesh" or makes us shiver. To your dog, shivering while he waits for you to come out for a run in the cold, the muscular action helps to keep him warm, although to you it acts rather as a warning to go in for another sweater. You lack not only his fur but also his thickness of tissue in the skin.

The sympathoadrenal system at the same time turns loose an extra supply of cell fuel, glucose, into the blood, thus speeding up the production of heat in the body much as we speed up the motor of an automobile by feeding it gasoline at an increased rate. When we are too warm, the mechanism goes into reverse and dissipates heat instead of conserving it: it dilates the billion tiny capillaries in the skin, allowing them to carry more blood to the body's surface and allowing more of the body's water to escape and evaporate there; it activates the sweat glands for still more rapid evaporation.

LINKS TO CONSCIOUSNESS

The adjustments and counteradjustments of the two autonomic arms go on all the time, waking and sleeping. Ordinarily they are too minute to be perceived. We become aware of their effects only when they are large-scale, when the heart thumps and the belly tightens in fear, or tears well up in grief. So impressed, indeed, were some of the early investigators by these bodily expressions of emotion that two of them—William James, the Harvard philosopher and psychologist, and C. G. Lange, a Danish physiologist—separately arrived at a theory that historically bears both their names, the James-Lange theory. They held that the bodily response comes first, and that we then experience the emotion in response to the physical changes within; in other words, that we grieve because we weep, rejoice because we laugh.

The debate went on through the turn of the century and for decades after. It fitted in with Darwin's interpretation of the slow evolution of structures and patterns useful for survival: emotion and conscious experience might well be secondary to the immediate automatic physical response.

The theory has never actually been proved or disproved. We

cannot ask the mother hen whether she feels love for her eggs before or after her ventral blood vessels dilate to provide a heating
system for their incubation. We can hardly ask her whether she
feels love at all. Even in human beings, there seems to be no
practical way to time the subjective awareness of an emotion in
order to discover whether it comes before, or after, or simultaneously with its physical expression.

But in its astringent, unsentimental way the theory may well
contribute to our awe and wonder at how we are made, at the
amazing elaboration of our unconscious nervous mechanisms, at
all the mysterious activities that go on without our control or
knowledge. And perhaps even more, at the singularly human
emotions, so powerful and yet capable of such subtlety and nu-
ance, that may after all have grown out of the unconscious operation of this life-sustaining, challenge-meeting autonomic nervous system.

We are probably on the brink of finding an explanation for the
even more puzzling phenomenon that occurs when, under quite
special conditions, the unconscious, involuntary responses of this
underground system seem to come under conscious control. When
the Hindu mystic, after a lifetime of intense self-discipline, walks
on burning coals or lies on a bed of nails without flinching, it is
quite possible to believe that he has learned to suppress his bodily
sensations, such as pain. But under hypnosis any average subject may allow a needle to pierce his hand and not only not feel
pain—he does not even bleed. The hypnotized subject is of course
not conscious, but in some way the suggestion has been conveyed
from the cortical centers of the brain to the autonomic system,
and there is the bloodless pinprick to prove it.

The medical uses of hypnotism have only begun to be exploited, but meanwhile a recent discovery in brain physiology
may lead to an understanding of this baffling phenomenon. There
appears to be a complete representation of the autonomic nervous system in the cortex, so that even the mechanisms that were
believed to be forever insulated from consciousness or voluntary
control are evidently integrated with the highest centers. When
we come to consider these highest centers we shall find further
evidences of this awesome interweaving of conscious and unconscious, voluntary and involuntary—of *psyche,* the mind, and *soma,*
the body.

MUSCULAR AUTOMATION

Even in the voluntary department of the nervous system, that branch that controls the skeletal muscles, there is an astonishing amount of activity that we can control only by a powerful effort of will, and some that we are no more aware of than we are of the autonomic system's functioning. These muscular responses are grouped under the name of reflexes. We are most familiar with two of them, the knee jerk that the doctor tests with his little hammer, and the hot-stove reflex which pulls the hand away from the hot surface even before we feel the sensation of burnt fingers.

The knee jerk is the simplest of our muscular reflexes. Essentially it involves only two neurons, the receptor nerve that receives the stimulus and transmits it to the spinal cord, and the motor nerve that carries back the impulse to contract the quadriceps muscle on the front of the thigh and jerk the leg up. It is all very rapid, though not instantaneous, but then the stimulus and response do not have far to travel and only one synapse between nerve fibers to leap over.

The knee jerk is one of the stretch reflexes; all the skeletal muscles respond in the same way. We mentioned earlier the unconscious interaction of pairs and teams of muscles that it takes merely to keep us standing up. As we bend, sit, rise, take a step, reach or lean, to maintain balance in the ordinary changes of posture—or even to stand still—the same reflex goes on in these many muscles that we see in simplest form in the knee jerk. Every time a muscle is stretched, it reflexly contracts. So, if you reach or lean, or if you are being jiggled in a vehicle, muscles that are stretched by the motion will tense and tighten to hold you and keep you from falling.

Even when we are standing or sitting still we are never perfectly still. We are top-heavy as to the distribution of weight, and the body skeleton is not a rigid structure but a springy, flexible system of joints and levers. Between the pull of gravity outside us and the pulsing of blood and muscular activity of organs within us, we are constantly swaying a little even when we are not aware of the least motion. Against this sway, the stretch reflexes are always being called upon to pull one or another muscle or group of muscles taut. We are aware of the position of the body in space and of each part of the body in relation to the rest, but we are not aware of all this reflex muscular action—fortunately, or we would have no mind to give to anything else.

The hot-stove reflex is nowhere near as simple, even though we go through the whole performance automatically before we are aware of the sensation of pain. Just to pull the hand away, an impulse must go from the sensory nerve endings in the skin to a center in the spinal cord, and thence an impulse must pass to a motor center and out along the motor nerves to shoulder, arm, and hand muscles. Trunk and leg muscles also respond in order to support the body in its sudden change of position. And we usually turn the head and eyes to the spot that caused the reflex; more often than not, we also utter an exclamation of pain, annoyance, or at least surprise.

All of this, involving so many responses, is still automatic, involuntary; we become conscious of it as it is happening. But we can control this reflex consciously—and indeed we do, every time the doctor or his nurse jabs us with a needle or the dentist touches a tender spot with his drill. These are the *nociceptive* reflexes—the responses to injury—and they clearly have a protective value to the organism. They would appear to belong to the earliest, simplest responses of the living cell. Yet in our highly complicated nervous system even a pinprick can excite this reflex, and the response involves the whole elaborate motor mechanism of hand, arm, shoulder, trunk, neck, eyes, tongue, larynx, and breathing. Every little nerve end, every tendril of the fibers of every receptor nerve, is in almost instant communication with motor nerves throughout the body, by virtue of the interlocked, interacting pathways of the nervous system.

This is so in the innate reflexes which, so far as we know, are not based on experience or learning but are born in the individual. It is all the more evident in the whole series of conditioned responses that are part of our ordinary daily lives. The Russian physiologist Pavlov first identified the conditioned response in his famous experiment, in which he rang a bell each time he presented food to a dog, and showed that eventually the dog would salivate at the sound of the bell alone, without the food.

It would be almost impossible to count the number of acts we perform every day that are conditioned responses, between brushing our teeth in the morning and brushing them again at night. Walking, running, going up and down stairs involve great numbers of learned muscular co-ordinations that have become automatic. We suddenly realize this when we are brought up short in the middle of one of them, as when we are going down the stairs and expect a step which is not there. We dress and undress, turn lights on and off, open and close doors in a series of learned but automatic acts.

Some of our most complicated learned skills, such as driving a car, are a series of conditioned responses of which, once learned, we are no longer aware. Red and green lights, signals from other drivers, turns and grades in the road—to most of these an experienced driver responds automatically.

Conditioning—learning by experience—enters into our lives so early that it is hard to tell what part of our automatic behavior is inborn and what is learned. A zoology professor in a women's college once kept a boa constrictor in an egg crate in his office. The snake was well fed, sleepy, and harmless, and when students came to see it the professor—perhaps with malice aforethought—invited them to stroke it. There were always some students who had to force themselves to touch the snake, and whose hands involuntarily jerked back from the touch; only afterward did they realize that the snake's skin was smooth and dry, not at all the cold slimy thing they had expected. Here was the hot-stove reflex, true enough, but the hot-stove situation that stimulated it was purely imaginary and certainly learned.

The simple inborn reflex is in fact too simple to be of very wide use even to many species of animals, let alone man. Touch a sea anemone and it shrinks back. The knee jerk with its two-cell arc is just as incapable of variation: tap the knee and it jerks. But an organism living a more ambitious life than a sea anemone—a crab, for example—already has a choice of responses. Touch a crab—as we inadvertently do sometimes while walking on the sandy bottom close to shore—and he may not draw back; he is more likely to turn and pinch the offending toe in his claw. For this the crab's nervous system needs more than a two-cell reflex arc.

ARC OF LEARNING

The first expansion of the two-cell arc is a third cell interposed between the sensory and the motor nerve, called an "internuncial" cell, like a diplomatic envoy or go-between (for example, the Papal nuncio). This cell may receive information from elsewhere that alters the situation. When the puppy takes your hand in his teeth, your response may be not to pull your hand away but to admonish the puppy with a slap from your other hand so that he lets go. You have learned that by that method you stand less chance of a scratched hand. Incidentally the puppy, too, is learning to modify his responses. If he is slapped when he nips and praised when he merely nuzzles, his internuncial cells begin operating on new pathways, and these pathways are traced over and over by experience. In time he becomes a mannerly dog, who automatically inhibits his first primitive impulse, the biting impulse, and enjoys more polite kinds of play.

This, in its simplest form, is the mechanism of learning. Out of the most primitive needs of the organism—to avoid something, such as injury, or to get something, usually food—more and more elaborate motivations develop on the basis of experience, memory, and association. The thirsty deer does not run straight to the water hole. He stops to sniff first for danger. The hungry leopard lets the stag with cruel antlers go by and waits for the less dangerous doe or fawn. The reward for learning, in the wild natural world, is survival.

In the world of men the motivations and rewards of learning are vastly more complicated and subtle, and they change from age to age, from culture to culture. The human infant is born with the most primitive branches of his nervous system developed and functioning, the basic reflexes and the autonomic system that control his heart and respiration, his digestion and body chemistry. He grasps a finger that touches his palm. He turns his head toward a touch on his cheek and opens his lips to grasp and suck his food. He also has at birth the whole complement of nerve cells for his entire nervous system, brain and spinal cord, sensory and motor cells. They await the growth of the white covering along their fibers, the essential myelin sheath that insulates the nerves, before they can serve him.

The sensory and motor areas and certain other regions of his higher brain, the cortex, are also mapped out, although their nervous connections will be established only gradually as he develops. But there are vast numbers of brain cells, as yet uncommitted, capable of receiving the new imprint of experience, association, and memory—in other words, learning.

The nerve cells are fixed in number but they are not limited in the growth and diversification of their extensions. Their fibers will spread and branch, finding new pathways and new connections. Each time a new skill is developed, a new word learned, a new impression absorbed, it is entered somewhere in the convolutions of the brain and its route marked on the nerve pathways. A pathway first explored is traveled uncertainly at first, then with increasing sureness until the same or a similar signal regularly brings out the same or a similar response.

Animals of lower orders than man are born with many more patterned responses—instinctual forms of behavior—but on these patterns new pathways can also be traced. With the birds, for example, the elaborate patterns of migration, nest-building, even the characteristic themes of the species' song are built in. All of them follow in order, all are set in motion by the lengthening day after the sun has passed the winter solstice. In the tiny bodies of the warblers wintering on the Amazon, the reproductive glands begin to enlarge, extra layers of fat are stored in the tissues; the flocks gather and rise into the air for their flight of a thousand, two thousand miles to Iowa or Maryland or Connecticut, to nest again where they were hatched and to sing the song that warblers sing.

But the songs are not quite identical from one bird community to the next. Though they are all of the same species, and their basic song motifs are the same, there are differences, like the dialects that differentiate one human community from another even though they speak the same language. The birds sing by inborn pattern, and they sing the song of their own species, but they also learn variations of their song, and these they learn by listening and imitating. Birds reared experimentally, in isolation from their fellows, also sing the basic songs of their species, but their song does not develop fully until they hear experienced birds of **their** own kind.

The higher animals learn by imitation and by punishment and reward. The punishment may mean going hungry for a while, or it may be danger or pain. The reward in nature is usually a successful hunt for dinner or a mate. The human being also learns by the same routes. A parental warning of danger or expression of disapproval takes the place of literal pain or loss of satisfaction; the reward may be nothing more tangible than the approbation of his parents or his fellows. Eventually the highest reward, for a mature human being, is his own good conscience.

For the human child the important learning is how to behave in the society in which he is to live. He must learn its language, its skills and techniques, its customs and mores, its ethics. An ant or a bee is born to the pattern of its society and its own place in the society. The ant's 250 nerve cells and the bee's 900, or thereabouts, are enough to carry out the inborn activities of the social insects, however elaborate—and some are elaborate almost beyond believing, for example, the dance by which a worker bee communicates to his fellows in the hive the direction and the distance of a newly discovered, rich feeding ground.

The human infant has many systems of fixed inborn patterns, but he also has a much greater capacity for the development of new patterns. He can learn to live in an Eskimo or a Tahitian village or a Chicago suburban society. He can learn to speak Malay or Finnish or English, and the English he learns may have a Scotch burr or a Yankee twang. He can learn to prize a good rice field or a good automobile or a good book, and he can learn to fight with bow and arrow, bombs, intercontinental missiles—or not fight at all.

All this he can learn, because of his extraordinarily flexible, teachable brain. The Spanish neurologist Santiago Ramón y Cajal likened the human brain to a garden of trees which, with intelligent cultivation, "can increase the number of their branches, strike their roots over a wider area and produce ever more varied and more exquisite flowers and fruits."

19 | OUR MYSTERIOUS MASTER

F OR SOME TIME the electronics engineers and the mathematicians have been gleefully turning out more and more wonderful computing machines which they dub electronic "brains." They give their creations such fanciful anthropomorphic names as Maniac and Oracle and talk about their unpredictable behavior and "nervous breakdowns."

They point out that their machines can "learn" and "reason" and "remember," and within the strict definitions of these words the claim is justifiable. Some of the machines can make choices and develop short cuts, more efficient ways of performing a given operation than their designers foresaw. One day there will be a universal machine which can learn and imitate the operations of other machines. And a machine that, given the raw materials, can reproduce itself, not only its functioning parts but its very reproductive mechanism. Such machines exist not only in the designers' imaginations but on paper; theoretically they are quite feasible.

No sooner does art succeed in imitating nature in some new way than nature—as Oscar Wilde observed—begins to imitate art. From calling an electronic machine a brain it is only a short step to calling the brain an electronic machine. There are enough likenesses to make the analogy tempting, so tempting, in fact, that it gave rise to a lively branch of science, called cybernetics, devoted to studying all the ways in which machines and living organisms resemble each other, especially the computer and the brain. We can think of the brain's gray cells as vacuum tubes or transistors, can actually measure electrical waves given off by the brain and neurons. Many of the activities of the central nervous system become graphic to us in terms of feedback systems and closed, open, and reverberating circuits.

But sooner or later the analogy breaks down and the machine, however marvelous, dwindles to its true dimensions before the marvel of the brain. The electronic computer is only one more of the brain's many creations, a device that man has invented to save himself time and labor.

Man made the lever and the wheel, and harnessed water, steam, and electricity to mechanical devices to do the muscle work of animals, or of the thousands of slaves who built the Pyramids. Then he turned his ingenuity to inventing brain machines to save himself the trouble of tending the muscle machines. Safety valves, thermostats, electric eyes and automatic regulating devices are all varieties of brain machines, controlling and directing power.

Now, having invented first the vacuum tube and then the transistor, he is building brain machines that save millions of man-hours of brainwork. It would take fifty scholars forty years to index the works of St. Thomas Aquinas; machines are doing the task in a year. Machines are deciphering the Dead Sea scrolls, filling in as many as five words at a time where the erosion of centuries have made them indecipherable. It is exacting, time-consuming brainwork. But even though it is brainwork, it is still the kind of brainwork that a machine can do, and only after men with human brains have devised the formula and fed the machine its instructions. In other words, it is mechanical.

Imagination, feeling, creativity, laughter, conscience, and the power to invent new machines are still beyond the machine. The British brain physiologist Sir Geoffrey Jefferson put the difference in these words: "I might believe in man as a machine . . . explained by electronic science if I were to see an electronic machine behaving improperly toward another one or if one were pregnant."

THE EFFICIENT BRAIN

Even in the machine's own terms of mechanical efficiency the brain is still the unchallenged champion. Its billions of cells— somewhere between twelve and fourteen billions—operate on the equivalent of less than 100 watts of electrical power; a machine made of that many transistors would need some 100 million watts.

To be sure, the machine is faster. A nerve can recharge itself no more than a few hundred times a second, while a vacuum tube can be turned on and off a million times a second. But the machine's speed depends upon how many operations it has to perform, how frequently its instructions must be changed, how much it must "remember." The machine built at the Institute for Advanced Study in Princeton, the one called Maniac, has a much admired memory as mechanical memories go. It can figure out the positions of the planets in the solar system for the next million years without straining a tube, but when it comes to memory, it can "remember" only about a thousand numbers, of forty two-figure digits each—40,000 digits. The memory capacity of an average human brain has been estimated at perhaps 100 million "remembrance units," as we might call the brain's equivalent of the machine's digits.

A good part of what it has stored the brain can recall at will in a matter of seconds. Some memories take a little longer, as Freud and others have demonstrated, and some the brain will not relinquish without the prodding of special techniques of a rather mystifying kind—hypnosis, for example. But there are those who believe that everything we ever learn or experience is registered somewhere in the brain. Even if we remember only a conservatively estimated 10 per cent, no machine, today or in the foreseeable future, can match this.

We can scarcely imagine the monstrosity of size—and cost—of a machine that would even approach the brain's billions of cells, let alone the magnitude and variety of its operation. One brain physiologist, Professor Warren S. McCulloch, suggests that it would take all the power generated by Niagara Falls to operate a machine with a capacity like that of the human brain, plus all the torrents of water that rush over Niagara's lips to cool the tubes.

THE GREAT MUTATION

The human brain needs no such gargantuan paraphernalia. Physically it is anything but impressive. A soft spongy mass, pinkish gray, weighing about three pounds, in a little bony box that is neatly curved to fit—the brain presents nothing more awesome to the unaided eye than this. Yet in it may be contained a genius like that of Aristotle or Einstein, Moses or Michelangelo. Or the scarcely lesser genius of any ordinary everyday human being, thinking and acting, loving and hating, doing good and evil and knowing, for the most part, the difference between the two. In it are stored past and future, concepts of beauty and of truth, the science of atoms and metagalaxies and also the simple love of children, animals, and the green earth.

The wonder of the brain that was to become human began with a great mutation, a little more than half a million years ago. The dinosaurs had vanished, feathered birds instead of pterodactyls flew in the air, and the small mouselike creature, the first mammal, had come out into the open and fathered many species. The sea had given birth to life long before this, and life had been changing, but slowly.

"For three billion years, until an ageless watcher might have turned away in weariness, nothing had moved but the slime and its creations," writes the evolutionist Loren Eiseley. "In all that prehuman world there had been no animal capable of looking back or forward. No living creature had wept above another's grave. There had been nothing to comprehend the whole. . . . At the end of that time there occurred a small soundless explosion . . . in a little packet of gray matter that quite suddenly appears to have begun to multiply itself in the thick-walled cranium of a ground-dwelling ape."

In that quiet explosion were contained all the explosions yet to come, down to the searing flames of fission and fusion. But in it, paradoxically, were also contained the end of tooth and fang and claw, the beginnings of the human family and the promise of a family of man.

For with the unprecedented capacity of the brain to grow and elaborate its convolutions and its pathways, other changes came rapidly. The creature possessed of such a brain did not have to wait for the eons of evolution to bring improvements in the parts of its own body, a sharper claw or a stronger jaw. It could devise parts for itself as they were needed—in other words, tools. A man who could make a spear or slingshot or bow and arrow did not need the swiftness of the deer or the ferocity of the boar to defend his life and catch his food.

But he did need—and in order to survive he had to develop

—the love and tenderness that would keep his young safe through the years that it took this new, complex brain to grow to maturity. In most of the species of nature the young are born to fend for themselves. With few exceptions, fish and insect and reptile progeny need never know their parents or their parents know them. The higher the level of the species, the closer it approaches the family: the parent birds guard and feed their broods, the mammals suckle and defend their litters. Mother and father birds teach their fledglings to fly; the mother cat teaches her kittens to run, climb, and pounce. This nurturing takes a few months, a season, with some species a few years, and then the young are ready to make their own way in the world.

Only in the human family do we find children of widely different ages, from infants to adolescents, still under the parental roof. Only man keeps his children these many years; only the human young receive this long nurturing care. Parental love that continues for years has its survival value for the species, for the human brain needs years to grow and build the nerve pathways on which human survival depends.

This is so even in the most primitive cultures. Naked man without his skills and tools is among the most helpless of creatures in all the natural world. In swiftness and strength, keenness of senses and the cunning of instinctual self-preservation he is far inferior to his own dog or donkey; the owl has more distant vision and the bat has sharper hearing. His instincts, like the specialized parts of the body that he might have developed, were sacrificed to the learning capacity of his brain. Even his hand, that marvelously skillful and sensitive member, is in the evolutionary sense arrested, compared with the hand of his nearest cousin, the ape. An ape's hand, even with its short thumb, is nearly as good as man's at manipulatory skills, but it is a step further in evolution, specialized for clinging and swinging in the trees. Man's hand would be at a disadvantage in case he should take to the trees, but it is also the more flexible to perform the many tasks his endlessly curious, imaginative, and inventive brain can devise for it.

And if man is helpless through his childhood years in a primitive society, how much more helpless—and potentially dangerous to other men—he is in a culture in which science and technology have put fabulous tools into his hands, to say nothing of murderous weapons. In such a society his learning takes ever longer and longer. Today we think of our twenty-year-olds as still adolescents, and we question the maturity of men and women whose graying hair would make them automatically the elders and arbiters of other cultures.

With all that we know today and all that we have yet to learn, how can the human brain absorb and correlate and use even a fraction of it? In the 600,000 to a billion years since Dr. Eiseley's ground-dwelling ape sat on his haunches by a rock pile, chewing on a stick and *thinking,* such challenges have already been offered to the brain—and have been met and surpassed—that we can scarcely list the powers of that little packet of gray matter today. The evolutionists, the anthropologists, and the paleontologists have far to go still, merely to fill in the gaps in the fantastic journey of the brain from ape to man, and from the big-jawed, small-brained man at the dawn of his day to the man who painted slender-legged bison by firelight on the walls of his cave and the man who painted the creation of Adam on the ceiling of the Sistine Chapel.

THE ORGAN OF ADJUSTMENT

The brain is no mere decorative flower at the top of the evolutionary tree. Even if we never used it for thinking, we would still need it, merely to keep us alive. It is first of all the body's organ of adjustment: within its gray cells and branching nerve fibers it activates, co-ordinates, and regulates the body in all its functions within and all its relationships to the environment without. The cell's metabolism, the functioning of organs and systems are all watched over by the brain. We see, hear, feel, taste, and are aware of our body sensations and positions not at the ends of our nerves but in the brain. All the vital functions, some conscious, some unconscious, and some on the border line of consciousness, the human brain shares with other species.

We also share with the higher animals the brain's primitive ability to learn, to remember, and to reason. The intelligent chimpanzee piles up boxes one atop the other and climbs on them to reach the banana. To be sure, he does not do this at once, unless he has seen it done. If the banana out of his reach is on one side of his cage, and the boxes are on the other, when he looks at the banana he does not remember the boxes, and when he looks at the boxes he does not remember the banana. Only when he sees both at the same time does he make the connection between the two, that with the boxes he can reach the banana. Once he has seen the relationship, however, and acted successfully upon it, he can repeat the operation. He can even generalize from it and take other expedients like it to get his banana. One experimenter gave his chimpanzee a choice of three ways to get the suspended fruit, but the ape thought of a fourth. He took the professor's hand, led him to the spot, and climbed on his shoulders!

Man is far inferior to his animal cousins or even to his primitive relations in sensory perception; the difference appears in the comparative size of sensory areas in an animal's brain and in man's. In interpreting these perceptions, modern man has also lost much of his primitive cunning. The Australian police boast about their bushmen trackers, who have not only remarkably keen perception but even more astonishing deductive powers. They can tell, from signs imperceptible to modern men, how fast a man was traveling, whether he was tired, whether he carried a burden and in which hand he was carrying it, and they have given remarkably accurate physical descriptions of fugitives they had never seen.

Reason, perception, vocal expression, memory and learning we share with the higher animals. But the ability to symbolize, conceptualize, theorize, to imagine and believe in a world not present to the senses, whether it is a supernatural world or a world of science—these are human faculties. Only the human brain has been capable of creating words, and out of words language and numbers, the basic tools of thought. From the earliest cultures of which we have any knowledge, man has devised symbols, systems of communication, and interpretations of the world in which he lives, and has found ways to hand on his knowledge to his progeny.

EXPLORING THE DARK CONTINENT

Where and how in the brain all these operations go on, the physiologists and psychologists have labored long to discover. Until very recently the brain in its normal functioning was nearly as inaccessible to them as the far side of the moon. The great brain physiologist of the past generation, Sir Charles Sherrington, who won the Nobel Prize in 1932, wondered whether any of the work the physiologists of his time were doing on the brain was bringing us any closer to an understanding of the mind.

The scientists could describe the brain, its major segments from the medulla oblongata to the cortex, its tributary nerve centers—ganglia—in and along the spinal cord. They knew a good deal about the pathways of the great nerve trunks that go up and down the spinal cord and into the brain. They had isolated the separate branches of the system, the voluntary and the autonomic, the motor and the sensory, the automatic reflexes and their modification by learning, or conditioning.

Yet learning and memory, association and recall, the emotions themselves remained mysterious. So did waking, sleep, attention, consciousness. The higher centers of the brain were still largely an unexplored continent, and the fabulous interweaving of nerve fibers remained nearly undecipherable, a trackless jungle of neurons.

Within the past few decades the explorers have made more progress than for generations before. Electricity and electronics and advances in biochemistry and biophysics—the chemistry and physics of living matter—have put new tools into their hands. At last they can peer into the little dark box of the brain while it is whole and healthy and functioning normally. They can stimulate different regions of the brain and then observe the effects in behavior. They can give the brain tasks to perform and measure the activity of its various areas and pathways electrically to see how it performs the tasks.

Curiously the brain, which registers pain for the rest of the body, feels no pain itself. The same exquisite precision that makes brain surgery the art it is today has enabled investigators to study the brain in healthy normal animals. They can place wires as thin as threads in precise spots, without injury or discomfort to the animal, and activate an area or measure the activity going on there. They can work with their animals without anesthesia. They have mapped many areas of the brain that were previously dark and have traced many activities along their nerve pathways.

As long ago as 1929 a professor at the University of Jena in

Germany, Dr. Hans Berger, announced that with ordinary radio equipment he had detected and amplified electrical waves produced by nerve cells in action. His discovery was at first ignored as a useless mechanical trick, but today the electroencephalogram —the EEG—has vastly increased our knowledge of the brain in health, besides being a useful diagnostic tool.

The EEG machine is a listening device; it listens to the brain much the way the doctor with his stethoscope listens to the heart. But unlike the heart, whose functioning can be measured by ear as well as by electrocardiograph, the brain's rhythms are not audible and can only be "heard" electronically. The EEG machine picks up these signals through electrodes, small metal strips, taped to the head at designated spots, and the record can be made audible, through loud-speakers, or transcribed on tape. These machines amplify brain impulses approximately two million times. When a group of cells discharge their impulses in concert, their activity is recorded as a series of waves of recognizable form; it is as though a group of people were clapping hands together.

The orderly, organized working together of cells that gives off these regular waves does not begin with infancy. A newborn baby's electroencephalogram confirms what we already know of its undeveloped nerve pathways and its immature mental activity. The record is an aimless scribble with no pattern, indicating cells discharging at random, with an occasional spasmodic wave of cells acting for a brief moment in unison. At about the age of one month the baby begins to take note of what he sees with one or the other eye—he will not focus both together until some weeks later—and this first organized activity registers on the recording apparatus as the first regular rhythm, a wave of nerve cells discharging together at a slow rate of three impulses per second, localized at the back of the head in the occipital lobe, where visual perception takes place in the cortex.

Through the childhood years, as other areas of the brain mature and nerve cells become tuned to each other by their growing, interconnecting fibers, the rhythmic impulses spread and accelerate; a rate of between four and seven per second is typical until about the eighth year. Then the adult waking rate of ten impulses per second begins to dominate; these are the so-called alpha waves.

The ten-per-second alpha waves characteristic of most adults, a sequence of ripples, are called "waves of inattention"; they appear when the eyes are closed or when the mind is idling, not concentrating, and they are blotted out the moment some stimulus—a noise, for example—or a strong emotion or some form of mental activity focuses the attention. The alpha waves also dis. appear when we are falling asleep. They are the dominating rhythm given off by the brain when we are wide awake but not attending to anything in particular.

The chemists' discoveries in the functioning of the brain are equally significant though less easily understood by many of us. Despite its measurable electrical activity, the brain is after all a chemically functioning organ, mysterious in many ways and yet not basically unlike the other organs of the body.

A chemical compound, powerfully stimulating, was quite recently discovered in the brain and nervous system; given the name of *serotonin*, it is sometimes called the brain hormone. Another significant organic chemical, norepinephrine, was discovered in the central nervous system, and this one is virtually identical with adrenaline, the hormone that mobilizes the body's forces for emergency action. Until this discovery it was believed that this compound came only from the adrenal glands, at the prompting of the sympathetic nervous system. As in other systems of the body, these compounds have their opposite or antagonistic compounds. To the many theories of how the nervous system works, the brain chemists contribute the hypothesis that the nerves transmit their impulses from the nerve ending of one cell to the nerve ending of another, across the gap or synapse, by way of these chemical substances, one group chemically inhibiting, the other mediating the transmission.

Another tool of brain research also comes from the chemical laboratory, this one in the form of drugs. Again there are two opposite and apparently antagonistic groups. There are the tranquilizing drugs, and there are the drugs that produce hallucinations—"vest-pocket psychoses."

One of these latter, lysergic acid, was discovered by a Swiss chemist, in what might have been a serious incident but turned out to be amusing and also fortunate. In the course of a routine preparation he apparently inhaled some of the powerful chemical. Feeling strange, he bicycled home through a familiar world become suddenly and eerily distorted, and for the next two hours he experienced the first of the drug-induced psychoses that have since become a part of brain research. Closely resembling this drug (its symbol among chemists is LSD-25) is mescaline, an extract of the peyote, a variety of cactus; Indians of the Southwest and Mexico have traditionally taken this to induce religious visions, and the writer Aldous Huxley experimented with it.

Research workers have experimented with these drugs on themselves and on other volunteers. Hospital staff members, convicts in a state prison, and members of other groups have offered themselves as subjects for the model psychosis, with its hallucinations, loss of reality and loss of identity.

These efforts have been mainly directed toward discovering what goes wrong with the brain and nervous system physically— or perhaps we should say, chemically—in mental illness. By experimentally confusing the brain and interfering with its normal operation, investigators believe, the laboratory psychoses have given them valuable clues to the way the brain must work when it is well. These studies take us close to the border line between the physical brain and the subjective consciousness, the mind.

From the psychological laboratories have come some revelations that approach the same elusive boundary, but from the other side, the side of consciousness. These are experiments in sensory deprivation and deprivation of sleep.

College student volunteers, in one of these experiments, were offered twenty dollars a day just to lie quietly on a comfortable cot in a cubicle around the clock, for as many days as they could endure it. Their physical needs were attended to, they had no cause for anxiety, but they were also totally alone and shut off from the world, except that they could communicate with the experimenter if necessary. They wore goggles that shut out the shapes of things, though not the light, and cuffs that kept them from experiencing touch sensations; the steady hum of an air conditioner cut off all other sounds.

The idyllic prospect of doing nothing at all for real money attracted a good number of volunteers, but most of them gave up after one day, some after only a few hours. Of the original forty-six, only fourteen lasted long enough to report the experience: a gradual loss of the ability to think, to concentrate; growing mental confusion, finally the hallucinations—visual, auditory, and of body sensations—much like those of the drug-induced psychoses.

A distinguished brain physiologist subjected himself to an even more severe test of the effects of sensory deprivation: Dr. John C. Lilly, of the Institutes of Mental Health, lay in a tank of water of about body temperature, wearing a breathing mask which also covered his eyes. In three hours, Dr. Lilly reported, he experienced the gradual loss of control of his thought processes and ended with vivid three-dimensional visual hallucinations.

In still another experiment, some hundreds of soldiers at an Army installation participated in a staying-awake experiment. They experienced no particular fatigue, but they began to have delusions, mainly of persecution, and some became almost violent in acting out their fantasies.

So it appears that the mind can become confused through a variety of causes, not only by the interference of powerful chemicals, but also by being deprived of the normal everyday experiences that we scarcely even notice as we go about our business, the sounds and sights and contacts that feed our minds with information of the real world around us.

Thus from many directions the explorers are tracing pathways through the jungle and mapping the continent of the brain. What we know is still infinitesimal compared with what we have yet to learn. But it is possible now to sketch the brain as a mechanism that may some day explain the mind.

20 | MIND AND MECHANISMS

M ORE THAN two thousand years ago the Greek physician Hippocrates spoke to a world still far from convinced that the brain was the seat of the mind:

"And men ought to know that from nothing else but from the brain come joys, delights, laughter and sports, and sorrows, griefs, despondency and lamentations. And by the brain in a special manner we acquire wisdom and knowledge, and see and hear, and know what are foul and what are fair, what are bad and what are good, what are sweet and what unsavory. . . . By the brain we distinguish objects of relish and disrelish; and the same things do not always please us. And by the same organ we become mad and delirious, and fears and terrors assail us, some by night and some by day."

No one to date has described more eloquently the mysteries of mind that are somehow carried on within the brain. Where are all these subtle functions performed? How does the brain, a collection of living cells whose structure is basically like that of all living cells, give rise to the mind? How does it produce that strange, special amalgam of thinking and feeling, of sensation, experience, memory, reason and aspiration that means to each of us the self, the "I" of our identity?

BACKWARD THROUGH TIME

The brain, as we know, has a mixed pedigree. There is the "old brain," which man inherited from earlier species, and there is the "new brain," which in its fullest development is peculiar to himself. The new brain is the cortex, that covering of gray cells, several layers deep, that floods over the two hemispheres of the cerebrum and into each fold and fissure, following its many convolutions, finding space within the narrow compass of the skull for its billions of cells and their branching fibers.

The cortex sits like a thick gray cap, deeply folded down its center from brow to occiput, over the oddly shaped parts of the old brain. We know the cortex as the thinking and reasoning brain, the intellect, and also as the perceiving and performing brain which receives sensory information and directs the muscles of limbs and body, of eyes and speech and facial expression, to move and act. We think of the cortex as the conscious brain, that area in which are concentrated all our most human traits.

It is all of that. In its full human development it is the part of the brain that most clearly differentiates man from all other species, even from fossil man with his low forehead, apelike eyebrow ridge and heavy jaw.

The cortex alone does not contain the mind. The mind is the brain functioning on many levels, old brain and new. It is like a chorus of many voices, of different pitch, timbre, and loudness, speaking different words with different inflections, perhaps even in different languages, and some of them not speaking words at all but uttering inarticulate sounds. Or it is like a color separation, used in printing designs in several colors, in which each part of the pattern in its own color is spread on its own transparent sheet; when all the sheets are laid one on top of another we see the whole design in all its colors.

If we follow the curious design of the brain downward through its many levels, from the new to the old and older brains, we are unreeling its history, and we are also peeling back one by one the layers of the transparency, peeling away a color and shape and a fraction of depth of the mind, until we come to the simple first layer with no color or pattern that we can name.

IN THE OLD BRAIN

Leaving the cortex, the richly patterned overlayer, we find deep within the cerebral hemispheres a part of the old brain called the thalamus; the Greek word means merely "inner chamber." Like the cerebrum, the thalamus is in twin halves. Through here pass the body sensations; it is a relay station but it also integrates the sensory information on the way to the cortex. It is an organ of crude consciousness, of sensations of rough contact and extreme temperatures either hot or cold; it is principally here that we feel pain. In the thalamus, responses are of the all-or-nothing kind. Even mild stimuli would be felt as acutely disagreeable sensations unless they were graded and modified by the finely discriminating cortex.

Close by the thalamus, in a fibrous saddle or arch between the cerebral hemispheres, is an area of primitive pleasure sensations, like the thalamus in being crude and undifferentiated, but pleasurable rather than painful. It is so recently discovered that it is still without a name.

Below the thalamus at the base of the cerebrum is the hypothalamus, no bigger than a lump of sugar, but potent far out of proportion to its size. It takes part in such vital activities as the ebb and flow of the body's fluids, the regulation of metabolism, blood sugar levels, body temperature. It turns the wheels of the body's many rhythms: of activity and rest, appetite and digestion, sexual desire and menstrual and reproductive cycles. It has been called the body's metronome, thermostat, "appestat." And besides all this, the hypothalamus is the body's emotional brain.

Here is the center of the primitive emotions that are necessary for survival in a world of fang and claw. Some scientists have pointed out that the civilized world, too, has been shaken from time to time by hypothalamic statesmanship, for Napoleon, Bismarck, and Hitler were all given to outbursts of fury characteristic of this old emotional brain uncontrolled by the new.

The hypothalamus is only one three-hundredth of the brain's total bulk, but it sits in a seat of power. It is the principal center

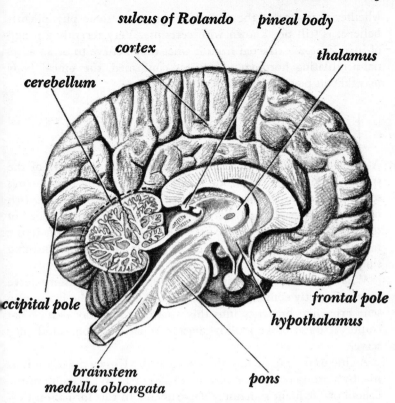

cerebellum

cortex

sulcus of Rolando

pineal body

thalamus

ccipital pole

frontal pole

hypothalamus

brainstem
medulla oblongata

pons

of the autonomic system, with its sympathetic and parasympathetic arms, and furthermore it is situated close by the pituitary
gland, the master gland of the endocrine system. This dynamic
heritage from the long-ago youth of the animal world knows neither good nor evil but only survival; like the genii in the bottle,
it is a powerful servant, exciting, potentially rebellious, putting
its drive and momentum behind every deep emotion that we
feel.

A small mystery, among many large ones still remaining in the
brain, is the pineal body. Tucked away in this second story from
the top, under the shelter of a mass of nerve fibers that forms the
center of the cerebrum, this little organ has as its sole claim for
attention a moment of historic importance. In the seventeenth
century René Descartes, philosopher and mathematician, found
his way to the pineal body and, by mathematical deduction, declared it to be the seat of the soul. What its function may be, or

whether it is part of the endocrine system as some physiologists believe, is still not known with certainty. Very recently a group of investigators extracted from it what they believe to be an adrenal-stimulating hormone. If this is confirmed, the pineal body may take its place at last among the endocrines.

THE GATEWAY OF ATTENTION

At the next level downward is the brain stem, that part of the spinal column that lies inside the skull. One of the brain stem's several parts is a peculiar cluster of cells which so baffled research men of a past generation that they named it the "manure pile" of the brain. Its closely woven network of nerve fibers won it the more dignified textbook name of "reticular formation," meaning simply a netlike formation.

What puzzled the investigators was that the great sensory nerve trunks, directly connected to the highest centers of the brain, also sent brushlike branches into this area on their way past. What could all these nerve endings mean? What function could they serve?

A clue to the puzzle was discovered at the University of California, by a group of scientists led by Professor H. W. Magoun of the School of Medicine's anatomy department. In this formation they found the arousal center for the brain, an area no larger than a man's little finger. They discovered that when the cortex is stimulated directly, the brain awakens, but in a blurred, gradual pattern of awakening brain waves unlike normal waking. When this "reticular activating system" was stimulated, however, the result was the normal, familiar pattern of awakening brain waves.

This netlike system in the brain stem might be described as the gateway to our attention, a crossroads between the high and the low centers of the central nervous system. Once we leave this level, we apparently leave consciousness behind. We do not consciously experience the operations of the central nervous system below this level. But this does not mean that the lower centers function independently of the higher brain, nor that the higher brain is independent of them. On the next level the cerebellum, the "little brain," gives us a particularly graphic demonstration of how the conscious and unconscious centers function in harmony.

THE "LITTLE BRAIN"

Tucked in at the back of the head, under the caplike occipital curve of the cerebrum, the cerebellum clings to the brain stem like a butterfly to a stalk; its design is very like that of a butterfly, with a slender body between two spreading wings. The great motor and sensory nerve cables go past it through the brain stem on their way to the higher, the conscious, brain. So far as we know, the cerebellum operates below the threshold of the conscious mind. But it taps in, so to speak, on both the sensory and motor connections to the cortex and performs a peculiarly interesting function.

We have said earlier that the voluntary muscles are all consciously controlled, and we have talked about the astonishing coordination of muscles involved in even the most commonplace movements; one of the examples we used was that of raising and lowering this book. A little later in this chapter we shall have a closer look at the part of the cortex that initiates all these movements, and the adjoining area that receives messages from all the sensory nerves in the body.

We are conscious of wanting to make a movement and also of making it. We are conscious of the position of every part of the body, and of every sensation in each of the parts. All this information comes to our conscious, cortical brain. All these sensations are necessary information when we want to make a movement.

But when we stop to think about it, we realize that with all our consciousness, with all our information from the senses and all our awareness of movement, we do not direct the actual execution of a movement with our conscious minds. When you lift your hand and turn a page of this book, you are perfectly conscious of making the movement. But you have no idea which of the thirty-two separate muscles in your hand, plus several in your arm and shoulder, have collaborated to accomplish it.

You may, if you concentrate, be able to move a particular muscle at will. But what you are concentrating on is the part of the body and the movement you want to make with it, rather than the muscle itself. The conscious brain does not think in terms of muscles. It thinks in movements.

Carrying out the movement is the concern of the cerebellum. The "little brain" translates the order for a movement, coming from the cortex, into an operational program. It is as though an executive sent a directive to his staff, and the staff then performed all the many separate tasks necessary to carry out his directive. If he is a good executive, he does not have to think of the details. He has a capable, well-trained staff to attend to them.

It is the cerebellum that does this staff work. On an order from the cortex, it mobilizes all the individual muscles necessary to carry out the order, and it also times and grades their contractions and co-ordinates them so that our movements are made smoothly and with precision. The cerebellum makes it possible for us to spear a morsel on the dinner plate and lift it to the mouth, to raise a foot just high enough and place it on the curb, without jerks or misses and without our being aware that we are doing anything particularly complicated. The cerebellum guides the muscles by which the fingers of the concert pianist race over the notes; in the most brilliant, difficult passages, he may play twenty or thirty notes a second, a feat that requires perhaps 600 motor actions. His conscious brain, drawing on his musicianship and artistry, directs the performance; but it is the cerebellum, operating over nerve pathways tuned by practice to instant, accurate response, that carries out the dazzling display.

To do the detail work of a virtuoso performance, or just to execute a simple order from the cortex to stand, walk, or turn the head, the cerebellum needs information from the sensory nerves. This it has. The great nerve cables, on their way to and from the cortex, send branches into this remarkable unconscious co-ordinating station as they go past it through the brain stem to which it is attached.

The nerve cables continue downward through the brain stem's several parts, the midbrain, the pons or bridge, and the medulla oblongata. In the brain stem the motor and sensory nerves cross over, left to right and right to left, producing the puzzling phenomenon by which the left hemisphere of the cerebrum controls the right half of the body, and vice versa. In this area are also nerve centers with special functions. In the midbrain, for example, are reflex centers for turning the head and eyes and pricking up the ears—this last being a lost art for most of humankind. In the medulla oblongata are centers for the heart, blood vessels, and respiratory system.

From the brain stem there emerge on their separate pathways most of the cranial nerves, nerves that arise within the skull and, with one important exception, serve the head. They are the sensory nerves of sight, hearing, and taste, and the ones that carry sensations of heat, cold, touch, and pain, of muscular movement and position from the head and face. They are the motor nerves that move the eyes and eyelids and all the fine eye muscles, that translate our feelings into facial expression, that move the muscles of speech and of eating and swallowing, and stimulate the salivary glands to secrete.

The one exception, the vagus nerve, carries among its mixed fibers the autonomic motor fibers that go to the bronchial tubes, the stomach, gall bladder, the small intestine and part of the large one. It carries secretory fibers to the gastric glands and the pancreas, and inhibitory—quieting—fibers to the heart. It is the great nerve of the parasympathetic, the conserving arm, of the autonomic system.

THE PROTECTED ENVIRONMENT

This is the brain, the new and the old, the heavy bulblike flower with twin hemispheres at its top and the many interrelated parts in its depths, rising above the spine's slender stalk. The whole structure is wrapped in three membranes, protected and buoyant in the cerebrospinal fluid, and set within the domed bony box of the skull.

A pint of blood flows through the brain every minute, carrying in nutrients and carrying away wastes, but while blood circulates through the brain's tiny blood vessels as it does elsewhere in the body, it does not release its nutrients directly to the brain cells. For their highly specialized work they apparently need a special environment, for there is a barrier of some kind that keeps some substances out of the brain entirely and delays the entrance of others for hours, sometimes days longer than it takes them to penetrate to the rest of the body. When sodium, for example, is experimentally injected into the blood stream it can be detected everywhere else in the body in about ten minutes, but not for sixty hours or more in the brain.

How the blood-brain barrier, as scientists call it, works or even of what it is made is not yet known. One of several theories is that certain star-shaped cells, called astrocytes, that are found by the billions in the nervous system, may have the function of selecting what shall be admitted to the cerebrospinal fluid that bathes the nerve cells. They cling to the blood-vessel walls with sucker feet, and apparently they are so closely crowded that there is little uncovered space along the capillary walls through which undesirable chemicals may slip. The astrocytes, in this hypothetical explanation, are so arranged chemically that they take into their own cell bodies only certain substances and release these to the nerve cells, like nurses that prepare the food for their charges and permit them nothing but the prescribed diet.

Some drugs, however, have properties that get them past the blood-brain barrier: the barbiturates that are the active ingredients of many sleeping pills, ether and nitrous oxide or "laughing gas" among the anesthetics, carbon dioxide, carbon monoxide or automobile-exhaust gas, the poisons cyanide and strychnine, alcohol in sufficient quantities, possibly some of the tranquilizers, and the hallucination-producing drugs or at least some of them, notably mescaline. These intruders may work in several ways to interfere with the normal functioning of the nerve cells. They may disturb the oxygen supply, for example, or they may act on any of the special enzymes that convert glucose into energy for the work the cells have to do.

The course of evolution that resulted in the blood-brain barrier did not, it seems, anticipate man's ingenuity in finding substances that would penetrate this highly specialized filter. Aldous Huxley pointed out, in a talk to a group of medical men on the subject of tranquilizers, that, long before history began, men had sampled every variety of leaf, root, berry, nut, fungus, and bark—and not only to cure disease or alleviate pain. In Mr. Huxley's view, man had scarcely achieved the self-awareness that makes him human before he began seeking to transcend himself, to reach toward a world of dreams, visions, and mystic ecstasies. Seeds of the opium poppy have been found in the kitchen middens, the refuse heaps, of the Stone Age lake dwellers of Switzerland. A sacred mushroom was eaten by wild tribesmen in Kamchatka as well as in Aztec Mexico, and some think a mushroom was the intoxicant that caused the berserk rages of the ancient Norsemen. Making an intoxicating beverage out of the fermented liquor of some grain or fruit is among the oldest arts known to men.

When in health and untampered with by its endlessly curious possessor, the human brain lives in a chemical environment quite different in certain ways from that of other organs. The cerebrospinal fluid is somewhat higher in sodium chloride and markedly lower in proteins than the blood plasma, and it has floating in it only a few lymph cells compared with the high number of cells of many kinds in the plasma. Its volume is kept constant at about 130 cubic centimeters in man; normally, any excess is allowed to filter away into the blood stream. It flows through the several intercommunicating cavities—the ventricles—of the brain, keeping them always filled, and it continues with the nerve cables down the spinal cord. It is at once a protective moat for the master organ in its bony castle and a more stable inland sea than might be provided by the blood that flows through the rest of the body.

KING OF THE CASTLE

We have seen how the new brain, the cortical thinker and doer of whose activities we are most aware, leans upon its older members, and how the complex pattern of the mind is drawn from all its parts, those that are conscious and those below the threshold of consciousness. The cortex is not, after all, the king of the castle, unless it is a constitutional monarch, bound to listen to his ministers. The white-sheathed nerve fibers, streaming out of the pinkish gray cells, push their branches and tendrils toward countless other nerve endings both nearby and far away. By them the cortex is joined to every part of the old brain, the spinal centers, and so to all parts of the body.

Remembering this, we are ready to explore the cortex with its special mechanisms and functions. We know a good deal about some of these, less about others, and about some we still have only interesting speculations.

The cortex is rather like a relief map, with one very deep valley dividing it longitudinally into symmetrical halves, and each of the halves again divided by two major valleys and many shallower folds. The very deep valley runs from brow to occiput, and in its depths is a bed of matted white fibers, the corpus callosum, that connects the left and right hemispheres. The hemispheres control opposite sides of the body, as we know, but they are also intercommunicating, so that the left hand does know what the right hand does. The upper half of the face, for example, has its connections in both hemispheres, and this is also true for the eyes. What we learn and remember seems to be recorded in duplicate, with carbon copies filed in each hemisphere.

Besides the central longitudinal fissure, each hemisphere is again divided by a fold midway between front and back, running across the top and down the side somewhat above and in front of the ear; this is the fissure of Rolando. Yet another deep valley runs laterally backward from the temple above the ear; this is the fissure of Sylvius. These major folds divide each hemisphere into four lobes: the occipital lobe at the back of the skull, the parietal lobe at the side, the frontal or forehead lobe which is all the area in front of the fissure of Rolando, and the temporal lobe at the temples below the fissure of Sylvius.

REALMS OF THE SENSES

Our two major senses of sight and hearing are well mapped in the cortex: we see with the back of our heads, in the occipital lobe, and we hear with the sides, in the temporal lobe. Two other areas have been explored, inch by inch. They are the sensory and motor areas for the body, and they parallel each other across the fissure of Rolando, the sensory strip following the fissure on its rearward or parietal side, the motor strip on the forward or frontal side.

In the sensory strip are registered all our sensations. In the motor strip are the nerves that control the voluntary muscles. In both, the parts of the body are represented in an orderly way but, oddly enough, upside down: beginning with the toes, tucked into the longitudinal fissure, across the top of the cortex go the foot, leg, hip, torso, shoulder, arm, and each of the fingers, then the neck, and a leap to the top of the face and downward to eyes, nose, mouth. The sensory strip has an area for genital sensation and another for intra-abdominal sensation.

As we might expect, the parts of the body that are most active in sensation and movement have the largest areas within the strips, so that a picture of the body as represented in these two strips in the brain would be curiously distorted, with the hands and face far larger than the whole length of torso and leg. In the sensory strip the foot is larger than all the body up to the head, the hand with its fingers covers more area than the entire arm (the index finger is dominant) and largest of all is the lower part of the face with its sensitive lips. In the motor area the well-muscled hand is huge, with a great thumb, and the face is again the largest, with all its muscles of expression, mastication, and speech.

It is in the sensory areas of the brain that all our perception takes place. Here is where we recognize sweet and sour, hot and cold, pain, the tactile form of an object held in the hand, the rough texture of tweed and the smooth of silk. Here we know that we are sitting or lying, stooping or standing; here we recognize that someone is shaking our hand or stepping on our toe. In the psychovisual and psychoauditory areas the brain sorts out the sizes, colors, depth and spatial relationships of what we see, and the timbre, pitch, intensity, the harmony or cacophony of what we hear.

More than this, the brain interprets the significance of these perceptions. We do not merely see a face; we recognize it as familiar, interesting, attractive, or none of these. We do not merely hear sounds the orchestra is making; we hear the music and we like it or we don't like it. A trained musician can also hear the instruments individually, and a Toscanini could hear which one was not in tune.

We also remember as we perceive with our senses; a scene, a sound calls up other times, other experiences. Many perceptions stir us emotionally. If this were not so, we would probably have no paintings or poems or jokes, no symphonies or hit parade songs, no art either long-hair or short-hair.

All these responses to our perceptions the sensory areas of the cortex do not bring us unaided. They draw upon other parts of the brain by way of the intricate communicating network of nerves.

A great part of the cortex that remains unmapped is thought to be involved in just this associative kind of response. If it is so, it should not surprise us, for much of our thinking and feeling is woven out of associations. Factual knowledge and technical skills depend upon a background of experience and relationships between one kind of thing and another, and certainly wisdom and judgment and the acts of making plans and decisions are not born out of a vacuum. The contents of the mind at any given moment, whether it is idly musing, thinking rationally, or experiencing a surge of emotion, draws upon an intensely personal and private background of association. The richer a life has been in experiences that have made their imprint on thought and feeling, the richer will be the patterns upon which the conscious mind can draw.

THE CENTER FOR SPEECH

For a long time the frontal lobe, which particularly distinguishes man's brain from that of the lower orders, was thought to be such an associative area. It was called a "silent" area because it seemed to have no specific function. This still appears to be true for most of the frontal area, but the exception is a noteworthy one: in the left frontal lobe, in a part close to the small center that the human brain has for the sense of smell, is the center for speech.

This center appears in no other than human brains, and for the lack of it, apparently, no other known species has developed true speech. All the animals, even the fishes of the so-called silent world, communicate with each other by way of a language of sounds and actions. Most fishes grunt, and the white whale has a lively vocabulary in a wide register of sounds. One species of squirrel varies its single chirped sound in as many as five different ways, each for a different kind of danger, and all the squirrels within hearing respond with appropriate behavior; at the sound that means a bird of prey, all run for cover, but at the sound that means a snake they stay where they are, alertly watching the foe on the ground. The birds have the most elaborate vocabulary of all creatures in the wild state.

But all these sounds are basically instinctive, and the behavior that they call forth in other animals that hear them is also innate and patterned. Both the call and the response are involuntary; they can neither be produced nor inhibited at will. The bird will call even if no other bird is there to hear it.

Animals that live with man develop an additional kind of language. Your dog's bark or whine or snuffle, your cat's meow or purr has a specific meaning and it is intended to tell you something or move you to do something, to open the door, fill the food or water bowl, scratch pussy's neck or come and play.

Parrots, and some other gifted mimics among the birds, even learn human words. All animals are mimics to some extent; imitation is a useful survival mechanism by which the experienced elders teach the young what they need to know. Parrots, crows and ravens, parakeets, and myna birds go further and use their gift of mimicry as a form of play.

But none of these is true language. No animal of the lower orders, however varied the sounds he makes, can tell a story, describe a place, give orders or instructions, communicate abstract ideas.

Animal psychologists have taken a great deal of pains to analyze this matter of speech. They began, many of them, by believing that the most intelligent species do have speech—the anthropoid apes, if no others—and one hopeful observer solemnly compiled a dictionary called *Do You Speak Chimpanzee?* which zoo visitors, at the turn of the century, carried with them in the expectation of conversing with their cousins, just as they would use a phrase book to talk to the natives in a foreign land. The apes, according to report, paid them no mind.

More recent experiments have been made in teaching animals human speech. Again, the chimpanzee has been the pupil of choice, or in one instance an orangutan; both these apes have vocal equipment like ours, and they are good mimics and highly intelligent. The first success was with a young female orang who learned, after six months of patient effort, to say two words. When she was frightened she clung to her teacher, kissing him and crying, "Papa, papa!" When she was ill she said, "Cup, cup," asking for a drink. She was learning to make the sound *th* when her death ended the experiment.

The most extensive experiment was that of a husband and wife team of psychologists who brought up a baby girl chimpanzee like a human child. In standard performance tests Viki at two and one half ranked as much as eight months ahead of human children of the same age, but her language development was that of a one-year-old, and it progressed very little farther. At the age of seven, when she died of encephalitis, she had a vocabulary of three words, "Mama," "Papa," and "cup," and several play sounds which were arbitrarily accepted by her foster parents as words: "tsk" for cigarette, "up" for a piggy-back ride. But she never made a sentence or learned a word that had not been painstakingly taught her. Her intelligence was far beyond her language, and she did have a lively language of action for communicating her wishes. Speech, however, was forever impossible for her, because she lacked the speech center in the brain.

The difference is apparent from infancy. Only the human baby coos and babbles and engages in vocal play; not even the chimpanzee does this, although it is born with the same organs and muscles of speech. The human baby practices every kind of sound and syllable until, listening and imitating, he drops those that he does not hear and concentrates on the vowel and consonant combinations of his own people's language.

THE UNSOLVED PUZZLE OF MEMORY

In the temporal lobe, close by the auditory area, is a recently discovered center for another faculty that we think of as distinctively human, the memory. Elephants have legendary memories, so have parrots, and the animals we know most intimately—horses, dogs, cats—remember many things we teach them and many that they learn without our help. But the capacity for memory of such an animal is severely limited, as is his capacity for experience. There is nothing in the world, natural or man-made, that matches the human memory.

The so-called memory center in the brain appears to be a storehouse where memories are stacked rather like furniture. When this area has been stimulated electrically, a particular event, a piece of music, an experience long forgotten or deeply buried has been brought to the individual's mind, complete in every detail.

But it is a mechanical kind of memory. When the stimulation is removed the memory ends. When it is applied again, the memory begins again, not where it left off but from the beginning. It is like a strip of film or recording tape being run off on a machine which, at an interruption, automatically rewinds and begins again. This is not the magic of memory as we have experienced it, unfolding at the stimulus of a fragrance or a face or a fragment of melody, bringing with it a welling of emotion. It is not even the magic of that practical memory for facts and events that serves us in everyday life and also, occasionally, fails us by pulling out the wrong card or sometimes a blank one.

Yet the recording that an electrode sets off in the brain, mechanical though it is, poses questions to which we have not yet found the answers. Our senses bring us millions of impressions in the course of a day, some familiar, some new, which in some way we classify and relate to what we already know. We see, hear, observe and absorb information of all kinds, from childhood on—facts, admonitions, relationships. Many of them are clothed in emotion so strong that although the original experience may be forgotten, the emotional aura can be evoked by the merest shred of an association.

We know from psychoanalysis, and somewhat from hypnosis, that the mind seems to store a great many memories of which we are not ordinarily conscious, including details which at the time we were not aware of observing. A story is told of a master bricklayer who, under hypnosis, described on request a particular brick he had laid ten years before in a particular spot in one of the many Gothic buildings of Yale University. He had laid close to two thousand bricks that day and probably on every working day before and since. Yet he remembered that particular brick, its color, a peculiarity of one face, a pebble imbedded in one corner. He recalled and described other bricks in equal detail and with equal accuracy.

Of all the experiences that we undergo and the impressions that pour in upon us, the probability is that we actually forget a good deal—in one estimate, perhaps 90 per cent. But even the 10 per cent that remains with us must add up, by middle age, to a fabulous sum of memories. Where do they go? How are they stored?

The temporal lobe seems to be a kind of memory center, but no recording or filing system that we can imagine would explain how any one group of cells could hold even a fraction of one individual's memories. The whole brain, with its billions of cells, would not be large enough if each memory had to have a cell to itself. One possible explanation to account for so many memories, and the ways in which we have access to them, is perhaps the chemical one.

The giant protein molecules, of which we talked in the chapters on the body's chemistry, make up the brain cells as well as all the other cells in the body. Each living cell, in the brain as elsewhere, contains great numbers of these long chain-aggregates of molecules. The brain alone contains an astronomical number of them, a thousand billion billion, or one followed by twenty-one zeros. The impulses that run along the nerves are of the kind that can change these molecules into new combinations and, as we have seen, the cells are continuously reproducing these molecules exactly, through the mediation of the genes.

This could be a chemical way, then, by which memories are imprinted: the nervous impulses of the experience or the perception would leave their traces in the minutely changed giant molecules within the cells. The molecules themselves need not last—indeed, the individual molecule in any cell may not last more than a day. But the molecules are steadily reproduced, each according to its pattern. And so the memory trace would, theoretically, remain.

Are the molecules reproduced exactly? Again theoretically, they are. But we know that the emotions are powerful editors of memory. A memory can become clothed in nostalgic longing and its less agreeable realities become veiled, blurred, perhaps erased. Or the darker aspects of the experience may be sharpened by grief, fear, loathing. A memory can be unbearable and sink without a trace, or so it appears until some dynamic event brings it to the surface again like the detonation of a depth charge. Or perhaps the memory itself, the fact or the experience, remains sunk and we are aware only of the emotion swirling around it, like waters swirling around a hidden reef.

We have been calling this hypothetical explanation of memory a chemical one, but it is both chemical and physical, or more accurately it belongs in that scientific limbo where chemistry and physics meet, because it deals with the changing of energy back and forth between chemical and physical forms. We accept this changeling character of energy every day of our lives when we turn on the electric range for heat to cook by, or the television set for images and sounds. We know very well that what comes through the wall outlet into the apparatus is not heat or light, or pictures, words and music. It is energy in the form of electricity, and the appliance converts the same energy into these other forms.

The concept that energy may be converted within the brain cells in much the same way is harder to accept. From the heat generated in a cooking stove to the heat generated in a cell is not so great a leap. But between energy converted into cellular heat or even muscular power, and energy converted into remembered facts and feelings, is such a jump that we cannot be surprised if the imagination boggles at it.

Can we really believe that the change of a single atom, or the position of an atom, in a giant molecule which itself is invisible, may be the means of a vividly remembered childhood scene? Yet man has found the way to store images in very small packets, on magnetic tape.

However memory may work, if the temporal lobe of the cortex is its center, its nerve fibers must reach into many other parts of the brain, old and new, to bring together those associations of fact and feeling that constitute our everyday, normal experience of memory. Sometimes the association comes instantly to mind: the name, face, occasion of a previous meeting, the incidents of a previous experience. On examinations some students have the happy faculty of summoning the right answers on demand. The memory can also be trained; most memory systems are based on associative cues of one kind or another.

Sometimes we have the experience of trying unsuccessfully to dredge up a memory, only to have it float to the surface hours or days later when we are not trying at all. A word, a tune, a telephone number or address will sometimes elude us in this way and come to mind when we are no longer struggling to recapture it. The associative pathways are twisted and winding, as are the nerves along which, we assume, they must travel. It is not remarkable that we forget. What is remarkable is that we remember as well as we do.

SLEEPING AND WAKING

The body needs rest; it is the brain, as we mentioned earlier, that needs sleep. In particular it is the cortical brain, the new brain, that first becomes disordered and chaotic in the experimental non-sleeping marathons.

When a man stays awake around the clock for 240 hours, as the scientific investigator Dr. Nathaniel L. Kleitman has done (or for 200 hours, as did disk jockey Peter Tripp recently in New York's Times Square) with a crew of relentless watchers to shake him when he dozes and catch him when he tries to steal away for a cat nap, what happens to him physically? The effects of such an ordeal on the body should be ravaging, or so we would imagine. The surprise is that there are virtually no effects at all, no remarkable changes in blood pressure, heart rate, or other significant indicators of physical fitness. The reflexes remain normal. He does not even lose weight!

It is the organizing, reasoning, remembering brain that suffers. On the second or third day the signs of cortical fatigue begin to appear—irritability, increased sensitivity to pain, loss of memory, and then hallucinations and delusions. An Army volunteer in one of many stay-awake experiments was convinced he was an FBI agent on a secret mission for the White House. Another believed he was the victim of a murder plot and became violent with the watchers.

And here we find a curious paradox. It is the brain that must have sleep, but it is also the brain that keeps us awake. One of the great achievements of man, compared with the lower orders, is that he voluntarily spends more time awake than asleep. His is a "wakefulness of choice" as against the "wakefulness of necessity" of animals, whose principal waking interest is to satisfy hunger.

Man with his highly developed brain is curious, seeking always to transcend his limitations in time and space; he is also sociable and talkative. And man alone, of all living creatures, is capable of boredom. With too much idling, or too long running on a treadmill of routine, characteristically he does not simply go to sleep as his dog or cat would do. His brain makes him restless and discontented so that he is driven again to find something new in which to be interested.

Man needs more than food to live on; his brain is greedy for stimuli. Unless it is fed it will give him no rest, or it will torture him with delusions; we remember the college boys on their cots, in the sensory deprivation experiment. The search for something to be interested in is not limited to scientific geniuses and intellectual giants. It is a trait shared by all healthy children, and there is a vast industry of leisuretime arts, crafts, sports, education, and entertainment, that has no other purpose than to cater to the same need in adults.

The human baby begins life by sleeping twenty or twenty-two hours out of the twenty-four, waking up only to eat. But very soon this changes, sooner, in fact, than even the baby experts used to think; by actual observation, most babies two or three weeks old are doing nicely on only about fifteen hours of sleep a day. And usually sooner than the baby books predict, the young child is fighting his nap and fighting his bed time. Many explanations of an emotional kind are offered for children's protest against sleep, and no doubt they are valid; but the obvious explanation is often lost sight of. The child's developing brain is discovering too many interesting things in the world, is drinking in too many lively new stimuli, to be able to go docilely to bed and shut down for the night.

What happens in the body when we go to sleep, we know in considerable detail. There is a general slowing down of all the body's rhythms, a diminuendo of all its processes. Heartbeat and respiration retard to a leisurely pace; blood pressure and temperature fall to a lower level; the level of adrenaline in the blood and the volume of urine also fall. But these changes come about when we are merely lying down and resting. What happens in the brain that makes the difference between resting and sleeping?

The electroencephalogram gives us the record of diminishing brain activity. When you close your eyes, the alpha rhythm of ten waves per second begins to break up; soon the ripples come, not steadily, but in bursts with pauses between. In a desultory way you may be scanning in your mind the events of the day just past or the prospects of the day to come. Then the ripples vanish and large angular waves appear, called "spindles"; these seem to represent incomplete thoughts, fragmentary ideas, again with pauses between. They give way to long, slow waves, "rollers" at the rate of three per second, as the sleeper sinks to a level of crude undifferentiated feelings, and after them a series of fine, irregular vibrations, very fast, about twenty per second, the last flickers of attention. Then these, too, flatten out, and the line traced by the recording pen becomes nearly horizontal, with long delta waves that may be as slow as one every two seconds.

This is the first and deepest level of sleep, lasting for an hour or two. After that the patterns go through cycles, sometimes close to waking, then back to deeper sleep again. The electroencephalogram refuted the old belief that we plunge to bottomless depths on first falling asleep and spend the rest of the night climbing slowly back to consciousness. The sleeper wavers from level to level, and now and then he seems to float up quite close to the threshold of consciousness.

We move about in sleep, once or twice every hour, more frequently toward morning; we change position on the average between twenty and forty times a night. A really immobile sleep is not necessarily the soundest or the most restful. The body needs to change position if it is to rest all its muscles and keep the blood freely circulating.

And we all dream. Those who believe their sleep is dreamless simply do not remember their dreams. Usually it is the fast wakers, or those who spend their first waking moments quickly orienting themselves, who forget that they have been dreaming. Nor do our dreams go by in a few brief seconds; this is another of the many old misconceptions about sleep. We have periods of dreaming that last for as long as half an hour at a time.

THE DREAM WORLD

Why do we dream? This is a point on which the physiologists and the psychoanalysts seem to meet. Sigmund Freud surmised that our dreams stand guard between our sleeping minds and the stimuli from outside and from within the body that might wake us; since the brain must have sleep, dreams are a mechanism to buffer it against being disturbed. Possible disturbances are harmlessly deflected by being woven into dreams.

In a University of Chicago experiment to discover whether this was so, the volunteer sleepers suffered noises, flashing lights, sprays of cold water—minor torments designed to twitch, though not quite to pull aside, the restful curtain of unconsciousness. Then they were awakened and asked what they had been dreaming. Not quite half the dreams they reported had incorporated the most annoying stimuli in their dreams. What kept the other volunteers asleep?

One speculation is that we enjoy our dreams and do not want to wake up. But according to Dr. Calvin S. Hall of Western Reserve University, who collected 10,000 dreams of normal people, and some other dream collectors, more than two-thirds of our dreams are apparently far from enjoyable, if we judge them by our waking standards of enjoyment.

Two out of three dreams are unhappy or unpleasant; they express fear, sadness, or anger. Sixty-three per cent of the acts performed in dreams are hostile. They outnumber friendly or loving acts by three to one. Two per cent of the unloving deeds we perform in our dream lives are downright homicidal.

If our dream world is more often painful than pleasant, what becomes of the theory that we cling to sleep because we enjoy dreaming? The contradiction may be only apparent. According to psychoanalytic theory, our dreams express our unconscious wishes and fears, and even though these are often angry, anxious, or sad, they serve a sleep-protecting function. These disturbing emotions and experiences stored in our unconscious are released in the safe symbolism of dreams, and so they do not disturb us. When they become too powerful, or perhaps too literally recognizable by our conscious minds, then we experience not a dream but a nightmare, and usually we are brought sharply awake. The most frequent sufferers from nightmares are little children, whose strong emotions are still close to the surface and who do not yet clearly distinguish between fantasy and reality.

Women dream more than men, and young people more than older ones; bright people do more dreaming than those with low I.Q.'s. In dreams we have the illusion of carrying on conversations, but we probably hear only one side of the dialogue, our own. Smell and taste sensations are comparatively rare. Under our closed eyelids our eyes move from side to side and up and down while we dream, as though we were actually watching the dream images move across a screen. Most of us dream in black and white. About one in three, especially women and young people, dream in color.

WAKING UP

Added to the many myths about sleeping and waking that have been punctured in recent studies is one more, the notion that a really healthy person leaps out of bed wide awake and full of energy after a good night's sleep. The evidence is that we all wake slowly, even after we are up and dressed and have breakfasted, and some of us wake much more slowly than others.

It takes time for body and brain to warm up to efficient working levels after the night's slowdown. Temperature and metabolism records show that the warming-up process requires a certain amount of time for everyone, but follows different patterns for different individuals. Some have a curve that rises through the morning, reaches a peak about midday and declines through the afternoon, while others are definitely at their best in the morning. Still others, the "evening people," wake up feeling wretched and are at their liveliest at night when the morning people are about ready for bed.

Submarine crews and polar explorers experience considerable variation in their sleeping habits when the natural rhythm of daylight and darkness—or an alarm clock and an eight-hour working day—is not there to keep them regular. There is nothing arbitrary, it seems, about when we need to go to sleep and how much sleep we need. Some individuals do well on less sleep, some require more.

Sleep needs are supposed to diminish with age, but there are elderly people who need as much sleep as any growing youngster. And there are young people who can dance or study all night and feel no ill effects. We can and do "catch up" on sleep; after a spell of late hours we snatch some extra hours to pay off the sleep debt.

All this we know about sleep; but the nature of sleep itself is still elusive. One of the oldest theories is that the blood supply to the brain diminishes, and so we sleep. But the volume of the brain actually increases during sleep, and this indicates not a reduced but an accelerated flow of blood to the brain. Another classic explanation is that fatigue toxins accumulate in the brain, in the same way that lactic acid accumulates in weary muscles; this may be true, although no such toxins have been found.

Still another speculation is that fatigue may take place at the synapses where the nerve ends communicate: either the nerve ends retract, breaking off communication, or else the chemicals necessary for carrying nerve impulses across the synapses become exhausted. There is also a possibility that we go to sleep because we are conditioned to do so by the clock, the darkness, and the act of going to bed.

And finally there is the closed-circuit theory, which may allow room for the others as well. According to this interpretation, the brain is kept awake and alert by stimuli from the body entering the lower centers, which then stimulate the higher centers, and the alert and active brain in turn sends impulses out to the body, keeping the muscles in a state of readiness, or tone. Fatigue may enter this circuit at either point: the fatigued muscles begin to relax and send fewer impulses to the brain, or the fatigued brain sends fewer to the muscles. Stimuli and responses continue to decline, feedback becomes less and less, and we fall asleep.

The same process works in reverse to wake us up: the rested body begins to respond to such environmental stimuli as light and noise, and peripheral nerves send an increasing volume of stimuli to the brain centers, which respond by sending increasing stimuli to the skin and muscles, and so the feedback accelerates until brain and body are wide awake again. Dr. Kleitman formulated this theory of sleep in 1939, and nothing that has been discovered in the many investigations since then has invalidated it.

Whatever its mechanism, sleep is not an absolute antithesis of waking. It is only a way station on the brain's scale of attention; there are many degrees of attentiveness even while we are, as we believe, fully awake. According to one estimate, we are altogether alert and attentive only about one minute out of every hour. The rest of the time we are operating almost automatically, by habit and training, with only a fraction of the mind.

And even when we are most deeply asleep, the resting brain is not totally unresponsive. It leaves some inner gates open, although the particular stimulus that finds entrance there is different for each one of us. A sea captain wakes at a change in the sound of his ship's engines; a mother wakes at her baby's cry. And, as Sigmund Freud pointed out long ago and recent studies have confirmed, there is one sound that will wake almost anyone, and that is the spoken sound of his own name.

21

THE WORLD PERCEIVED

THE WORLD is so full of a number of things, sang a favorite poet of childhood. His simple, happy phrase evokes the freshness of a child's perceptions, when so much of the world is encountered for the first time and every message from every sense is new and wonderful.

As we go our daily way, each one of us walks through the same steady shower of impressions on our senses, some gently persistent, some elusive, some aggressively demanding attention. Hundreds and thousands of sensations pour in at the open doors and windows of our senses and along the passageways of the nerves to the brain, where we sort them out and decide which are worthy of note.

Of necessity, in our busy lives, we become exclusive about what we will give our attention to. The thousands of sensations stream past; we select from them the practical and needful, the unusual, the especially pleasurable, the painful or those that threaten to cause pain. Both the continuous stream of sensations and the ability to select among them are essential to our survival. The whole process is so automatic that we are not in the least aware of how astonishing it is.

To begin with, the notion that we have five senses and only five is a misleading simplification. Each of the major senses—vision, hearing, taste, smell, touch—is not one but a group or family of receptors. Vision involves seeing form, color, distance, and seeing at varying intensities of light from brilliant day to nearly black night. Hearing implies pitch, timbre, intensity, and the direction from which the sound is coming.

Analyze any single sensation and you will soon see that it is not single at all, but a multiple of many separate factors. Many of these factors have their own mechanisms in the sense organs and make their separate contributions to the total perception. Nor is it easy to single out even a major perception. If you give your mind to the job, you can say what it is you see or hear, but in the ordinary course of experience your seeing and hearing come mixed. What you taste is rarely separate from what you smell. Touch is far from an adequate word for the combination of senses by which you know that you are holding a piece of ice in your hand, for example, and that it is cube-shaped, wet, and too cold for comfort.

The five senses are multiple, and furthermore they do not include the muscle senses by which we recognize the weight of things when we heft them, or the sensation of pain that may come with any of the other sensations when they are too intense, as well as from injury. There are interior sensations: hunger, thirst, nausea, satiation, fatigue, and the sexual sensations. These last, physiologists think, may be related to another special sense, a tickle sense. And there are senses of motion and balance and the position of the body and its members in space, the kinetic and the proprioceptive senses, by which the individual perceives not only himself but his relationships to the world around him.

All this is far more than a simple sum of five senses. It is an assembly of extraordinary special mechanisms, each distinctly adapted to its task, and each unique in its way. The receptor— that is, the end organ of the sense—is stimulated by a particular stimulus to which it is specifically sensitive, and this stimulus is relayed along the nerve pathways to its destination in a particular area of the cortex that is devoted to that special sense, with detours to lower levels of the brain on the way, as we have seen. The brain makes a double response: it assesses the quality of the sensation, and it decides whether the sensation is pleasant or unpleasant. These two responses may involve two separate brain mechanisms.

Some of the senses must be acted upon by direct contact with the stimulus, or very nearly so: the senses that we group as "touch" in the skin are of this kind. Two are acted upon chemically: taste, which is stimulated by molecules dissolved in liquid passing over the receptors, and smell, for which the molecules are diffused in air. Vision and hearing are distance receptors. The energy that stimulates them comes in the form of light waves for one, sound waves for the other, and the source from which they come may be nearby or as far as a clap of thunder in the upper air, a ray of light from a star millions of light years away.

The distinctions of near and far are learned by experience; to a baby, the objects he can touch, smell, or see all seem to be the same distance away. It is the distance receptors, and the ability of the brain to interpret the complicated messages they transmit, that give the higher animals their primary advantage over the more primitive forms of life.

We hardly ever experience a pure sensation, unless possibly a sensation of pain, and then it has to be simple, quick, and localized, like the prick of a needle, for us to experience it unmixed. Of the many messages the senses communicate to the brain, those to which we give conscious attention are so swiftly interpreted and related to memory, association, judgment, and especially to other sensations, that it is almost impossible to disentangle the original single sensation from the context in which we become aware of it. And it is almost impossible, too, to disentangle the pure sensation from the wealth of experience and learning that the brain immediately brings to bear on it.

How, for example, do you park your car? How do you know so swiftly that you must swing your wheel a fraction one way, then a fraction the other way, in order to slide into the limited space? How do you know, just by looking at it, that there is enough space? The answer is obvious—some learn this kind of spatial judgment more readily than others, but we must all learn it. Yet the same kind of learning goes into far less obvious acts that we perform automatically with every waking movement that we make. We could not pick up a pencil, flick a light switch, take a step up or down, or walk through a room without fumbling, stumbling, or bumping into things if we had not learned to judge distances.

A similar swift conversion of simple sensation into judgment and meaning is applied to all our other senses, though not to the same extent. Of all the senses, human beings depend most of all upon vision; it is our principal practical guide in the daily acts of living and working. Our other senses also make their steady contribution to our safe, comfortable, and efficient functioning in the world around us. And they enrich our lives immeasurably with esthetic experiences. Imagine a spring morning or a crisp fall afternoon, an evening at the ballet, a ski run over powder snow on a mountain trail, or a good dinner with good company in a pleasant place. How many kinds and qualities of sensation, how many facets of our senses contribute to any of these enjoyments? Just to list them would be a challenging exercise.

THE SENSES OF TOUCH

Eyes, ears, nose, palate come readily to mind when we are asked to name the sense organs; it would hardly occur to us to name the skin as one of them. Least regarded, yet intimate with every part of the body and most useful in keeping all parts comfortable is this sensory envelope. It is literally a sheath of sensation, alert and responsive from crown to finger tips to toes. Through its 3,100 or so square inches are threaded many thousands of sensory nerves. Their endings are dotted all over the body, thronging in some areas, thinly spread in others. Constellations of them are clustered at the base of every hair. The passage of even a breath of air stirs some of them, and others signal whether it is warm air or cool, moist or dry.

Until the end of the nineteenth century the sensations of the skin—warmth, cold, pressure, pain—were all thought to be aspects or subqualities of the sense of touch. Around 1890 experiments were carried out in which every square inch of the skin was marked off and tested for each of these sensations. The investigators found, to their surprise, that they were not at all the same. Different spots responded to different stimuli. Some, for example, were sensitive to warmth and pain but not to cold, others only to cold, still others only to pressure or pain. Touch itself was found to be a separate sensation from any of the others.

And the five separate sensations, although distributed all over the body, did not occur at all uniformly. Many more cold "spots" than warm ones were discovered on the back, and many more warm than cold ones on the front of the body. This is logical. By the very structure of the body, man's back is broad and relatively exposed, an ideal sentinel to warn him of approaching chilliness in his environment. The abdominal surface, by contrast, is a natural nest, cupped by the embracing limbs; it has been from the beginning, especially in females, the cozy shelter for the young, and hence the heat receptors here are a useful signal of degrees of warmth.

Similarly, the distribution of the other skin receptors was found to be quite uneven over the surface of the body, with some areas far better supplied than others. What is more, each of them is now known to have a different structure at the receiving end: a rather elongated bulb-shaped organ for touch, a squat bulb for cold, a mechanism like twisted threads for warmth, an ovoid corpuscle for deep pressure.

Only pain appears to have no special structure for its reception. The pain receptor is simply a nerve end stripped of its protective sheath and laid bare. The image that this calls up is in itself rather painful, but we must remember that the pain fibers are a network within the skin, not crudely exposed but sheltered under a reasonably tough layer of outer skin cells. People seem to have had some such idea about sensitiveness to pain long before the anatomists and physiologists told us it was so. We say that a hypersensitive person is "thin-skinned" or that "his nerves are raw."

This group of senses has in common a group of functions: they are nociceptive, that is, they warn us of possible harm and certainly of discomfort. They also tell us about the shapes and surfaces of things: large, small, angular or curved, smooth or rough or sharp or blunt, and degrees of wetness, coldness, warmth. With experience we learn to recognize objects and textures by their feel: china, metal, wood, flower petal and leaf. An experienced housewife can distinguish between good and poor qualities of linen tea towels and wool blankets by their textures; a printer can tell the quality of paper in the same way.

And since they are all located in or just under the skin, however unevenly, they usually send their messages to the brain in combination. There is no special end organ for wetness, for example, but we recognize well enough whether the object we are touching is wet or dry; psychologists think the sensation may be a combination of cold and pressure. Heat and cold are distinct, except when they approach extremes. A piece of ordinary ice is cold, but dry ice on the skin—solidified carbon dioxide, 109 degrees below zero—gives a "burning" sensation, and so does friction, as when a rope "burns" the hand, an experience with which riggers, sailors, and mountain climbers are familiar.

If the sensory nerves were evenly distributed, each half-inch square of skin would have a dozen heat receptors and a pair for cold, twenty-five for touch, two hundred for pain. Just how sensitive each spot is to each kind of stimulus depends in part upon how thickly receptors of that kind are clustered in that spot. The closeness of the receptors also helps us in locating the area of the sensation. Touch, pressure, and pain can be quite accurately located, but cold and heat sensations are more diffuse. The tip of the tongue is most thickly supplied with touch receptors, after that the palm side of the finger tips.

The thinness of the skin in a given area and its supply of hairs also contributes to its touch sensitivity. A touch as light as two milligrams—one fifteen-thousandth of an ounce—on the thin skin of the forehead, for instance, can be felt, while a five-milligram touch, two and one-half times as heavy, is the lightest perceptible one on a finger tip. Hairs grow virtually everywhere on the skin except the palms of the hands and the soles of the feet; they grow at a slant like grass swept by a breeze, and touch spots cluster in the skin on the windward side of each one of them. Thus even a light touch on the tip of a hair bends it back, and like a tiny lever it communicates the touch to the receptors.

How do we know whether it is one or two objects that we are touching? Aristotle solved this little riddle long ago with his experiment with the pea, and children have been playing the trick on each other ever since. When the fingers are in their normal positions, the old Greek scientist discovered, an object held between the forefinger and middle finger touches the adjacent sides of both of them, yet we know it to be a single object. But if we cross these two fingers, and then put the object between them, with the eyes shut the feeling is that there are two objects— because ordinarily it takes two objects to stimulate the touch receptors on the opposite sides of the fingers.

What this means is that learning and experience are a vast part of our perceptions; even so minute a discrimination as this one is the result of learning. Touch the skin of your forearm with two objects an inch apart: the sensation will be that of a single object touching you. In the middle of the back, on the upper arm and the thigh the touches may be still farther apart, and the sensation will still be that of a single touch.

The finger tips, the lips, and especially the tip of the tongue can distinguish separate touches that are barely separated. These areas are most richly supplied with touch receptors. Furthermore, from birth they have had the most practice in exploring our immediate environment for us. The baby pops every new object he picks up into his mouth, not to taste, but to feel it; his lips are an additional set of finger tips and his tongue is even more sensitive.

It is not hard to see how the skin, with its other functions, also developed into a receiving apparatus for the body's direct contact with its environment. The first, most primitive receptivity of an organism is to these very stimuli of touch, pressure, and temperature. In the course of evolution the protective value of these receptors became more and more important to living creatures as they ventured into new environments, from the soft, warm sea, for example, onto the land with its rough, hard surfaces and its extreme temperatures.

The crustaceans and the insects needed no sensitive skin, since they wore their skeletons on the outside. The soft-skinned vertebrates had to develop specialized senses in their outer covering if they were to survive. Or, to put the case with more Darwinian precision, their chance for survival depended on how well their skins kept them informed of changes, especially dangerous changes, in their environment.

From survival to comfort is a step many of the higher animals have taken; puss purring by the fire is a traditional symbol of comfort. The further step, of using his tactile senses in the development of fine skills and exquisite esthetic pleasures, is a privilege reserved for cortical man.

THE CHEMORECEPTORS: TASTE

This high-sounding word is the label that physiologists give to taste and smell; it is useful as a reminder that these two senses are stimulated by chemical means.

It is useful, also, in reminding us that these two senses are most often stimulated jointly, one reinforcing the other, so that we often confuse them. With them go certain tactile sensations that are also hard to separate. When you complain, "This coffee is cold; it tastes awful," you are reporting two sensations and the absence of a third that you have reason to anticipate. There is no chemical difference between hot and cold coffee; the coffee would have the same effect on your taste receptors no matter what its temperature. But the hot-cold receptors in your mouth have given you the wrong reaction—you have a cool sensation when you anticipated a hot one. And your smell receptors, which should have reported the delicious aroma of coffee, have reported nothing at all. No aroma rose to your waiting nose, because there was no steam to carry it.

The same confusion occurs when toast or bacon seems tasteless because in fact it has merely failed to be crisp and crunchy, when a pastry has no flavor because it is heavy and soggy instead of light and flaky. Many people think they dislike the taste of cabbage or of fish when what really displeases them is the smell; the same goes for many cheeses. Some restaurateurs trade on the fact that people will relish a tough and virtually tasteless steak if it has a charcoal or hickory-smoke fragrance. Taste is often overwhelmed by smell because, of the two, it is far less sensitive.

Like the end organs of the tactile senses, the taste receptors are differentiated. Each responds only to the kind of taste for which it is specialized. There are four fundamental tastes: sweet, salt, sour, and bitter; alkaline and metallic are sometimes included as basic taste sensations. All other tastes are combinations of these, often with sensations from other kinds of receptors. The taste of ice cream involves cold receptors in the mouth; ginger "burns," that is, it excites other sensory nerves in the mouth, and this sensation is part of our perception of the taste of ginger; lemon juice puckers the mucous membrane by its astringent action, as do other acid substances, and this is part of the taste of sourness. With oils, custards and gelatine preparations, with chewy caramel or melting chocolate, the texture—a tactile sensation—is inextricably associated with the actual taste recorded by the taste receptors.

These receptors, called buds, are bundles of slender cells with hairlike branches, packed together in groups called papillae at various places on the tongue. Each of the four tastes has its own buds: sweet and salt receptors cluster most numerously on the tip and fore part of the tongue; sour receptors are mainly along the edges, and bitterness is tasted at the back of the tongue and on the epiglottis. We taste bitter-sweet substances in two stages, first sweet, then bitter. The solid center of the tongue's surface has little or no ability to taste.

The most sensitive taste buds are those for bitterness: they can detect the taste when it is only one part in two million. A good deal more sweetness is necessary before it is perceived, one part in two hundred. In order for the taste buds to detect any taste at all, the molecules of the substance must enter the pores of the papillae and stimulate the hairlike processes of the taste buds directly. Thus the substance has to be dissolved in liquid; if it is not liquid when it comes into the mouth, then it is chewed or it melts and becomes mixed with saliva. If you put a solid substance into your mouth and no part of it, not even a molecule, became dissolved, you would not taste a thing.

Taste buds are apparently supplied to animals according to their need. Whales swallow their food whole and so they need few if any taste buds. The antelope, on the other hand, is highly sensitive to taste and has 50,000 taste buds. A pig, more discriminating than he is given credit for, has 5,500. Man possesses only 3,000, unfortunately for his vanity; but what he lacks in the physical equipment for a gourmet he more than makes up for in cultivation.

It is this cultivation that not only sets man's taste apart but makes taste itself a more complicated affair than the purely sensory stimulations, complex though they are, of vision and hearing. From infancy we associate the chemical stimulation of the taste buds with touch, pressure, cold, heat, all of them tactile senses, and smell. This mixture becomes ever more refined, and reaches its peak in the wine experts who, with one meditative sip of a wine, can tell the vineyard it came from and the year in which it was harvested. Another group of experts can discriminate among the sixty-four varieties of pepper.

Most of us are content just to enjoy a well-planned, well-cooked dinner, but even this is not a simple sensory experience for the diner—or the cook. The four fundamental tastes, plus weight and fluidity, mildness and sharpness, temperature, texture, and a number of other subtle attributes, and finally the elusive influence of smell, all enter into our appreciation of a meal.

SMELL

The sense of smell once dominated the brain, and for many higher animals it still does. Even the fishes follow their noses. Salmon swimming upstream will not go through water saturated with man smell or bear smell. We surmise that when man's forebears took to the trees, their sense of smell was no longer an adequate guide. Among tree dwellers, those with the keenest distance receptors—sight and hearing—were the ones who survived and procreated. Thus the "nose brain," as it is called, of the ground-dwelling species was bred out of the tree dwellers, little by little through the millenniums.

The distance that ultimately separated the species is apparent in a man and his dog. The dog's contact with the world is by way of his nose; his olfactory apparatus occupies a large part of his brain and most of his instinctual and reflex behavior is tied to what his sense of smell tells him about his environment. Not so with man. His eyes have a far larger area in his brain, and his other sense organs are on the whole more highly developed.

The external organs of smell are comparatively simple: they occupy an area no larger than a fingernail, on each side of the far interior of the nose. Ordinary air currents do not flow directly over them as we breathe, and for this reason we sniff when we consciously want to detect an odor or to enjoy a fragrance to the full. Convection currents are set up when the cool air we inhale meets the warm air within the nose, and thus the molecules of odorous substances, diffused in the air, are carried into the inner chamber to mix with the mucous fluid and so act on the olfactory cells, in much the same way that substances in solution act on the taste buds.

The olfactory receptors adapt to a particular odor rather rapidly; although an odor seems quite strong at first, it soon begins to fade. This is not true for everyone, or for every odor, but it is a familiar experience for many. Oddly enough, while one odor fades away another may be detected, so the reaction is not one of olfactory fatigue, but only of adaptation to a particular substance and its chemical action on the cells.

Odors are harder to classify than colors, the pitch of sounds, and the four primary tastes. Most investigators believe there are as many different odors as there are odor-exuding substances. A number of classifications have been attempted. Here is one that lists eight kinds of odors: ethereal, as of fruits; aromatic or resinous, as of camphor or bitter almonds; fragrant or balsamic odors, as of flowers and flowery perfumes; ambrosial odors, such as musk; garlic odors, in which are included garlic, onions, and also sulfur and selenium compounds; burnt odors, as of tobacco, roasted coffee, roast meat, also burning feathers; goat odors, from sweat, ripe cheese, and caproic acid which comes from fatty animal tissue and cocoanut oil and is used in artificial flavoring (its name is taken from the Latin word, *caper,* for goat, because of its smell); finally, foul odors, from decaying meat or vegetable matter and from excrement.

Neither this list nor any other appears to satisfy everyone. There seems to be more individuality in the way odors affect people than in almost any of the other sensory perceptions. What is more, most of us react rather strongly to odors. The sense of smell seems to have gained emotional and esthetic power as it has lost in practical value. A disagreeable odor does not merely displease us, as might an unpleasant sound or an ugly sight; it disgusts us. When there is a pleasant scent we can hardly get enough of it; our olfactory cells stop reacting to the salty sea breeze, the piney wood, the flower garden—or the perfume that costs many dollars per ounce—long before we tire of it. Part of the charm of a fragrance is that it is so elusive.

Individuals differ enormously in their keenness of smell, but there is one curious aspect of this sense that almost all of us have experienced, whether or not we have good noses, and that is the power of an odor to call up memories. Sometimes the odor is actually present, sometimes it is only remembered by association, but either way it seems capable of arousing peculiarly poignant feelings. Some scientists, in a speculative mood, have suggested that the history of the olfactory sense may account for this. Although it has lost most of its ancient realm in the brain, and has been superseded in the cortex, it may still retain some remnants of its past powers through connections with the lower centers, those that have to do with our most basic emotions.

However that may be, although the sense of smell has lost most of its practical value for humankind, it remains a source of pure sensory enjoyment which no animal, however keen its nose, seems able to share except perhaps the cat, which apparently shares man's delight in flower fragrances and perfumes.

THE DISTANCE RECEPTORS: VISION

Compared with the chemical responses of taste and smell, the distance receptors present wonders of a different order. How does the ear bring us bird song and baby's cry, footsteps and fire sirens, and a passage from Shakespeare? How does the eye capture for us the forms and colors of images nearby and far away, in sunlight, twilight, or almost no light at all?

Scientists pondered for some two thousand years before they devised a dark box, with a hole and a lens, that could reproduce on its inner surface an image of outer reality. They tinkered for nearly three hundred years longer before they had a camera that could photograph that image. Living matter long ago changed and molded itself into just such a mechanism and, clever as he is, man has not been able to match it. The living camera of the eye photographs fleeting images by the thousands, between one moment and the next, and it makes its own adjustments, automatically and precisely, with each change in distance, light, and angle.

Leonardo da Vinci, as good an anatomist as he was an artist and physicist, described an experiment to illustrate how the eye works. He held a piece of paper before a small hole in the wall of a darkened room, and on it he saw the images of objects on the other side of the wall, in their exact forms and colors, with the single remarkable difference that they were reversed.

This is still a good way to understand the principle by which the eye—or a camera—captures and reproduces an image. The eyeball is the darkroom, the pupil is the small hole, and Leonardo's piece of paper is the layer of sensitive cells at the back of the eyeball, the retina.

There is nothing magical about this principle. Light rays pour through any opening, but if the opening is large and the chamber into which they come is light, the images that they might throw are diffused so that we do not see them as images but only as light. When we shut all other interfering light out of the chamber, and narrow the opening to a tiny circle, then we eliminate all other rays except those that come together at that tiny opening.

Light rays travel in a straight line. They come to the opening from all directions and, unless there is a lens over the opening, they travel straight on through it. Light reflected from the part of the scene that is directly opposite the opening will continue straight through in a horizontal plane, but rays from the top and bottom and sides of the scene come to the opening at an angle. Traveling on in the same direction, they spread out again on the inner side, exactly as they shone from the original scene, in the same relationships and color values, except that now the top of the scene is at the bottom, the left is at the right. If, like Leonardo, you were to hold up a piece of paper on the inner side of the opening, you would see the upside-down, left-to-right reproduction.

That is how the eye sees. The images on the retina are reversed, as they were on Leonardo's paper and as they are through the lens of a camera. The brain automatically turns them the right way around. In a psychological experiment some years ago, the volunteers were given spectacles which turned the world upside down before the picture reached the eye, so that the images on the retina came out right side up. The effect at first was confusing, probably dizzying, but within a day the volunteers were seeing the world right side up again even through their image-reversing spectacles. The flexible, self-adjusting cortex had adapted to the new conditions and learned to accept the unaccustomed right-side-up image directly from the retina. In this it had the help of experience, judgment, and the evidence of the other senses, especially the proprioceptive ones, which told the brain that its owner was not standing on his head.

The images that the eye sees are not simple and static like an object before a camera obscura or a picture posed for a photographer. The scene is fluid and changing; the object of our gaze is constantly shifting, and the head that holds these two living cameras is almost never still. Furthermore, the distance from the opening—the pupil—to the screen on which the image must be thrown—the retina—is fixed. It can be neither shallower nor deeper than the depth of the eyeball, whether the image comes from far or near.

Like a camera, the eye has a double convex lens to bend the

rays so that they will fall on the sensitive plate, the retina. But the lens of the eye is made of elastic living tissue and is held by a ligament, also of living tissue. It is the lens itself that makes the adjustment for distance. When you turn your gaze on a distant scene or on anything more than twenty feet away, the ligament tightens, pulling the lens out flat enough so that the light rays, coming almost directly to the eye, are bent only very little as they go through the lens to the retina. For near vision the ligament relaxes, and the lens through its own elasticity becomes more convex and bends the rays more sharply so as to bring them into focus within the shorter distance.

Our good vision both near and far depends upon this adjustment of the convexity of the lens to the depth of the eyeball. In nearsightedness—myopia—the distance from lens to retina is greater than normal and the image falls somewhere in front of the retina; in farsightedness the eyeball is shallower than normal and the focusing point of the image is somewhere behind the retina. In presbyopia—old-age vision—it is the loss of elasticity in the lens itself that causes blurring of the image of print and nearby objects.

The eye also has to adapt for the amount of light coming from the object, and for this it has the iris, a muscular diaphragm that hangs before the lens like a little curtain with a round hole in it; the hole is the pupil. The muscle fibers of the iris are of the smooth kind that are operated by the autonomic nervous system, and there are two sets of them, a circular group like a sphincter that constricts the pupil, and a radiating group that dilates the pupil. The stimulus is the amount of light that falls on the retina: when there is too much light for a clear image the sphincter muscle contracts; when there is too little, the dilator muscle pulls the opening wider.

But the pupils alone do not account for the eye's extraordinary adaptation to light and darkness. For this the retina itself has the special equipment of two sets of receptor cells. The retina developed originally from brain tissue and it is composed almost entirely of nerve cells, but of a very specialized kind. They are long and narrow, lying parallel like matches in a box with their heads, the receiving ends, in the depths of the retina and their transmitting ends toward the pupil. In front of the receptor cells are transmitting nerves that pick up the impulses across the synapses; the nerve fibers gather like wires in a trunk line to form the optic nerve, and where the optic nerve leaves the retina we have, in each eye, the curious phenomenon of the blind spot.

The receptor cells are the sensitive plate, the film of this living camera. They are of two kinds, cone-shaped and rod-shaped. Between them they cover the full range of light adaptation, the cone cells being sensitive in bright light, the rod cells in dim light. The cone cells are also the color film of our eye camera. At twilight, as the light fades the colors of things also fade because, as the light dims below their threshold of sensitivity, the cone cells cease to operate. The rod cells, taking over, respond only in black, white, and shades of gray that are mixtures of the two.

Vision is a photochemical reaction. In the rod cells the chemical involved is a rose-colored pigment called visual purple; the scientists' name for it is rhodopsin, from the Greek words *rhodon,* a rose, and *ops,* the eye. The cell synthesizes its pigment from vitamin A and a protein. Bright light "bleaches" the rhodopsin— splits the substance into its two components—and in the dark the cell resynthesizes it; this is what we experience as dark adaptation, during the several minutes it takes us to accustom our eyes to the change when we go from a light room into a dark one.

In the cone cells the sensitive pigment is called iodopsin, from the Greek word for violet, because that is its color. In bright light, as the rods lose their sensitivity, the cones gain theirs. The rods are spread around the periphery of the retina, and thus in dim light we have general vision but it is not very sharp or clear. The cones are clustered most thickly in the center, where the cell layers are thinnest and the sharpest vision occurs. When we turn our eyes and focus them on the object that we want to see, we bring the image onto that central area of the retina, and it is the cone cells with which we see most clearly.

It is with the cone cells, too, that we see color. The most generally accepted of a number of theories about color vision is that there are three types of cones, each containing a substance that reacts to light of a different color, one set for red, one for green, the third for violet. In light these are the primary colors which, mixed together, give white (in paints they are red, yellow, and blue). White light stimulates all three sets of color cells; any other color stimulates one or two. Color blindness, which is mostly inherited and mostly among males, is usually a lack of either the red or the green cones, but most color-blind persons see some difference between the two; otherwise they would not be able to distinguish traffic lights.

One of the most obvious facts about our eyes is that we wear them both in front of our heads, but the happy consequence is not so obvious: it is thanks to their position that we can see in depth. Probably the change came when our remote ancestor lived in the trees, for the ability to see in depth and to judge distances accurately must have been a considerable advantage while swinging from branch to branch, many feet above the ground. With both eyes in front, their separate fields of vision overlap. We see two images superimposed one upon the other, but because of the space between our eyes the image from each eye goes a little way around its own side of the object. Close this book, hold it in front of you, and look at the title on its spine first with one eye closed and then with the other; you will see that one eye gives you a little more of one side of the book, and the other a little more of the other side. With both eyes open, you see a little of both sides at the same time.

This is our gift of stereoscopic vision, which we share with our simian cousins. Fish and most other animals do not have it—to them the world appears flat. One of the few exceptions is the owl, which outsees all of us; he has not only stereoscopic but telescopic vision. Oddly enough, during the first few days after birth the human infant also has telescopic vision. Recently some tests were devised which revealed that babies three or four days old have an acuity for objects 450 feet away, but soon afterward they need binoculars!

Our judgment of distance depends with near objects upon our vision in depth; but as the distance increases there is less and less difference between the left-eyed and the right-eyed view, and so we depend upon other factors as well. Experience tells us that the farther away an object is, the smaller it looks. Its color also changes, its details disappear, its outline softens. Nearer objects, on which our depth vision is more effective, give us a measure by which to judge the remoteness of farther ones. Then there is perspective, the familiar illusion that parallel lines converge toward the horizon. And the other curious illusion that as we are moving, for example, in a car, the trees and houses nearest us go by in the opposite direction while the mountains in the distance and the sun in the sky seem to move with us.

All these are learned criteria, but we accept them automatically as we accept all the other wonders of our power of vision, including the remarkable mobility and co-ordination of our eyeballs. We can turn our eyes together in any direction, up and down and sideways, thanks to six fine little muscles with which each eye is equipped. These muscles, tiny but powerful, give instant co-ordinated obedience to our will.

From our knowledge of other body mechanisms we would expect this delicate, finely adjusted mechanism to be protected like a precious jewel, and it is. To begin with, it has three layers: the sensitive retina on the innermost side, the choroid coat which contains mainly the eye's blood vessels, and finally a tough fibrous outer coat, the sclera, which we see as the white of the eye; the cornea is the transparent round window at its front.

The eyeball itself is filled with fluid, the vitreous fluid, drawn from the blood plasma and automatically maintained at the correct pressure to keep the eyeball round. Here we have again, as with the foetus during pregnancy and indeed with the brain it-

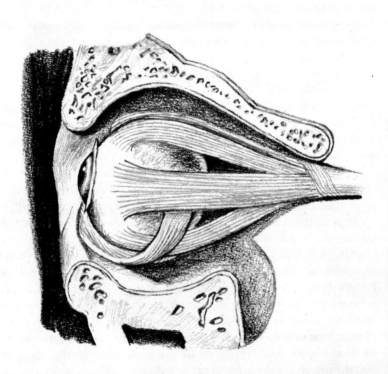

self, the simplest and surely the most efficient protective device for delicate structures, a tough flexible fibrous bag filled with fluid. As with the brain, too, the sac is nested in a bony shell, in this case the orbit, and a small pad of fat cushions the back of the eyeball against the bone.

With the eye, the bony case is necessarily open at the front, and this situation calls for additional protective devices. The cornea, transparent and somewhat bulging, is part of the sclerotic outer coat and just as tough, and it has behind it, moreover, another small chamber of fluid, the aqueous humor, insulating the iris and its opening, the pupil, immediately behind which is the lens. A continuous membrane, the conjunctiva, covers the exposed part of the eyeball and extends onto the inner surfaces of the lids.

The muscular curtain of the eyelids opens and shuts in a regular rhythm and in addition blinks reflexively when an object comes threateningly close. A broad circle of muscle tissue, the orbicular muscle, surrounds the orbit, and this shuts the lids; each lid is additionally equipped with its own muscle for opening. Unlike the muscles of the pupil, which are of the smooth type and unconsciously controlled, these are voluntary muscles and we control them consciously. The wink reflex is one of the inborn reflexes, as automatic as the stretch reflex in our body muscles that keeps us from falling over when we sit and stand.

Since the front of the eye is exposed to the air, it also has the device of the tear gland, which provides a continuous supply of fluid to wash over the exposed surface. Each wink of the eyelids swabs the eyeball, keeping it moist and keeping it clean of dust and particles. The gland is just above the eye, under the outer rim of the eye socket; two small ducts at the inner eye corner drain the fluid away through the nose. The tears contain lysozyme, a natural antibacterial agent which is also present in the saliva.

One more, rather odd protective mechanism was discovered by physiologists who were curious about the way we express emotions with our facial muscles. They observed that in expressions of strong emotion—anger, grief, laughter—and in violent physical exertion like that of the sprinter or the pole vaulter at the peak of his effort, the eyelids press down tightly on the eyes, squeezing shut or almost shut. One explanation offered for this reflexive tightening of the orbicular muscle is that in all these intense states the blood pressure rises considerably. The pressure of the eyelids against the eyeball could have the protective effect of counteracting this pressure from the blood vessels of the eyes, and thus keeping the delicate tissues within from being damaged.

The functional beauty of their structure is one more to add to the many beauties of the eyes that poets have sung and painters have painted lovingly through the ages. Set jewellike in their orbits between the accenting lines of brows and lashes and the planes of forehead, temple, and cheek, they gleam with colored irises and shining whites and reflect from their moist surfaces pinpoints of light and tiny, brilliant facets of their surroundings. They are the esthetic focus of the human face and its expressive focus as well; to read another's feelings we look into his face and most particularly into his eyes. Through our eyes the world sees each one of us as surely as we see the world.

HEARING

Compared with the lyrical orbs of vision, the organs of hearing seem slightly absurd. Their only beauty is to be as inconspicuous as possible; unless they are small and cling closely to the sides of the head we laugh at them and find them grotesque. Within, there is an elaboration of connecting parts that is positively fanciful, like the machines the comic artist Rube Goldberg used to draw.

First there is the tympanic membrane or eardrum. Then come three little bones, the hammer, the anvil, and the stirrup, called collectively the ossicles. These lead to the cochlea, named for a snail shell which it resembles almost perfectly; it is a tube coiled in two and one-half turns. Deep inside its fluid-filled convolutions, which are further complicated by dividing membranes, we finally come to the organ of Corti, containing the nerve ends of hearing which convert sound into impulses for the acoustic nerve to carry to the brain. Besides all this, there is the curious device of the semicircular canals, plus two other small organs, the utricle and the saccule, and a tube—the Eustachian tube—that communicates with the outer atmosphere by way of the nose.

We could call this fantastic structure nature's folly, but we would be wrong. It is in fact a brilliant solution of a formidable physiological problem, the problem of hearing. If the eye is admirable in its functional design, the ear, end product of a tortuous evolutionary history, is fabulous.

The ear began as a breathing apparatus, the gills of the fish. In the course of time it acquired the function of an organ of equilibrium, and in the fishes this is still its entire function; the finny folk apparently hear with their bodies by bone conduction. The semicircular canals which serve as our balancing mechanism are still structurally part of our labyrinthine hearing apparatus but they are functionally quite distinct, and we shall talk about them in later pages of this chapter.

The principle of the drum, a membrane stretched over a hollow, as a trap for sound waves appeared two separate times in the course of evolution. The grasshopper's eardrum differs from ours by being on his belly, and his tympanic membrane is part of an organ by which he receives the sensation of his own body move-

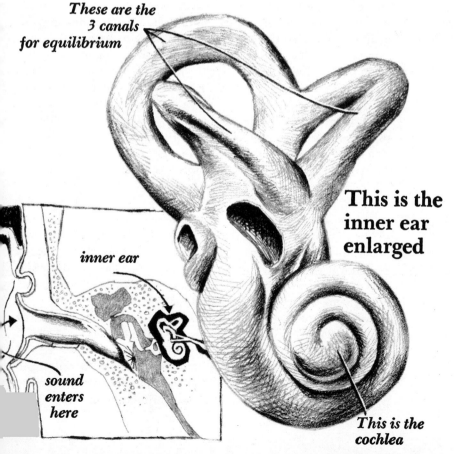

These are the 3 canals for equilibrium

This is the inner ear enlarged

inner ear

sound enters here

This is the cochlea

ments, by way of his outer covering. The katydid has its hearing apparatus on its forelegs, equipped with not one but two tympanic membranes, and with this it can hear sounds up to 55,000 vibrations per second, far higher than the human ear's upper limit of between a usual 20,000 and a possible but extremely rare 30,000. Grasshoppers, and also roaches, respond to much lower tones than our lower limit of about sixteen cycles per second.

The upper and lower limits, and especially the lower ones, of our hearing are a physiological necessity. If we could hear all the low tones the cockroach hears we would be constantly assaulted by a din of thumps and rumbles from our own bodies and every step we take would set up a reverberation from our skulls. If you doubt this, put your fingers in your ears and listen to the rumble and roar of your finger joints and muscles as you flex them.

But even with the development of the tympanic membrane, the problem of hearing was not solved. Most of the sound waves striking the membrane simply bounce off; what remains may be an infinitesimal vibration of the drum. But, to be useful to the living animal, the ear had to be sensitive to the lightest possible sounds, the rustle of leaves, crackle of branch, or stealthy footfall that might mean danger or dinner. At the other end of the decibel scale the ear had to be able to survive a sound violent enough to burst the drum; in nature this might be a clap of thunder or the explosion of a volcano. The ear actually is protected against such violent assaults with two tiny muscles that damp the vibrations in the tympanum and the ossicles. Only man makes noises too sudden or too protracted for this protective mechanism. The crack of a rifle, a bomb burst, or the continuous high level of some factory noises are all potentially destructive to hearing.

The solution of the main problem, that of hearing, is the ear's astonishing transmitting chain of membrane-ossicles-cochlea, a mechanical transformer that converts the large-amplitude sound waves striking the drum into smaller, more concentrated vibrations. Some frequencies of sound set the tympanic membrane vibrating less than one-billionth of an inch, and this unimaginably tiny vibration is converted into a sensation of hearing.

The ossicles, the three little bones in a row, act as a series of levers, each one multiplying the minute movement of the membrane as they pass it on, so that by the time the stirrup taps the window of the cochlea it has twenty-two times the pressure of the original vibration. The thin, oval-shaped window membrane vibrates in turn, setting the cochlear fluid in motion along its tortuous spiral, whose constricted winding channel multiplies the pressure still further, until the original vibrations reach the nerve ends in the form of quite powerful sideways motions—shearing forces—rubbing against the sensitive hairlike cells of the organ of Corti. The vibrations are transmuted into impulses that pass on along the acoustic nerve to the brain, and the waves of pressure within the cochlea are released by way of a second membrane-covered little window, the round window, at the other end of the cochlea. The Eustachian tube, no mere useless remnant of evolution, has the important function of keeping the air pressure on the inner side of the eardrum equal to that of the outer atmosphere, not only for our comfort—as we realize when we travel by plane—and for the safety of the membrane, but also so that the membrane may be free to vibrate.

Astonishingly, through this lengthy transmitting chain, the multitude of sounds are carried along, separate and distinct, instead of in the jumbled confusion that we might expect. Somehow the nuances of timbre, pitch, and intensity are maintained with each amplifying step so that when the impulses arrive in the auditory area of the cortex we distinguish a violin's note from a clarinet's, an automobile horn from a foghorn, and the fine shadings of accent, inflection, and expression in each other's speech.

Exactly how these distinctions are conveyed to the brain remains something of a mystery. We know that loudness is determined by the size of the sound waves, timbre or quality by their shape, and pitch by their frequency, the number of waves per second. The difference between a noise and a musical tone is in the regularity of musical sound waves, plus the overtones that accompany each note of music in a regular mathematical ratio. We hear these, too, as part of our musical perception.

The eye, as we noted, has its separate photochemical substances for different colors and its separate cells for different degrees of light. But the ear apparently must transmit the equivalent distinctions in sound all by way of the same set of hair cells in the organ of Corti, the end organ of hearing deep within the cochlea.

Just one of these questions—how we hear pitch—has kept generations of physicists and physiologists in lively debate. The ancients had an echo theory, a forecast of the resonance principle that the physiologist-physicist Helmholtz formulated in 1857. Helmholtz demonstrated that a sound of a particular frequency will set up sympathetic vibrations in, for example, the particular string of a piano that is tuned to the same frequency. The membrane on which the organ of Corti rests, deep within the cochlea, is shaped like a piano or harp, with long fibers corresponding to the bass, graduating to the short fibers of the treble. Conceivably each fiber might respond to a sound of its own frequency. But these graduated transverse fibers of the membrane are interwoven with longitudinal fibers, as if your piano's wires had another set of wires woven across them. Held fast in such a fabric, the fibers can hardly be expected to vibrate independently, each one to its own frequency.

Another theory is that the frequencies of pitch are transmitted in nervous impulses of the same frequencies to the brain. This is called the "telephone" theory because it is the way the telephone transmits sound, by way of electrical impulses corresponding in frequency to the sounds. But the nerves do not transmit continuous current, as we know. They discharge and then rest to recharge. The highest frequencies measured in nerve fibers are only a few hundred cycles per second. This might account for the low notes, but it can hardly explain how we hear the high ones.

The two theories are not mutually exclusive, nor do they exclude other possible ways in which the various sounds can be transmitted. Scientists today believe that several mechanisms may contribute to our hearing. For example, the long fibers may give us the frequencies of low notes by sympathetic vibrations, the shorter fibers may respond on something like the telephone principle, and the two ways of responding may overlap in the middle register, where our hearing is, in fact, most acute. Each one of the hair cells of hearing seems to have its representative spot in the auditory area of the cortex, so that the brain may interpret the pitch of a note according to the spot that is stimulated, in the same way that we locate the position of a touch on the skin.

Besides this, the whole cochlea vibrates to the sound wave pressures that are transmitted to it. The original sounds can be played back electrically, as though the cochlea were a microphone. This highly advanced form of physiological sound transmission is called aural microphonics; only birds and mammals have it. This is generally accepted as having a good deal to do with the musical perception which we share with the birds.

One of the puzzles especially tantalizing to musicianly scientists is that of perfect or absolute pitch, an inborn gift by which its possessor can tell you with his back turned that the note you strike on the piano is an A; he may also mention that your automobile motor is humming in E flat. Comparatively few people have absolute pitch, but musical training can develop relative pitch to a point very near perfection.

By all these curious mechanisms in the ear, and the subtle coordination in the cortex of our experiences from birth onward, we are able to distinguish more than 1,500 separate musical tones, besides sorting out, interpreting, and appreciating an infinite variety of sounds in our environment. Incidentally, the fact that we have two ears, one on each side of the head, helps us to determine the direction from which a sound is coming.

We do not hear nearly so wide a range of sounds as many other creatures. The bat, for example, guides its swift darting flight by its own faint supersonic clicks and even catches its dinner by the echo of its tiny sound from the body of a passing insect in the dark. We do not even have the hearing acuity of our own ancestors, for whom alertness to the slightest sounds might mean life or death.

If we have lost our primitive sharpness of hearing, we have gained in cultivation. The birds participate with us in appreciation of musical sounds, but even the warbler, practicing his turns and trills in the spring, cannot enjoy his own music in quite the way his human hearers do. And we can be certain that neither he nor any creature, other than civilized man, has an ear for a Bach fugue or a Gershwin blues.

Almost as wonderful—and for practical purposes, certainly as useful—as our ability to hear is our ability not to hear, that is, to shut out or ignore a vast amount of sound. The city room of a metropolitan newspaper is a bedlam of sound—phones, buzzers, voices calling, conversation and laughter, and from the pressroom the roar and rumble of the presses—and yet men and women can carry on at telephones and typewriters, apparently hearing nothing unless they are directly addressed.

Partly this is a development of inhibitory mechanisms in the cortex, by which familiar sounds of no particular meaning are suppressed. A laboratory cat learns to drowse undisturbed even by a pistol shot, if it hears the shot often enough. But part of the ability to shut out sound is the individual's development of his own powers of concentrated attention. There are vast differences between one person and another in sensitivity to sound. Some ears are so intensely responsive that their owners suffer something very like pain from certain kinds of noise, and it is a fatiguing effort for them to concentrate against distracting sounds. The eccentric novelist Marcel Proust surely had his nerves to contend with when he was finally driven to line his room with cork, but he may also have had the unfortunate gift of hypersensitive ears.

Architects and acoustic engineers are increasingly paying attention to the problem of noise. A British commission measured the distances at which houses should be placed from ordinary traffic and from truck traffic, and fatigue studies in industry make a strong case against uncontrolled factory noise. Man is a noisy animal at best, and the more civilized he is, the more noisy. He will have to be increasingly alert to protect his fine mechanism of hearing, the product of millenniums of evolution, against his own roaring progress into the twenty-first century.

THE SELF-SENSES

As though hearing were not enough of a task, the ear continues to serve its more ancient function as the organ of equilibrium. The three semicircular canals, with their little appendages of the utricle and the saccule, are structurally part of the labyrinthine system of canals that includes the cochlea. While in the course of evolution the cochlea became a specialist in hearing, the canals remained at their original task of keeping us in a state of balance.

The canals function with the beautiful simplicity of fluid in a tube: on the principle of inertia, when the container moves in one direction, the fluid is pressed back in the opposite direction, and this pressure against hairlike nerve cells in one end of the tube is what gives us our sensation. The three canals are placed at right angles to each other, one in each dimension of space—forward, backward, and to the side. With a set of these in each ear we are equipped to perceive motion in any direction, and automatically our body muscles respond to keep us in balance.

On the principle of momentum, we continue to feel that we are moving in the same direction for a moment or two after we

have stopped; the endolymph, the fluid in the canal, is still pressing against the cells. If we have been spinning hard in one direction, the act of stopping releases the pressure on the hair cells
suddenly so that for a moment we feel we are spinning in the opposite direction, although we are standing still. Dizziness and
staggering may follow too long or too rapid spinning—that is, too
intense a stimulation of the horizontal canals. A more spectacular
effect can be achieved by bending over and circling around a mark
on the ground. This brings the vertical canals into action, and
the unusual disturbance may upset the autonomic nervous system and bring on a number of disagreeable sensations, along
with a fall in blood pressure.

The canals provide us with our kinetic sense, the sense of motion. The organ of our static sense, which tells us which way is up,
is the utricle, a small chamber just below and connected with
the canals. In it is a plaque of hair cells covered with a gelatinous
layer, and clinging to this are crystals of carbonate of lime, the
otoliths or ear stones. The pressure of these crystals on the hair
cells tells us the position of the head in relation to the earth's
gravity. This is the stimulus that sets in motion the righting reflex, by which a falling cat turns in the air and lands on its feet,
also by which a diver on hitting the water turns and swims upward to the surface. It is the erratic, intermittent stimulation of
this sense that gives some persons motion sickness in a car, train, or
plane. In fact, both the canals and the utricle promise to be such a
nuisance to interplanetary travelers of the future that some specialists in space medicine believe these organs have outlived their
usefulness and may well be jettisoned.

The saccule, another small chamber below the utricle and with
a similar sensory apparatus, is connected with both the utricle
and the cochlea. It is the only remaining anatomical connection
between the organs of hearing and of balance, in the highly
evolved human ear. It may have to do with the static or kinetic
senses, or it may be part of the apparatus of hearing. It is one of
the many physiological puzzles that still baffle the students of the
ear.

Combined with the kinetic and static senses in the ear, the
nerve ends of sensation in all the muscles of the body give us our
proprioceptive senses—literally, our self-senses—the perceptions
of the body and its parts in space and in relation to each other.

All our muscular co-ordinations are based on signals from these sensory nerves. Their impulses stream into the lower brain, which sorts them out and organizes them on the way to the cortex, just as it organizes and co-ordinates the muscular instructions sent out by the cortex.

All unnoticed as we give our attention to the important business of living, these senses guide every motion and gesture that we make. Thanks to them and to the watchful centers in the brain, we move smoothly, efficiently, and sometimes gracefully on our way.

PART VI

RETROSPECTS

AND

PROSPECTS

22

THE UNIQUE YOU

THE BIRTH OF A CHILD, says Dr. George Draper, confronts us with an amazing circumstance. All at once there is a new presence in the room, "a new, complete individual, with moving arms and legs and a perfectly well-defined and unique individuality."

The uniqueness of that kicking, crying, brand-new little individual is not simply a sentimental fiction in the minds of his admiring parents. Every scientist will agree with them. Among the nearly two and three-quarter billion human beings on earth there is no other individual exactly like him. Nor was there ever, among the billions that have already passed this way. Nor will there ever be, among the billions yet to be born.

This is true for the newborn, and for you who are reading these words, and for everyone you know. Theoretically there is a chance that two human beings might be identical, but the odds against it are astronomical.

Each human being inherits, in his twenty-three pairs of chromosomes, many thousands of different genes—the estimated numbers are between 10,000 and 40,000—and these determine the constitutional equipment with which he enters the world. The possible variations in anatomy alone are almost beyond computing. One anatomical atlas shows diagrams of six different ways in which the major arteries branch out of the aorta, five different variations in one single muscle of the index finger, eight versions of the branching and connections of the facial nerve. All were found in different individuals, and all were normal. These are only a fraction of the individual differences in anatomy alone, and there are, besides, the inborn functional differences.

Consider blood typing. For most practical purposes we have been content to list five groups: A, B, AB, O, and Rh. A more detailed differentiation brings the number to nine. But 475 patients in a London hospital yielded 296 different blood types. Some were extremely rare—211 of them occurred only once each in that particular sampling. But they did occur. On the basis of some English laboratory studies there may be as many as 300,000 different types of human blood.

Not even identical twins are identical. They grow from the same fertilized egg, inherit the same genes, belong to the same blood group and inevitably to the same sex. They are, as we shall see, the only individuals who have so far been able to exchange organs, specifically a kidney. Yet their fingerprints are distinguishable; so is their handwriting. So are many detailed measurements. For example, only 64 per cent of identical twins have matching blood pressure. Occasionally one twin is both larger and more vigorous than the other, an anomaly that is hard to explain except by some inequality in their blood supply within the uterine environment that they shared before birth. We realize nowadays that children of the same parents, growing up in the same home, nevertheless do not have the same environment. Now we have reason to think that even the uterus, that most controlled environment in the human being's entire history, may not be the same for two embryos growing side by side within it.

The uniqueness of each individual is a scientific fact. To each of us, as individuals and as members of the human family, it is very likely the single most remarkable fact of life. It adds the spice of unpredictability to every encounter with a stranger and even to our relationships with those we know best. It creates values and standards and ethical systems. Without individual differences there would be no arguments and no opinions, no judgment, no taste, no need for conscience, common sense, or the wisdom of sages. There would be no approval or disapproval, no liking and disliking. It is hard to see how we could ever fall in love.

Because of our individual differences we have Beethovens and Einsteins, Napoleons and Gandhis, and also, now and then, a Hitler. Because of human variability we have—within limits, which are also variable—freedom of will, of thought, of action, and such documents as the Bill of Rights.

All this, by the ineluctable logic of physical and cultural evolution, we owe to the uniqueness of each one of us as individuals. And to it we also owe our most precious individual possession: our identity.

ONE BIG FAMILY

Man's variability is one of the wonders of the biological world; if we had no other distinction, this alone would make us remarkable among living species. To some degree every living organism, even the simplest, is unique. As we follow the evolutionary scale through forms that are more and more complex, the differences fall into patterns, which we call species. When individuals diverge far enough from the patterns of their kind, a new species—or genus, or family—is born. No longer do these new individuals mingle and mate with the older branch. Birds do not mate with reptiles, though in evolutionary terms they are closely related.

Granted that a goldfinch does not mate with a lizard. But neither does a goldfinch mate with a sparrow, although both belong to the finch family. In nature, goldfinches do not mate with bullfinches or linnets, their closest cousins. Canary fanciers tried for centuries to cross the pretty singer, also a finch, with its wild relatives; until recently all they got for their pains was the linnet-canary mule, an attractive pet but sterile. Not long ago a cross between the canary and still another finch, the Venezuelan siskin, resulted in fertile males, and now there is a new breed of canaries ranging in color from deep tomato red to pale pink. The breeders justly consider this a triumph over the ways of nature. They achieved it only after generations of experimental mating.

In domestication we bring about many fertile crossings of types which might not interbreed in nature, but once they have evolved beyond a certain point they become mutually infertile. When we cross a donkey and a horse the offspring is a mule, useful but sterile. The separateness of these two branches of the family *equus* is final. They can no longer produce fertile offspring that mix the genes of each.

This evolution toward mutual infertility appears virtually everywhere in the animal kingdom, until we come to man. Even in his evolution man is unique: with all their variety, human beings have never, it appears, diverged into separate species. Accidents of geography isolated some branches of the family at various times in history: the Australian and African aborigines, for example; the Eskimos, the Lapps, and the many Indian peoples on the American continents. But the main streams of mankind have been flowing together, mingling and parting and mingling again, across the continents and down through the centuries.

Men seem to have been born restless; their wandering groups never remained apart long enough to develop mutual infertility. It is the roving foot of mankind, its never-ceasing search for a greener valley or a forest richer in game, that we may thank for our individuality. When they were few, and roamed in small bands over vast land areas, their differences became quite marked. That was when human evolution progressed to its farthest points along the paths of divergence. It produced the subspecies that today we call Caucasian, Negroid, and Mongoloid, and within the subspecies such types as Alpine and Mediterranean and Indo-European among the Caucasian, Eskimo and American Indian among the Mongoloid.

Then as the species multiplied the peoples overran each other. Mating with the stranger, extraordinary among other animals, with man was normal and sometimes mandatory; among some primitive peoples there is still a powerful taboo against marrying within the tribe.

History and even prehistory can be read in waves of peoples sweeping across the lands, Gaels and Celts, Greeks, Romans, Goths, Saracens and Turks, Tartars and Slavs. And where they came together, no differences of color, creed, custom, much less of language and national allegiance, kept them from mingling and mating whether by conquest, capture, enslavement, concubinage, or simply living side by side. Throughout history they mated as they do now, within each of the three great branches of the human family, and they mate across those dividing lines, too, wherever they meet in the world's melting pots. Custom erects its barriers, but nevertheless people mate with exotic strangers, as they always have.

The result is a common human pool of genes of immeasurable variety, a huge grab bag out of which each new individual gets his chance assortment. He is more likely to resemble his own parents than others in many characteristics, but he will be a mixture of both and will not duplicate either. And no one can predict what characteristics, from which of his many ancestors, will emerge from the mists of time to add a new seasoning to this absolutely unprecedented combination. There is also the possibility, even a probability, that he may contribute some mutation of his own, not necessarily significant, to the mixed packet of hereditary characteristics that he will pass on to his children in due time.

To man as a species, this gift of hereditary variability was an unmatched kind of survival insurance through the perilous years when he was struggling to gain a foothold on the earth. For so highly developed an animal, he remained marvelously adaptable. He never became so specialized as to be caught, like the dinosaurs, by a change in the weather. The main branches of the family made their rapid advances in the Temperate Zone, but scions took root and survived in desert heat and equatorial jungle, in the thin air of mountain heights and at the frozen poles. Everywhere they became the dominant species.

And that is how we all became members of the most highly individualistic club in the world, the club of man.

THE HOMOGENIZERS

Our individuality is by no means a free gift; it has its price. Our differences make life interesting, but they also make it difficult. The earliest bands of men were probably homogeneous enough not to make too much trouble for each other, but as soon as the differences began to be noticeable they had to be controlled.

Man is a social animal, and no society can continue for long without some degree of conformity. The bees and the ants have very complex societies but they have the inborn, fixed reflexes to go with their fixed social patterns. As for the birds that migrate in flocks and often breed in colonies, the deer that go in herds, the wolves that hunt in packs, there are learned or conditioned reflexes blended with the instinctual patterns, in various proportions. At the same time the kinds of behavior required of the members are still simple and few, and they are virtually all directly connected with the immediate needs of the individual in relation to the environment. Also, these small, inbred groups are quite homogeneous, and there are few individual differences to give trouble to the society.

Not so with man. He is born with a minimum of fixed reflexes and a maximum of potential for learning new behavior. The distinction of the human brain lies in the great areas of cortical cells that are not committed at birth to rigid patterns. Add to this his constitutional individuality, born of the mixed genes of his great family, and it is quickly apparent that human societies must have had their problems from early days.

In the world of fang and claw, surrounded by animals more powerful, swift, and fierce than themselves, men had to function in groups in order to survive at all. A few superior ones—the most cunning hunters, the most skillful weapon-makers, the most imaginative magic-thinkers—could serve the group as leaders. The rest had to submerge what differences they had, and obey. The demands of survival were the first homogenizers of human behavior. After that came taboos, traditions, rule by force, and rule by law. And eventually the laws could take account of human differences, and guarantee individual freedoms that were not destructive to society, as in our own Constitution and its Bill of Rights. From the long corridor of social evolution man emerged at last with a concept of the individual.

THE CLASSIFIERS

The scientists have also found human individuality a problem. Knowledge advances by the organization and classification of facts so that generalizations can be made from them, and theories are developed which can then be proved or disproved by observations and experiments. The scientists interested in man have been trying to organize and classify him for as long as they have been studying him.

The physicians, for obvious practical reasons, were among the first who tried to classify man. Hippocrates, sitting under his plane tree on the sea-girt island of Cos, in classical Greece of the fifth century B.C., described for his pupils "the white, the smooth, the lentil-like" who were susceptible to disease of the lungs, and other types prone to other diseases. He divided men into types according to which of the four humors predominated in their constitutions: blood, phlegm, yellow bile and black bile. His humoral theory lingered on in medicine into the nineteenth century, and we still describe people as sanguine, phlegmatic, chol-eric, or melancholy.

The classifiers have tried all kinds of systems. Johann Kaspar Lavater, the eighteenth-century Swiss theologian, wrote a great tome on physiognomy, a method of typing people by their facial features. Somewhat later came phrenology, which deciphered characteristics by the bumps on the skull; both had an enormous vogue in scientific circles until they descended to the fortune-telling level. The Italian criminologist-physician Dr. Cesare Lombroso believed he had found the clues to men's criminal tendencies in specific physical traits such as left-handedness or the shape of an ear lobe.

The "average man" was a product of nineteenth-century science, and this one has persisted in ways that are often as troublesome as they are helpful. The statistical basis for the concept is that when we plot any set of human measurements, the largest number of individuals are found to cluster around the center, and the numbers become fewer as we approach the extremes. One result of this statistical approach is the ubiquitous height-weight-age tables, into which we have been trying to fit our growing children and ourselves for generations. Another is the Intelligence Quotient, and its numerous offspring in the form of aptitude and other psychological measurements. The great complaint against all of these is that they do not make sufficient room for human diversity; they lose sight of the individual in concentrating on the statistical average. As a way of describing the human population they have their value, but as guides to the understanding of an individual or the management of his life they occasionally create more difficulties than they solve.

Somatotyping—classifying human beings according to body types—is the name for the modern science of fitting human diversity into categories. There have been several systems; the most recent and probably the most complete is Dr. William Sheldon's. He divides human beings into three types: the fleshy endomorphs, who run to fat and crave affection and companionship as well as food; the muscular mesomorphs, energetic, extroverted, and likely to be insensitive to other people's feelings; the thin, nervous ectomorphs, sensitive, shy, and inclined toward solitude and moodiness.

Correlated with these body types are three terms for tempera-

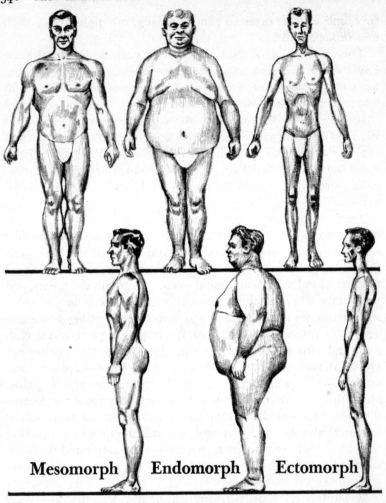

Mesomorph   **Endomorph**   **Ectomorph**

ments. The fat fellows are viscerotonic, or gut-centered; the extreme endomorph is likely to have an intestinal tract that is twice as long and twice as heavy as the extreme ectomorph. The muscle men are somatotonic, or body-centered. The ectomorphs are cerebrotonic; they have been characterized as hardly more than a thin layer of flesh and skin wrapped around a nervous system.

For his exhaustive *Atlas of Men* Dr. Sheldon weighed, measured and photographed 46,000 male Americans, and correlated their body types with behavior patterns, proneness to diseases, and the changes effected on each type with the passage of time. But to get all his 46,000 dissimilar individuals into classes, he had to divide the body into five regions and make measurements of each of these. Then by certain mathematical procedures he determined how much of each type—endomorphy, mesomorphy, ectomorphy—each individual mixture contained, measured on a seven-point scale. Thus an extreme endomorph would be represented by the formula 7-1-1, a muscular type like Superman would perhaps be 3-7-1, and a slender, tender ectomorph might be represented as 1-2-7. An all-around, well-balanced, presumably ideal human being is 4-4-4, a category in which we are likely to find very few real living people.

The result is a dizzying parade of diversity. As Dr. Sheldon himself points out, the individual is bound to defy the statistician in the end. Such an assemblage of organized measurements has its possible value in the study of man in all his aspects, but the exceptions are likely to be more impressive than the rules. For example, the mesomorphs are ideally equipped to become our great explorers, but Admiral Richard Byrd had a temperament closer to Hamlet's than to Superman's. The individuals who leave their imprint on history seem to be precisely the ones who cannot be fitted into any category. Why should we believe that the rest of us, whose gifts and opportunities are modest, can be any more definitively typed?

The best that the scientists can hope for is not a division into separate and mutually exclusive classifications but a continuous curve, along which each one of us fits at various points, depending upon which aspect of us is being measured. In biological science we use the term "normal" for any feature or measurement—or range of measurements—that is characteristic of 95 per cent of the population. Thus a pulse rate of about 70 per minute is normal. If we add another randomly chosen measurement, for example, acuteness of hearing, then we find that only about 90 per cent of us fit into the range established as normal for both items, pulse and hearing. With each feature or measurement that we add to the list, fewer individuals are "normal" in all of them. Increase the number of measured items to ten, and the percentage of normal individuals drops to sixty. If we measure 100 different characteristics, then only fifty-nine people out of a thousand are normal in all of them.

And there are thousands of measurable factors. Dr. Roger J.

Williams, an authority on biochemical individuality, concludes with a glint of triumph, "Practically every human being is a deviate in some respects."

INDIVIDUALITY'S ESSENCE

Thus the normal, like the average, turns out to be a fiction, convenient for scientists and statisticians but not of great value in describing an individual. And so the scientists turn to exploring the mystery of individuality.

The uniqueness of each one of us has been defined as being of two kinds. There are the multiple differences of anatomical structure, of organs and systems, the many ways in which nerves and blood vessels may branch off and communicate with one another, the variations in how muscles divide into bundles and how they are attached to bones, the blood types and the levels of chemicals in the body fluids. All these, fitted together, form a mosaic of individuality. Each of us shares many of these characteristics with others, but we do not share them all with anyone.

Besides these many separate differences, each of us has an overall difference, a kind of essence of individuality. Just what this is remains a mystery. It has to do with the organism's functioning as an integrated whole, and its nature is apparently chemical. This may be what the bloodhound scents with his remarkable nose, because he loses it when the individual he is trailing is no longer alive. Or so the handlers of bloodhounds tell us.

If this is what the bloodhound recognizes, then he shares that recognition only with the body itself. For it is the body's own tissues that infallibly identify and reject anything that is not of their own special chemical essence. This is the immune reaction by which the body defends itself against invading microorganisms of disease. Unfortunately it has the same reaction to our medical efforts to replace damaged skin and organs by graft and transplantation. Blood transfusions may not be repeatedly accepted by the body even when the blood is of the same type.

Some years ago one of the present authors co-ordinated a group effort of Harvard scientists in kidney transplantation. The first success, after many tries, was with a pair of identical twins. Since then other such twins have successfully shared one pair of healthy kidneys between them, and one happy patient went on to enjoy a normal pregnancy.

BANNERS OF IDENTITY

We are still seeking ways to circumvent the body's hostile reaction to needed tissue from a donor. And the biochemists are still seeking to penetrate the secret of the peculiar chemical essence by which the body identifies its own tissues.

For practical purposes, however, we need no such mysterious clues to our own identity or that of others. Every one of us flies identifying tags like a string of regatta pennants on a yacht. Face, features, coloring, body build, the way the hair grows on the head and the shape of the fingernails on the hand, the set of a man's coat on his shoulders and the hang of a woman's skirt from her hips—all these advertise our identity. Not only the way we look but each sound we utter and each gesture we make is strictly our own.

We may speak the same language, even the same dialect as thousands of others, but each of us speaks it in his own way. "From the timbre of their speech one can differentiate all one's friends, and in fact no one in the world speaks the same as anyone else," muses the hero, a professor of linguistics, in Guy Endore's remarkable suspense story, *Detour at Night*.

He goes further: "And indeed we . . . never pronounce the same word the same way. So that every word uttered in the history of mankind by all the human beings who ever lived on this globe, every single word was a unique phenomenon that will never be duplicated, and this uniqueness of every word not merely in sound but in its exact shade of meaning will continue until the last flicker of the last star. Go now and explain all this!"

So much uniqueness is rather dizzying. Luckily we recognize each other's speech no matter what the nuances, and usually we know how to interpret the nuances as well, in the speech of those whose utterances are important to us. In the same way we understand the shades of facial expression and of gesture, for these are also languages in which each one has his characteristic speech. We can even read, in the handwriting of someone we know, whether the writer is well or ill, joyful or sad, troubled or serene.

Handwriting, like speech, is an intricate collaboration of mind and body, nerve and muscle, a blend of learned and innate movement. Like speech, it identifies the individual and also reveals many things about him. It is so individual that some characteristics are recognizable even if the writer writes with his toes. Like speech, gesture, and facial expression, it can be masked by the individual himself and it can be imitated by others. But like a clever actor, a clever forger cannot duplicate the original exactly. Undoubtedly there have been forgeries that fooled the experts, but the positive identifiability of handwriting is a cornerstone of our legal and economic system. Without it, none of us could have a checking or a charge account, or ever be held to a contract.

Fingerprints were a legal identification on contracts as long as 1,200 years ago in China. The French criminologist Alphonse Bertillon developed a system of identification by body measurements for police purposes, but fingerprinting was not part of it until the 1890s, and soon afterward the efficient, virtually infallible fingerprint replaced Bertillon's measurements. Of the many millions of fingerprints on file in law enforcement and other agencies around the world—about a hundred million in the Federal Bureau of Investigation files alone—no two are exactly alike. Theoretically there might be a pair of identical prints from two individuals, but again, the odds against such an occurrence are so high that for practical purposes we rule out the possibility. The same individuality identifies the sole prints of infants in hospital records.

Other physical characteristics may be almost as specific and individual. Hair, for example, is accepted as circumstantial evidence in the courts; but fingerprints, palm prints, and sole prints are depended upon as convincing identification. Furthermore, fingerprints do not change, as do features and even body measurements. They can be identified so long as there is even the smallest bit of tissue. In the annals of crime there have been malefactors who tried to destroy the skin patterns of their fingers with acid or by cutting, but there was always enough skin left for indentification. One went so far as to have the skin of all his finger tips replaced with grafts from his chest. The grafts were a complete success, except that the man was identified anyway, by the original skin on other parts of his fingers.

These highly individualistic areas of our skin are identifiable because of a built-in nonslip mechanism. This is our friction skin; unlike the epidermis elsewhere on the body, this skin has no hair follicles or oil glands. Instead, it is corrugated over its whole surface by narrow ridges. Like the knurling on a tool handle or the tread on an automobile tire, this makes for increased friction, a great advantage in gripping which incidentally we share with the other primates and some lower animals. The differentiation of this skin develops during the third or fourth month in the uterus, and it is one of the many admirable properties of the human hand.

It is only incidental that the design of loops, whorls, and arches and the arrangement of sweat pores is so absolutely individual and final an identification tag. There are ethnic and family resemblances and even a differentiation between the sexes: women have more arches and fewer whorls than men. But among all the resemblances, each of us still has his own private and individual pattern spread out on his friction skin.

PRIVATE WORLDS

The farther the scientists pursue this matter of individual differences, the more it appears that each of us inhabits his own private world. Each human being, growing up through the childhood years, passes through the same sequence of stages from birth to adulthood and virtually in the same order. Each child "punches the time clock," as one authority put it, but each child does it at his own pace. And just as each individual matures at his own pace, so also he eats, sleeps, metabolizes, all in a rhythm of his own.

Each of us has his own inner environment, and it is astonishing how different these can be and still function within the healthy range. Nine normal young men gave samples of their blood cells, plasma, urine, and saliva to be analyzed for four common chemical components. Some had three times, and some even had six times, more than others in the group, of one or another chemical in such excretions as urine and saliva. Yet all were healthy, normal young men.

Nutritionists are constantly challenged to set standards for optimum diets, and yet we know that one individual gains and another loses weight on the same number of calories, that one hungers for meats and another for sweets. A normal basal metabolism is anything between plus ten and minus ten, but even within this normal range it does not tell us much about individual differences. It tells us how much oxygen the individual burns while he is lying still and consciously relaxing in body and mind; but it tells us nothing about his metabolism when he is normally active or when he is under stress. Each individual responds to stress in his own way, and even that way changes unpredictably. Some get thin, some get fat, some suffer from gastric ulcers and some from hypertension. Usually these are quite distinct kinds of people, but sometimes the same individual reacts with one stress pattern at one stage of his life and with an opposite pattern at another.

We have a rule of thumb about the amount of sleep people need at various ages, from the infant's eighteen or twenty hours to the five hours, more or less, of the aged; adults, we say, need between seven and nine. But some babies sleep much less than eighteen hours, and some old people sleep more than the average adult in his prime, while many hard-studying, hard-playing high school and college students get along on half the normal eight hours for weeks and months at a time. The best we can make of it all is that sleep needs are as individual as almost everything else about us.

Even the pattern of sleep seems to become anarchic as soon as artificial routine is removed. On the North Greenland expedition in 1952-54, during the spring and autumn most of the men were in bed by ten or twelve o'clock at night and up again in eight hours. But during the long summer day and the long winter night each man followed his own preference, with the result that, as the expedition's Dr. Harold Lewis observed: "There was never a time when someone wasn't in bed or someone out of bed."

Would all our other rhythms, given the chance, take as individual a course? To live with each other and get the world's work done, we must all accept some degree of imposed routine. Most of us have little choice about our mealtimes, our hours of work and leisure, of sleeping and waking. The question is, how well do we live within these artificial patterns?

An experiment to see what happens to body rhythms was carried out some time ago, this time in Spitzbergen; twelve people were divided into two groups, one group to live on a twenty-one and the other on a twenty-seven-hour day. From an individual's excretory rhythm we learn a great deal about what is going on inside his body, and the records of the Spitzbergen groups were revealing. Of the twelve experimenters, only three were able to adapt their excretory rhythms to the abnormally short or the abnormally long day. And a curious disorganization developed in the chemical components. Instead of water, chloride, and potassium excretion running comfortably together in timing and amplitude, the water and chloride rhythms took one course and the potassium another, usually staying stubbornly close to the normal twenty-four-hour cycle. What this suggests is that for a good many people, some artificial routines must throw the smoothly running body chemistry into wild disorder, with consequences about which we can only speculate.

The temperature curve, also highly individual, turned out to be less resistant to change. As we know today, our body temperature does not stay at the normal 98.6° Fahrenheit, but follows an individual curve through the twenty-four hours, falling lowest during sleep in the small hours of the night and rising at each individual's own pace during the day. When it is at its highest, we are most alert and efficient. But this peak during which we give our brightest performance, with reflexes snapping and brain cells clicking, lasts only about two hours, and it does not come to all of us at the same time of day.

As we noted earlier, there are "morning people" and "evening people" and all degrees between. Some people bound out of bed almost fully awake, the body temperature already well up, while others stagger miserably through the morning hours and scarcely feel human until late in the day, sometimes not until eleven o'clock at night, when the rise-and-shiners have run down again and are creeping off to bed. This particular difference has raised havoc in many an otherwise happy marriage, until the early bird has learned to endure a glum monosyllabic partner at breakfast, and the night owl has learned to channel his evening spirits in some acceptable way, or at least to tiptoe to bed. Some early risers are clever or fortunate enough to be able to break the day with a cat nap and enjoy a second rising curve in the evening.

The temperature curve does become adapted to a changed routine for most people, as some have discovered who alternate between day and night shifts at their work. In the Spitzbergen study the temperature curve of all but one of the twelve experimenters quickly became adjusted, both to the short day and the long one. But not everyone can make the switch. The sleep expert, Dr. Nathaniel L. Kleitman, and his associate Bruce Richardson set up housekeeping on a twenty-eight-hour day in the dark depths of Mammoth Cave in Kentucky. Richardson quickly developed a new temperature curve, but Dr. Kleitman never did, although the experiment lasted more than a month.

If the inner environment of each one of us is so much a law unto itself, how differently must we each respond to the outer environment! How different, indeed, must be our individual information about that outer environment! Each individual's sensory equipment has its own degree of acuity. Eyes, ears, touch, responses to heat and cold, all are different, depending upon the sharpness of each of the sensory organs and the individual's responsiveness to each one. An experiment in tasting revealed that some individuals needed a flavor twenty times stronger than others, in order to taste it at all. Similar variations occur with responses to loudness and pitch, to light and color, to temperature, touch, and pain. Each of us has his own set of thresholds for each of the senses.

Nor do laboratory tests tell the whole story. It is not enough to discover how well a person hears. We must also ask how well he listens under various circumstances and in various states of body and emotion. The brain must perceive what the senses convey, and in the brain the patterns of receptivity and responsiveness to one or another stimulus are being laid down from the first hours of life. Experiences from the day we are born, memories, associations, emotions color all our perceptions, and no one of us can disentangle all the threads of past and present that are woven into what we see or think we see, what we hear or believe we hear.

And so even the environment we share remains for each of us a private environment. Six people sitting and talking together in a room are six separate worlds, each one receiving impressions and responding to them in his own way, according to his own chemistry and his own patterns of thought and perception and his own receptivity of the moment.

The wonder is not that people misunderstand each other, that relationships grate and grind and sometimes come to a screaming stop. Nor is it remarkable that the body sometimes falters, and its rhythms stutter, under the unremitting pressure to fit into one or another arbitrary pattern. The wonder is that with all their differences the organs and systems do mold themselves to the patterns we demand of them. And human beings do communicate, and tolerate, and even learn to appreciate and enjoy each other's uniqueness.

MAN OF THE FUTURE

THE UNIVERSE was born in clouds of hydrogen ten billion years ago, so the astrophysicists tell us. Our earth is four billion years old, and for a billion years, perhaps two billion, it has supported life. Men like ourselves began to leave their records in caves and burial mounds only 50,000 years ago. In terms of the universe, we are a very new phenomenon.

We are new even in terms of living species. The oyster and the horseshoe crab are two hundred million years old, and there are fish and reptiles flourishing today that have eons of seniority over us. The first man-ape or ape-man, a creature that walked upright and used its hands, emerged only a million years ago, and it was another half million years before a genus that could be called *Homo*, the Peking man, appeared on earth. He lived in caves and he made stone tools for cutting and chopping, and we believe that he talked with his kind in some sort of language of perhaps a few hundred words. He also used fire; presumably when he encountered a natural conflagration he dared to carry burning brands to his cave for warmth and protection from marauding beasts. But he did not build and light a fire at need, and he still ate his food raw.

The Neanderthal men, the big-game hunters of Europe from two hundred thousand to fifty thousand years ago, were far more like us. Indeed, the anthropologists assure us that if a Neanderthal man appeared beside us in a bus or subway, bathed and shaved and dressed in a suit of clothes like anyone else, we would probably not give him a second glance.

But the men from whom we date our ancestry are the men of the Old Stone Age who unknowingly left messages for us to read, in the caves of Spain and the Dordogne, along the shores of the Mediterranean and in the chilly north of Europe as the Ice Age receded. Some paleoanthropologists believe that they may have made a much earlier appearance, perhaps 250,000 years earlier, and struggled to survive in a hostile world of icy tundras, of huge ferocious beasts like the mammoth and the cave bear that were also struggling to survive. Life was hard, and there must have been times when those early men were few in number.

When we meet them they had already begun to dominate their world. They were not the strongest or the swiftest; they were merely the cleverest. They had the brains and hands of men, and what they lacked in strength and speed they could more than make up for with weapons. They could learn from experience, and with language they could pass on what they had learned. They could observe and remember how things were and plan ahead for how they were likely to be again.

They were still hunters, and some of them were cannibals, but they had bodies and brains like ours. They had fires and lamps and created a habitable environment in the most unfriendly climates. They had good hunting weapons and good tools, even a fine bone needle with which their women sewed animal hides into coats and kilts to keep their hairless human bodies warm. So well did they manage that they even had leisure to decorate their weapons with carvings and to string sea shells and animal teeth for their own adornment.

Most marvelous, there were artists among them who left on their cave walls a graphic record of the animals they hunted, and of themselves hunting, running, dancing, wearing animal masks and costumes. Across the space of thousands of years we respect them for their skills, their artistry, and their daring.

It was men like these who ventured out of the caves about ten thousand years ago to live in shelters built by themselves, who discovered that they could plant grain and herd animals and thus insure their food supply. That was when man, the new kind of animal, began to learn what he could do. That was when he began to take control of his environment and direct the course of his own evolution.

FASTER, FASTER

From then on the wheel of change rolled faster and faster. In a few thousand years men were living in cities. They were trading and keeping business records, devising new tools and new engines, writing down laws and recording events, studying the heavens and the seasons and the world of nature. They journeyed long and hazardous distances by caravan and by ship. They populated the lands they knew, and they ventured out to discover new lands and populated those. Their numbers multiplied, and they fought wars for land, for goods, for slaves, perhaps for other reasons. And still they continued to make new engines, seek new knowledge, and explore across new seas.

Faster and faster the changes came, until now, in one century, we have gone from travel by horse and camel to railroad to automobile to airplane to jet to rocket. After eons of slogging over the surfaces of land and sea, of climbing perhaps to the height of a tree, in less than a century we have learned to travel high in the air and deep under the ocean. And in one generation we have finished with the conquest of the air and are standing on the brink of space.

When we look back only a little way, it seems that twentieth-century man has made an incredible leap into the future. When we look back somewhat farther we see something still more awesome. Twentieth-century man, poised for his journey to the moon, the planets, and perhaps to solar systems beyond, is biologically the same creature as that man of 10,000 years ago who planted the first seeds. He is the same, too, as that man of 50,000 years ago who groped his way deep into the caves to paint his wall paintings and build his ritual altars.

The same restless brain and clever hands, the same hunger to see what is yet unseen, to know what is yet unknown, to explain what is yet mysterious—these are common to the man of prehistory and the man of the future. No animal before man had this questing mind and the genius to devise tools for its quests. The men who plan and build the space ships and the men who will ride in them were implicit in the men who tamed fire and made tools out of stone and bone and hide and antler.

In these thousands of years the body has changed little, if it has changed at all. With the emergence of the human mind, evolution was converted from a procession of species to a procession of cultures.

The next step on man's evolutionary journey is surely the most daring—or so it seems to us as we stand on the earth's rim and look outward. But we may believe that Columbus setting out toward the horizon of the western sea undertook a journey as daring to the men of his time. They could not know with certainty that he might not sail straight off the edge of the earth into horrors unknown and unguessed.

And what shall we think of those first explorers, the men of the caves? Some of their paintings are two miles within the bowels of the earth. Modern archaeologists, fully armed with ropes and axes and high-powered electric torches, have slithered on their bellies through these labyrinths at the peril of life and limb, to find that the artists of prehistory had already been there. What terrors must the caves have held for those explorers, creeping through a darkness that for them was filled with demons and animal spirits and the ghosts of their own dead? All the light they had was from a wisp of fiber flickering and smoking in grease in a hollowed-out stone.

Man is the first animal that questioned and sought answers to his questioning. In the beginning his imagination ran far ahead of his knowledge. He conjured up explanations for himself that were both wonderful and terrifying, and in spite of his terror he ventured forth.

Today we extend our sensory powers with instruments. We know the solar system as the Greeks of Ulysses' time could not know even their own Mediterranean. We feed tons of accumulated data into machines and we map the universe we are about to explore. What we know in advance about the hazards of the journey into space is more than enough to make the mind reel. And there is still a vast unknown, which we cannot know until our venturers go and return to tell us about it. Yet there are venturers eager to go, as Columbus was eager, and as we imagine the Stone Age men of the caves were eager. This is the nature of man, the animal whose wondering mind drives first his imagination and then himself to see what is really there.

Through his whole history man has hungered for knowledge as

though it were essential to life, like food and air. In every era there have been individuals willing to risk life itself in satisfying this hunger. Man wants knowledge for its own sake, because he is curious; but also he wants it for the power it gives him over his environment. We can read man's past as a continuous striving to unlock nature's secrets and thus take control of its blind forces. As he has done in the past, so he probably will continue to do in the future. Paradoxically, the drive to know and to manipulate has led the human species into its greatest progress and also its greatest peril.

EARTHLINGS IN SPACE

Paradoxes go with man right into space; the project bristles with them. For example: the interplanetary pioneer, on his way to explore the vastness of the very heavens, will travel in the most wretchedly cramped, constricting vehicle that possibly ever held a living man. Every pound of cargo, every cubic foot of space that might make him more comfortable increases many fold the thrust that is needed to hurl him from the earth. He will sail through space not in a ship but in a capsule.

And a second paradox: this most advanced human voyager, with our most glittering technology at his beck, will possibly have as his teammate one of the oldest, most primitive forms of terrestrial life, the tiny marine algae. The reason for this is that an earthling, to survive away from earth, must take with him everything earthly that his body requires. The terrella or "little earth" in which he travels must provide him with oxygen, water, food. It must be self-sustaining for as long as the journey requires. There will be no supply stations on the way.

Hence the algae. The man and the plant together would form a closed cycle, reproducing in miniature the cycle of plant and animal life on earth. There is the respiratory part of the cycle: the man breathes out carbon dioxide and water vapor, which the plant must have to live; the plant converts these by photosynthesis into carbohydrates and it throws off oxygen, which the man must have to live. And there is the nutritional cycle: the man feeds his wastes to the algae as fertilizer, in particular the urea from which the plant can extract the necessary nitrogen, and in return the algae serve as his food.

About two and one-half pounds of algae could keep one man supplied with oxygen. Anything more he could grow would contribute to his food supply, and one variety has been found that multiplies itself a thousandfold a day. Algae vary in taste; one kind is peppery, another has the flavor of mushrooms. This space-capsule type of farming would have the essential virtue of compactness, for the vegetable garden is nothing more than a tank with a bright light shining on it. And here is our third paradox, embarrassing to space scientists: our astronauts on their journey into the future may have to rely for their lives on agriculture, the most primitive of man's techniques.

Probably the most embarrassing paradox, to the technologists, is that technology can do nothing to improve the traveler himself. They have hinted that the astronaut would do better without the vestibular organs in his ears, the utricles and the semicircular canals that tell him whether he is on his head or his feet and in what direction he is going. All the canals will do for him on a space voyage is to make him very, very sick.

Beyond this, there is nothing much about the man that can be changed. The human body is remarkably adaptable, and it can absorb a good deal of stress, but on some matters it is stubbornly uncompromising. It cannot be reduced in size, or dismantled and packed in a more convenient shape. It must have its air, water, and essential nutrients, or it will not continue to function for long.

The mind is scarcely more co-operative. Some polar explorers, though not all, have successfully endured long periods of isolation, monotony, confinement, and lack of intellectual and sensory stimulation. But no earthly experience can compare with a journey through an infinity of silent emptiness, with only the hypnotic faces of instruments to watch.

There are no changes of day and night for the space traveler to see, no phenomena of weather. He will hear no sounds except those he makes himself, and his own breathing and heartbeat may well reverberate with deafening monotony inside his space suit or his pressurized space cabin. Once away, he will have no sensation of movement at all, although he will be going faster than sound, faster than any human being has ever traveled. His principal sensation will be that of weightlessness, and most of those who have experienced it, even for less than a minute, have found it more disagreeable than not.

Of leisure he will have enough and too much. He will have little to do except check his instruments, and plenty of time to consider his perilous situation. Supposing that all the technology functions as planned, he will still be aware that only his tiny cockleshell of a space cabin protects him from cosmic rays, meteoric bombardment, and a temperature that ranges from 67° below zero to 23,000° above.

Even more stressful than anxiety is boredom. The mind too long deprived of stimulation becomes listless, inattentive, irritable. It begins to manufacture its own hallucinatory world. Even the personality changes.

Early in this space age, E. B. White wrote a story in which he imagined a conversation between two young Air Force officers stationed on a space satellite. They felt no pull of gravity, and neither did they feel the pull of conscience, duty, or sex. They did not *want* anything. They looked down at the earth and agreed that they did not feel drawn toward it in any special way. "Then what are we waiting for?" asked one, and they thereupon fired the Weapon that destroyed the earth.

What the literary artist knows by intuition, science has time and again confirmed. Whether it is brought on by boredom, stress, or the lost hope of ever returning, this separation that dehumanized two normal young Americans in White's story has been experienced by real young men in jet planes and on isolated tours of duty. It manifests itself in various ways, none of them an improvement over the normal, functioning human mind. It has a name; Air Force men call it the "break-off" phenomenon.

Why, in the face of all this, must earthlings fly into space? They must go, as men have always gone in the past, to find out what is there. They must explore the soundless frozen turbulence of the moon, must clamber over its bleak gray, gouged and cratered landscape, even though every step may smother them in clouds of lunar dust, and the smallest rip in their space suits may cause their tissues to swell and their blood to "boil" in a cosmic case of what on earth we call the bends, because the moon's atmospheric pressure is only one-millionth that of earth.

They must go to discover, on a dead satellite which like the earth is four billion years old, what clues there may be to explain the earth's and the solar system's beginning. They must go to see, in fierce clarity, the universe that we on earth see through our atmosphere as through a frosty windowpane. They must go to see how the earth whirls in its orbit and turns on its axis, and discover what we may not yet know about our own beautiful and still mysterious planet. They must go, as pioneers have always gone, to show that it can be done and to pave the way for others to follow.

The trip to the moon is only a beginning. There will be the trip to Mars, where there may or may not be life, perhaps more advanced than ours, and to Venus, which may still be steaming in a version of the earth's own youth and the birth pangs of life. We may begin to communicate with living creatures on planets like our own, in the galaxy of which our solar system is a tiny fragment. And when the sun expires—in some six or seven billion years—the genus man may save itself from extinction by emigrating to another planet within another solar system.

That is, if men do not first do themselves some irreversible mischief here on earth.

MAN ON THE EARTH

In Thornton Wilder's lighthearted parable *The Skin of Our Teeth,* Mr. Antrobus and the human family are confronted with one disaster after another: the Ice Age, the Flood, even a political convention in Atlantic City. They survive them all, but just barely.

Survival, but by the skin of his teeth, describes the first several hundred thousand years of man. For the close calls of the past he was in no way to blame. Ice, flood, drought, and famine, epidemics that depopulated cities and toppled empires were natural disasters and he was an innocent victim. His wars and persecutions were often indefensible on moral grounds but they were, comparatively, the games of children playing with fire.

Now we have our choice of man-made suicides. We can choose swift extermination in a nuclear war, or slower destruction by various means. Some of these are the result of callous uncontrolled technology, and some, ironically, proceed from our most humane endeavors.

For technological suicide the means are ready at hand. We can contaminate soil, sea, and air with radioactive wastes that destroy the species genetically. We can pollute our foods with the pest killers, weed killers, antibiotics and a host of powerful chemicals by which we often shortsightedly try to circumvent nature and increase the earth's yield for a quick profit. By a long list of preservatives, additives, and chemical tampering with the products of daily use, we can so disarrange our body chemistry as to create a whole new vocabulary of diseases.

Some of this has already come to pass. But with the nick-of-time technique that is characteristic of the species, the probabilities are that we will stop short of poisoning ourselves out of existence. The dangers of uncontrolled technology are too obvious to be ignored for long.

Uncontrolled good will presents another set of dangers. The very cherishing of life, it seems, places the species in peril. By bringing disease under control, by spreading the benefits of epidemiology and sanitation around the world, the humane medical sciences are letting loose an explosive growth of population that the earth may one day be unable to support. At the dawn of history the entire world was peopled by perhaps twenty millions. In 1850 the population was a billion, in the 1920s it had doubled, and by the year 2000 there may be six billion people shouldering each other for standing room on earth.

Thus man has been dogged by contradictions ever since he took over the management of his social evolution; he seems doomed as surely by his good works as by his evil. As he toilsomely conquers the blights of the past—plague, pestilence, famine, war—he finds that he has been eliminating things that are biologically necessary for his survival. Every step he makes in his striving toward the better life is an interference with the balance of nature, and so he finds himself in one impasse after another. But history gives us hope. Until now he has managed to wriggle out of each impasse, if only by the skin of his teeth.

THE BODY'S EVOLUTION

What biological changes the future will bring is anybody's guess. Since the Old Stone Age the human body has not changed significantly, not even as to the size of the brain. Cro-Magnon man had a brain as large as that of any twentieth-century nuclear physicist, or larger; his skull capacity was 1,600 cubic centimeters, compared with 1,500 for the average modern cranium. We have fossil evidence that a race of men, living in South Africa 150,000 years ago, had the skull capacity for a brain one and one-half times the size of ours.

Man is an enormously varied species; he has been intermingling his genetic strains since paleolithic times. The scientists are still debating, for example, the fate of Neanderthal man, that great European hunter. Was he exterminated by the more skillful Cro-Magnons, Aurignacians, and the rest who came into dominance as he faded? Or was he absorbed by them and are his genes part of our common heritage? How different was he, in essence? He had a brain as large as ours, although possibly not so well developed in the higher centers. He was heavy-boned, stocky, probably a powerful, muscular man. He even shared our ills. For a while he was described as shuffling, bent-kneed, scarcely able to walk erect, but the fossil bones that sat for this portrait turned out to be the remains of an old man with a bad case of arthritis.

Looking backward, we are inclined to accept the many human differences not as evolutionary steps but rather as genetic variations, brought into the pool of our inheritance by the many different strains of men. Looking forward, we may well apply the same rule for our picture of the man of the future.

There is a popular image of a creature with a ballooning skull to house his splendid brain. Correspondingly, his face is a cluster of infantile features; his babyish jaw holds few teeth; his torso and limbs are puny. It is quite true that the brain is continuing to develop, but in complexity, not in size. A new mutation is always possible, and there may be in man's future a race of big brains yet to come. Yet it is hard to imagine how such a mutation would be an advantage. The brain we have seems possessed of almost infinite potentialities, and what our brain cannot do it devises machines to do for it.

There are many possible improvements on the human body; it is no champion compared with some other animals. We cannot leap as high as the kangaroo or see as keenly as the hawk, but the brain compensates for these shortcomings. It invents machines that take us farther and faster than any animal has ever gone, and builds telescopes that see billions of miles into space.

Human beings are taking ever longer to mature and longer also to grow old. The future may have a population of vigorous centenarians, and sages of a hundred and fifty. With a mountainous and still growing mass of knowledge and technical skills to absorb, the men and women of the future may increase still further their "wakefulness of choice," in the sleep expert Dr. Nathaniel Kleitman's phrase, contrasted with the lower animals' "wakefulness of necessity" for the activities essential to sheer survival. With chemical aids the men of the future may be able to cut their sleep needs down to perhaps two hours out of twenty-four, and thus add still more years of activity to their lives.

The body is growing, not smaller, but measurably larger: two inches taller and as much as ten pounds heavier, according to the height-weight tables for the past fifty years. A college athlete of today can not squeeze into the armor in which medieval heroes fought their tournaments. Of the so-called "tigers" of the Air Force, the men who fly highest and fastest and carry out the most daring experiments successfully, only 5 per cent are of average height and weight. The other 95 per cent are taller and heavier than the norm for the general population. This is a disadvantage in space pioneering, but it indicates the trend toward largeness.

American children are consistently taller than their parents. Even those strains that are characteristically small, for example, the people of Mediterranean stock, are taller with succeeding generations in the United States. Some of this is due to the mingling with larger-bodied northern European stocks, but the simplest explanation is that a richer diet makes for larger people, as in the laboratory it makes for larger mice.

This does not necessarily mean that men will continue growing until they become giants. Each species seems to have its built-in limits. We would have to mix our genes with those of a giant species in order to grow giants. A mutation might accomplish the same change, but a mutation has to be advantageous to the species if it is to survive and spread, and it is doubtful whether gigantic stature is an advantage anywhere in our culture except on the basketball court.

What we see, looking ahead, is more of what we have already seen, more blending of strains within the human species, more mixing of genes, and ever more individual variety. We surmise that the world's three main streams—white, Mongoloid, and Negroid—will eventually flow together so that they are indistinguishable, and the average skin color will be coffee tinted. But genes do not mix like paints, and the coffee-colored average will embrace an infinity of shades from very light to very dark. The same will be true of the colors of eyes and the shapes of noses, the differences in statures, in talents and temperaments, in foolishness and wisdom.

To the wonderful diversity of human beings housed within human bodies, there is no foreseeable end.

INDEX

Abdominal cavity, 38
Abdominal salivary gland, *see* Pancreas
Acetyl coenzyme A, 179
Acid, neutralization of, 138-139
Acid-alkali balance, 138-139
Acoustic nerve, 322, 325
ACTH, 201, 207
Adam's apple, 203
Adaptation, 337
  dark, 318
  to dry environment, 86-87
  to high altitude, 83, 94, 100-101
  reproductive, 234-236
  to stress, 209-213
  and water balance, 137-138
Adenosine triphosphate, 179
Adrenal cortex, 196, 206, 207-208, 213, 242
Adrenal glands, 126, 194, 197, 200, 205-208, 259
Adrenal hormones, 206-208
Adrenalines, 64, 126, 206-207, 277, 299
  aftereffects of, 211
Adrenal medulla, 206, 207, 211-212
Adrenocortical hormones, 138, 154, 196
Adrenocorticotrophic hormone, 201, 207
Afterbirth, *see* Placenta
Agglutinins, 57
Aging, 194, 216, 227-229, 317
Airplane travel, 100, 329
Air sacs, 88
Alcohol, 108, 114, 117, 288; alcoholics, 130
Algae, 231, 354-355
Alimentary canal, 106-

110, 114; *see also* Digestive system
Alkaline balance, 138-139
Allergic reaction, 97
Alpha waves, 276-277, 299
Altitude, high, adaptation to, 83, 94, 100-101
Alveoli, 88
Amino acids, 23, 120, 126, 129-130, 135, 139
  digestion of, 109
  synthesis of, 7-8, 161-162
Amman, Jost, 133
Ammonia
  production of by kidneys, 139
  in stomach, 108
Amnion, 17
Amniotic fluid, 17, 39, 87, 184
Amniotic sac, 39
Amoeba, 49, 56, 158, 160, 231, 249
Anabolism, 174
Anal sphincter, 18, 112
Anatomy, differences in, 333-335, 342-343
Androgens, 215
Androsterone, 221
Anemia, pernicious, 127
Anger, 206
Angle of sorrow, 98
Animals
  and care of young, 233-234, 272-273
  courting rituals of, 233
  learning by, 265-267, 273-274
  mating of, 335
  memory capacity of, 294
  menstruation in, 225
  nervous systems in, 250-251
  reproductive cycles of, 215
  sense of smell in, 313
  sex life of, 232, 238
  sounds produced by,

101-102, 104-105, 292-294
  taste buds of, 312
  and temperature, 171-172, 259
  vision in, 319
Anterior-pituitary-like hormone, 242
Antianemic factor, 127
Antibiotics, 49, 50
Antibodies, 57-59
Antithrombin, 44
Antitoxins, 57
Anus, 18, 112
Anvil bone, 322
Anxiety
  and heartbeat, 67
  and space travel, 356
Aorta, 70, 71, 74-75
Apes, 5, 272, 293-294
APL, 242
Appetite, 115-116
Aqueous humor, 321
Aristotle, 198, 309
Arms, origin of, 15
Arsenic, 156
Arteries, 7, 69-72, 74-76, 127
  composition of, 75
  protection of, 39
  See also Circulatory systems; names of individual arteries
Arterioles, 75
Arthritis, 208
Articulation, 15, 25-28; *see also* Joints
Arytenoid cartilages, 102
Aschheim-Zondek test, 242
Astrocytes, 288
Athlete's foot, 49
Atoms, 144, 145-146, 148-152; *see also* names of elements and substances
ATP, 179
Attentiveness, 303, 328
Aural microphonics, 326

ABOUT THE AUTHORS

DR. BENJAMIN F. MILLER *has, since 1954, been Director of the May Institute for Medical Research of the Cincinnati Jewish Hospital and Associate Professor at the University of Cincinnati College of Medicine. Born in Massachusetts, he had his medical training at Harvard Medical School, the Cornell Medical Center and the Rockefeller Institute for Medical Research. During World War II he served with the rank of major in the U.S. Public Health Service. In the years following, he was lecturer on medicine at Harvard Medical School and served on the staff of the Peter Bent Brigham Hospital and the Massachusetts General Hospital. He has practiced medicine in various parts of the country, written many articles on medicine for popular magazines and published several books, including* You and Your Doctor *and* When Doctors Are Patients, *which he co-edited with the late Dr. Max Piner. His recent book,* The Complete Medical Guide *(1956), has established itself as a standard home medical book for the layman.*

MRS. RUTH GOODE *is a senior staff writer on the magazine for doctors,* MD. *A born New Yorker, she learned her trade in the city room of a metropolitan newspaper after being graduated summa cum laude from Smith College. She is author and co-author of a score of books, both fiction and non-fiction. Among them are half a dozen volumes in the fields of medicine and psychology, all aimed at the general reader. She is married to a former newspaperman and theatrical press agent and has two children.*